Scanning Electron Microscopy

APPLICATIONS TO MATERIALS AND DEVICE SCIENCE

P. R. THORNTON

S.R.C. Senior Research Fellow
School of Engineering Science
University College of North Wales, Bangor

CHAPMAN AND HALL LTD
11 NEW FETTER LANE · LONDON E.C.4

TO ANN, FOR
JULIE AND TREVOR

First published in 1968 by
Chapman and Hall Limited
11 New Fetter Lane, London E.C.4
© *1968 P. R. Thornton*
Printed in Great Britain by
Willmer Brothers Limited
Birkenhead

Distributed in the U.S.A.
by Barnes & Noble Inc

Scanning Electron Microscopy

Preface

In October 1965 the author established a research group at Bangor concerned with the application of the scanning electron microscope in the microelectronic materials and devices field. This book developed from informal seminars given to this group during 1966 and early 1967. At the same time outside organizations, both Government laboratories and industrial concerns, showed a growing interest in the possibilities inherent in the scanning electron microscope. As a result a number of pilot studies were made at Bangor, some of which turned into full-time projects. From this outside help and by letting the students have their head, so to speak, the projects soon ranged across a very wide field, from metallurgical and crystal growth problems, through cathodoluminescence studies to microcircuit studies with occasional excursions into the realms of zoology and marine science. As a result of the experience gained in this way, it was felt there was a need for a book which outlined the physics of the applications of the scanning electron microscope (SEM) in such a way that the capabilities, limitations and foreseeable extensions of the techniques were illustrated for a wide audience, including materials technologists, surface physicists, device engineers, metallurgists and possibly others.

Although this is a book about the applications of scanning electron microscopy it is, more specifically, a book about the fundamentals of the applications. It is the physical ideas underlying the application of this instrument that are stressed throughout. The range of ideas involved is considerable, stretching as it does from surface physics, secondary electron emission, electron-beam energy absorbtion, through luminescence studies to device physics and failure analysis. To this range we have to add a knowledge of the limitations imposed by electron optics and an insight into vacuum technology. To provide an introduction to the application of the SEM the author has sought to do two things. One was to provide a brief introduction to those aspects of each of the above topics which are relevant to scanning electron microscopy, and the second was to give a fuller discussion of the topics that are central to the SEM, in particular of the interactions between an electron beam and solid specimens.

vii

To those who find this particular topic difficult, and the treatment given overlong, the author would stress that it *is* a complex subject, but is basic to the applications particularly if valid quantitative data on semiconductor specimens are sought. Subsequently this background is used to discuss the abilities and limitations of the technique.

One final comment; no complete bibliography is given for the simple reason that Dr O. C. Wells has already compiled and cross-referenced an excellent bibliography which is readily available (See *Proc. I.E.E.E.*, 'Ninth Symposium on Electron, Ion and Laser Beam Technology, Berkeley, Calif.', edited by R. F. W. Pease).

Many people have directly or indirectly contributed to this book. Pre-eminent among these are the author's ex-students, D. V. Sulway, R. C. Wayte, D. A. Shaw, N. F. B. Neve, I. G. Davies and Htin Kyaw, whose energy and curiosity were continual sources of stimulation. Professor Gavin encouraged the author's efforts and freedom of action, while Dr K. A. Hughes contributed on the electronic side. On a more formal note the help given by the S.R.C., C.V.D. Office, the Cambridge Instrument Company, S. E. R. L. Baldock, Mullards (Southampton) and S.T.L. is gratefully acknowledged. The author has benefited from contacts with T. E. Everhart, A. D. G. Stewart, O. C. Wells, R. F. W. Pease, A. N. Broers and R. F. Thornley, who with others, notably K. C. A. Smith and D. McMullan, under the leadership of Professor C. W. Oatley at Cambridge were responsible for the basic research and development programme which has led to the introduction of scanning electron microscopy as a powerful addition to the existing range of electron-optical instruments.

Finally thanks are due to Mrs June Grindley who typed and checked a very untidy manuscript.

P. R. THORNTON

Anglesey 1967

ERRATA

page 36, *line 8 from bottom*

for $d_{\text{eff}}^{\text{th}}$ read d_{eff}

page 37, *equation (3.7)*

should read

$$d_0 = \frac{I_{\text{th}}^{1/2}}{\left(\dfrac{\pi}{4} \cdot \dfrac{eV}{kT} J_c\right)^{1/2}} \cdot \frac{1}{\alpha}$$

page 53, *equation (4.2)*

should read

$$f(R, z_n) = \exp\left[-(R/z_n)^p\right] \text{ or } R = z_n \left| \ln f \right|^{1/p}$$

page 53, *line 2 from bottom*

for CE_{n_0} read $CE_0{}^n$

page 54, *equation (4.4)*

should read

$$dg/dz = pz^{p-1} (CE_0{}^n)^{-p} \exp - [z^p/(CE_0{}^n)^p] = (p/z_n) \chi^{p-1} \exp - \chi^p$$

and on the next line

for X read χ

page 55, *equation (4.8)*

should read

$$E_{z'} = \left(\frac{z' - z}{\left| \ln f' \right|^{1/pC}}\right)^{1/n}$$

page 58, *line 10*

should read

$$\bar{\epsilon} = \frac{\bar{E}_z}{E_0} = \frac{1}{E_0} \frac{\int_0^{E_0} E_z h \, dE_z}{\int h \, dE_z}$$

page 62, *line* 6

   for $\hbar\nu$ read $\hbar v$

page 81, *last line*

   for   faster than R_z and E increase

   read faster than R_z as E_0 increases

page 147, *line* 23

   for   humidity   read   voltage

page 203, *line* 2 *from bottom*

   for   ● $= 10$ V

   read ● $= -10$ V

page 211, *line* 4

   for R_{app}

   read $d_{\mathrm{r}}{}^{\mathrm{app}}$

page 228, *table* 9.1

   final line should read

$$SiO_2 \qquad \sim24\cdot0 \hspace{4cm} [20]$$

page 269, *last line*

   for $\tau/2\displaystyle\int_\lambda n_\lambda d\lambda$

   read $(\tau/2)\displaystyle\int n_\lambda d\lambda$

page 270, *line* 2

   should read $\sqrt{(n_\lambda\tau/2)}$ and $\sqrt{\{(\tau/2)\int_\lambda n_\lambda d\lambda\}}$

equation (10.11), *second line*

   should read

$$(S{:}N)^1 = \sqrt{\{(\tau/2)\int_\lambda n_\lambda d\lambda\}} = \sqrt{\{(5/2\Delta f)\int_\lambda n_\lambda d\lambda\}}$$

page 271, *equation* (10.14a)

   for $d\lambda.\,d\lambda$ read $\delta\lambda.\,d\lambda$

Contents

PLATES

between pages 320 and 321

CHAPTER 1

Introductory

1.1 General Introduction

Part of the challenge in many scientific and technological problems today arises from the way in which some small, microscopic part of a component controls the macroscopic behaviour of the whole system. It is easy to cite examples from a very wide range of disciplines. For example microelectronic devices are getting so small that the active volumes are now of the order of $1,000$ Å $\times 2\mu \times 10\mu$. (1 Å $=$ one Ångström unit $= 10^{-8}$cm; $1\mu =$ one micron $= 10^{-4}$cm.) Such devices can be adversely affected by the presence of thin layers of contamination a few microns in diameter and some tens of atoms thick. Physical metallurgists are interested in micro-precipitates and other defects which have dimensions of the order of tens or hundreds of Ångström units and in the way in which these defects can strengthen or weaken a macroscopic structure. The defects introduced by irradiation damage can be of the same order of size. There is increasing evidence that the superconducting properties of type II superconductors are controlled by arrays of filaments approximately 500 Å in diameter and about $1,000$ Å apart. In another field, workers are interested in blood cells which are of the order of 8μ in diameter while the parasites that can exist in these cells can be $\lesssim 1\mu$ across. Viruses and chromosomes have significant detail of the order of 100 to $1,000$ Å and the diameter of the DNA molecule is ~ 50 Å. In insect and plant morphology complex shapes have to be studied to resolutions of the order of $1,000$ Å with a large depth of focus. And so on. The list can be made quite formidable and can be extended over most currently active research fields. And, over this whole range of scientific activity, electron-optical instruments are playing a highly significant role.

The optical microscope has, of course, contributed immensely to scientific progress and will continue to do so, but it is limited to a resolution of $1,000$ Å to $2,000$ Å by diffraction effects and its depth of focus is very restricted. As a result this versatile, cheap, and reliable instrument is being complemented by its electron-optical counterparts. By using electrons, diffraction effects only become important at resolutions of the order of a fraction of an Ångström unit (1Å = 10^{-8} cm). In practice the resolution obtained depends on the way in which the electron beam is used. Table 1.1 lists the major electron-

Table 1.1. The major electron-optical instruments in current use or development

Transmission electron microscope
X-ray microanalyser
Field-ion microscope
Field-emission microscope
Reflection and mirror electron microscopes
Electron diffraction systems
Scanning electron microscope

optical instruments currently in use or being developed. It should be stressed that this table does not do full justice to the range of high-resolution instruments available because it excludes instruments employing ion-beams or x-rays. For a detailed account of the instruments available the reader is referred to *The Encyclopedia of Microscopy* [1]. In order to assess the worth of scanning electron-beam instruments, particularly of the scanning electron microscope, it is necessary to know something of the capabilities of other electron microscopes.

1.2 General characteristics of the available electron-beam instruments

1.2.1 *The transmission electron microscope*

When scientists and teachers talk about electron microscopy, most of the time they are referring to transmission electron microscopy. This preoccupation with the transmission instrument reflects, quite rightly, the highly significant work that has resulted from its application. In this instrument [2] a beam of electrons is focussed onto the specimen which usually consists of a thin foil ($\sim 1,000$ to $5,000$ Å thick) or of a 'replica' of a specimen surface. The latter is made by forming a 'mould' of the surface using an organic or oxide film which is then metallized by evaporation. A ray-diagram showing the optics of the transmission electron microscope is given in figure 1.1. The electron beam (of small numerical aperture) passes through the specimen, an objective lens, an intermediate lens and finally, a projector lens. This projector lens, as in an optical projection microscope, throws a greatly magnified view of the specimen area irradiated by the electron beam onto a phosphor screen, below which is located a photographic plate for recording the image. The contrast in this instrument arises from several causes. Any perturbation in the lattice such as precipitates, dislocations, groups of point defects, surface or interface faults can, under suitable conditions, lead to the scattering of electrons out of the projected beam and hence to observable contrast. Interference effects between coherently scattered electron

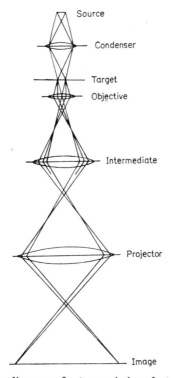

Figure 1.1. Ray diagram of a transmission electron microscope.

waves have to be considered as does the role played by inelastic scattering. The resolution obtainable is 4 Å in transmission and about 30 Å when replicas are used. Usually, transmission electron microscopes use beam potentials of the order of 80 to 100 kV. More recently instruments working at 0·25 to 1·0 MV have been developed.

The transmission electron microscope can also be put to other uses.

One of the more important techniques is limited area electron diffraction. The well-known ability of crystalline specimens to act as diffraction gratings for electron waves is exploited here. The diffraction pattern, which occurs in the back, focal plane of the objective lens, can be made visible by inserting an aperture just below the focal plane and positioning it to receive the diffracted beam. In this way the diffraction pattern from a given surface area of the order of a micron or less in diameter can be obtained and compared with the transmission micrograph. Finally it should be noted that the transmission electron microscope can be used to cast shadows or silhouettes of a specimen surface. If a relatively bulky specimen, such as a crystal growth, part of a razor-blade edge or a cleaved surface is inserted into part of the electron beam then a one-dimensional shadow of the edge intersecting the beam is projected on to the final screen.

1.2.2 *The x-ray microanalyser*

The x-ray microanalyser [3] uses a scanning electron beam to generate characteristic x-rays in the specimen. These x-rays are then examined by x-ray spectrometers so that the intensities of the characteristic lines can be measured. By the use of calibration specimens and after making corrections for the background signal, quantitative estimates of the specimen composition can be obtained. The spatial resolution obtainable is $\sim 1\mu$ and, under good conditions, impurity contents of the order of $10^{19} \rightarrow 3 \times 10^{18}$ atoms/cm^3 can be detected. Modern x-ray microanalysers have facilities for detecting primary electrons so that micrographs of the surface topography can be obtained and compared with x-ray distribution. The limiting factors in the performance of the instrument arise in the x-ray spectrometer. To cover the complete range of atomic numbers a series of crystals (used as diffraction gratings for the x-rays) is required. As both the efficiency of characteristic x-ray production and the ability to detect them deteriorates as the atomic number is decreased, extra care is required with low atomic number specimens.

Microanalysers usually require beam currents of the order of 10^{-8} to 10^{-6} amps, but, since all the major electron optical components are present, it is possible to convert a microanalyser into a somewhat rudimentry SEM by the incorporation of secondary electron detectors and by using lower beam currents.

1.2.3 *The field-emission and field-ion microscopes*

Field-emission is the name given to the emission of electrons from solids under the action of a high electrostatic field. Fields of the order of 0.5×10^8 volts/cm are required. Under these conditions the surface barrier is highly localized and the electrons can tunnel through the barrier. Field-ionization is a related phenomenom which occurs at somewhat higher field strengths, typically 5×10^8 volts/cm. Here the effect results because electrons tunnel from a gas molecule on or very near to the surface into the solid. Both these phenomena have been exploited [4] to make microscopes of incredible fascination and, in the field-ion microscope, of immense resolution. These microscopes differ in two ways from the electron microscopes described so far. Because the physical mechanisms on which they depend are surface phenomena and are very sensitive to small changes in surface properties they are used to study surface behaviour, its dependence on surface contamination, evaporation as a function of temperature, etc. The information comes from the top two atomic layers whereas other systems obtain information from layers of hundreds or thousands of Ångströms thick. The second difference arises from the complete absence of electron lenses as we normally understand them. Figure 1.2 shows the basic elements of a field-emission microscope.

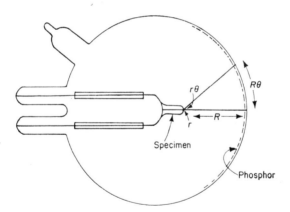

Figure 1.2. A schematic diagram of a field-emission microscope showing the geometry and method of obtaining high magnification.

The central element is a thin wire that has been etched to a fine point, ~ 400 Å to $1,000$ Å. A potential of several kV is established between the pointed 'tip' and the phosphor screen deposited on the inside of the outer bulb. The resultant lines of force are radial. Consequently electrons emitted over a distance $r\theta$ on the tip, to a first approximation, are received on a length $R\theta$ on the screen giving a magnification of R/r (10^5 to 10^6 in practice). The resolution obtainable is between 20 and 50 Å, being mainly limited by the spread in transverse momenta. In the field-ionization microscope H_2 or He atoms in the neighbourhood of the tip are ionized and the resultant ions accelerated towards the screen, which in this case is kept at a negative potential. Partly as a result of the increased mass of the charge carriers used, the transverse velocities are reduced when compared with the field-emission microscope. Theoretical predictions give a resolution of $\leqslant$ 4 Å. This value has been realized in practice.

The requirement of very high fields and localized emission imposes the need for specimens of considerable mechanical strength. This requirement is stringent enough to limit the specimens to high melting-point metals (W and Mo etc.) of to 'whiskers' of the lower melting-point materials. (Whiskers of a given material have increased strength compared to bulk specimens because of the absence of mechanical defects.) The technique can be generalized to some extent by evaporating other materials on to a tungsten filament and obtaining a field-electron or ion image of the individual molecules.

1.2.4 *Electron reflection and mirror microscopy*

As implied in the name, the reflection electron microscope [5] uses reflected electrons from bulk specimens to obtain an image of the surface. The beam is static and inclined at approximately 10 to 30° to the specimen surface. The reflected electrons are then imaged and projected by an electron lens system. Resolutions of the order of several hundred Ångströms can be obtained. The limitation arises from the spread in energy of the reflected electrons. We shall see later that electron lenses can only give good resolution when using electrons with a narrow energy spread. Attempts to limit the spread by use of apertures reduce the image intensity. The use of glancing angles of incidence increases the intensity but increases the image distortion because of the geometrical 'foreshortening'. The use of low angles also restricts the area of the specimen that can be retained in focus.

A variant on the reflection electron microscope is the electron mirror microscope [6]. In this case the specimen is biassed slightly negative with respect to the cathode so that it or, more correctly, the field distribution in front of it, acts as an electron mirror and reflects the electrons back along the axis whence they came. A magnified image of the field distribution is displayed on a phosphorescent screen by a system such as that shown in figure 1.3. Contrast arises from any

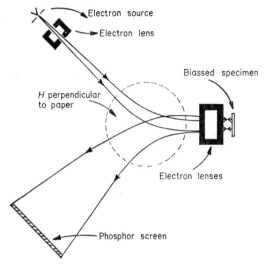

Figure 1.3. Ray diagram of one type of electron mirror microscope [6].

factor which perturbs the local field distribution near the specimen surface and hence disturbs the electron trajectories. The surface topography is one such effect and cleavages steps of ~ 25 Å can be detected. Electrical and magnetic distributions can also be revealed. Contact potentials and surface charge distributions have been observed. The magnetic field distribution on magnetic recording tape, domain patterns in barium ferrite and Ni alloy films have been studied. The resolution obtainable at present is $\sim 1,000$ Å which is of the order obtained optically, but it can be obtained with magnetic and field distributions as well as with surface detail. Because the beam does not touch the specimen, no change is induced in it. The technique can be extended to the study of slowly changing field distributions. The disadvantages arise from difficulties in the interpretation of the observed contrast, from difficulties of surface cleanliness and from limitations imposed by the technique on the nature of the specimen, in particular, from the need to have relatively flat and smooth surfaces.

This brief and oversimplified introduction describes the background against which the SEM must be judged. The introduction is oversimplified in that it neglects instruments in which combinations of these techniques are included in the one instrument. The author excuses this neglect by arguing that in these 'combination' instruments no new physical ideas are introduced, only a wealth of ingenious engineering which is outside the scope of the present book. This introduction is too brief in that it does not do justice to current work in which ion and electron beams are used concurrently to examine, diagnose, or etch to a required shape, specimens of widely differing types.

1.3 The history of the scanning electron microscope

The initial suggestion that an electron microscope could be made by focussing a scanning electron beam onto a specimen surface and recording the emitted current as a function of position was first made by Knoll [7] in 1935. Three years later v. Ardenne [8] built the first scanning electron microscope which used two magnetic lenses to provide a small electron spot at the specimen. Two sets of magnetic coils were used to scan the beam across the specimen in a television-like raster. The specimens were thin sections and the transmitted current was used to obtain micrographs. A recording film on a rotating drum was placed immediately below the specimen. The movements of the drum were coupled to the movements of the electron beam so that the magnification of the instrument was given by the movement of the film divided by the corresponding beam movement. No facilities were incorporated for focussing the beam. This could only be done by repeated trial and error. As the transmitted current was low, the recording time was high, about 20 minutes. Although the performance of this instrument compared unfavourably with the conventional transmission instrument, it was the first scanning electron microscope and v. Ardenne indicated how improvements could be made. It was suggested, for example, that opaque specimens could be examined if the secondary electron current from the top of the specimen was collected, amplified and used to intensity modulate a CRT. In 1942 this idea and others were incorporated by Zworykin, Hillier and Snyder [9] in a SEM using two electrostatic lenses and in which the effective beam energy was lowered by 'floating' the specimen voltage to within 800 V of the gun potential (10 kV). This arrangement was tried in order to enhance the local differences in secondary electron yield. In order to reduce noise problems in recording the secondary electron signal, the secondary electrons were accelerated onto a phosphor screen held at 10 kV and the resulting light emission used to give a photocurrent in a photomultiplier. The scanning time required was of some minutes. Focussing was carried out by observing the waveform from the photomultiplier and varying the lens voltages until the high-frequency components were maximized. The instrument gave resolutions of about 500 Å, but problems due to oil contamination complicated the interpretation of the contrast observed.

The post-war years saw further work in both France and at Cambridge. In 1946, Lecaute and co-workers (see reference [10]) reported a resolution of a few microns. In 1957 Davoine obtained a resolution of $\simeq 2\mu$ and, in 1960, Davoine and colleagues used the approach to study cathoduluminescent processes in crystals. The Cambridge work began in 1948 under Oatley and largely as a result of this group's efforts the first commercial SEM [11] became available in 1965.

The first major improvement made by the Cambridge group was in the collection or utilization of the emitted secondary electrons and so to decrease the noise problems which had plagued the earlier instruments. McMullan [12] using a modified two-lens, transmission electron microscope with electrostatic focussing, obtained a good signal-to-noise ratio by using a secondary electron multiplier which could operate in a demountable system. The multiplier used was the beryllium-copper dynode system developed by Baxter [13]. This system gave good performance and removed the limitation imposed by the slow response time of a phosphor screen when used at low excitation. Also, by tilting the specimen the collected fraction of the electrons emitted was considerably increased. Smith [14] improved the instrument and obtained resolutions of the order of 250 Å. Further improvements in instrumentation and in the understanding of the factors contributing to contrast resulted from the work of Smith [15] and Wells [16]. At about the same time Oatley and Everhart [17] first reported the ability to detect changes in surface voltage and Everhart and Thornley [18] developed a collector system using a scintillator-photomultiplier combination which is the system most commonly used at present. Recent years have seen continued application studies by the Cambridge group [19, 20] and, using a four-lens system, Pease and Nixon [21] have obtained a resolution of $\sim$ 60 to 100 Å.

1.4 Plan of the book

The present chapter does no more than set the scene by indicating the way in which the SEM fits into the existing family of high-resolution instruments based on the use of electron beams. The next chapter gives a general description of the component parts of a modern scanning electron microscope which serves as a background for a more detailed description later. The third chapter describes the type of electron column used in the SEM. As in the rest of the book, the treatment seeks to establish the physical principles exploited and the fundamental and practical limits on performance. No detailed design considerations are given but indications are outlined of the practical difficulties and the ways in which compromises have to be made. Chapters 4, 5 and 6 deal with the interactions of electron beams with solids. The first two chapters in this group deal, in some detail, with the very complex way in which fast electrons penetrate solids, are reflected from them, and how they give rise to secondary electrons. The significant experimental data are presented, and compared with theoretical predictions. It is shown that the theories require modification in detail and the difficulties in making valid calculations are stressed. In these chapters, the specimen properties are not given in detail. An oversimplified picture of the specimen is assumed in that no distinction is made between bulk and surface properties. This limitation is removed in Chapter 6 which surveys briefly the surface properties of a wide range of materials, particularly semiconductor and insulating specimens. The emphasis is again on the type of physical situation that can exist at specimen surfaces, rather than on the detailed facts about any one or group of materials. The treatment describes not only the equilibrium state but indicates the ways in which this equilibrium can be perturbed by the electron irradiation inherent in the SEM.

Chapter 7 deals mainly with the practicalities of ensuring that a suitably prepared specimen can be moved about and examined over a wide range of experimental conditions in environments which do not complicate the observations or the interpretation of the observations.

The next three chapters (8 to 10) can also be taken as a group, as each deals with one way in which the electron beam induced excitation can be used to examine specimens. Chapter 8 deals with the use of electrons emitted from the specimen to obtain information about the surface topography, surface voltage distribution, etc. Chapter 9 shows how the various electrical currents induced in the specimen can be exploited, while Chapter 10 illustrates the use of the cathodoluminescent properties of materials in the SEM. In each of the chapters the detection systems used are considered in detail and the factors limiting contrast and resolution discussed.

Chapters 11 to 13 can also be grouped together because they all deal with applications of the SEM. The examples chosen are all selected from the fields of materials science and device or surface-physics, but the techniques used have a wider applicability. Chapter 11 deals mainly with materials problems and Chapter 12 with device or surface-physics problems. Chapter 13 widens the field of application by describing uses of the SEM to fabricate very small devices and to store information.

REFERENCES

[1] *The Encyclopedia of Microscopy*, (ed. by G. L. Clark), Reinhold, New York, (1961)

[2] M. KNOLL and E. RUSKA, *Z. Phys.*, **78**, 318, (1932)
    E. BRÜCHE and H. JOHANNSON, *H. Naturwiss.*, **20**, 49, 353, (1932)
    L. MARTON, *Bull. Acad. Belg., Cl. Sci.*, **20**, 439, (1934)

For general reading:
    V. E. COSLETT, *Practical Electron Microscopy*, Butterworths, (1951)
    M. E. HAINE and V. E. COSSLETT, *The Electron Microscope*, Spon, (1961)
    P. B. HIRSCH, A. HOWIE, R. B. NICHOLSON, D. W. PASHLEY and M. J. WHELAN, *Electron Microscopy of Thin Crystals*, Butterworths, (1965)
    R. D. HEIDENREICH, *Fundamentals of Transmission Electron Microscopy*, Wiley, New York, (1964)

[3] R. CASTAING and J. DESCAMPS, *J. Phys. Radium*, **16**, 304, (1955)
    R. CASTAING, *Advances in Electronics and Electron Physics*, **13**, 317, (1960)

[4] R. H. GOOD, JNR., and E. W. MULLER, *Encyclopedia of Physics* (2nd ed.), **21**, 176, Springer-Verlag, Berlin, (1956)
    E. W. MULLER, *Fourth International Conference on Electron Microscopy*, 820, Springer-Verlag, Berlin, (1960)
    E. W. MULLER, *Advances in Electronics*, **13**, 83, Academic Press, New York, (1960)

R. GOMER, *Field Emission and Field Ionization*, Harvard Univ. Press, (1961) and ref. [1]

[5] E. RUSKA, *Z. Phys.*, **83**, 492, (1933)
    E. RUSKA and H. O. MULLER, *Z. Phys.*, **116**, 366, (1940)
    B. VON BORRIES, *Z. Phys.*, **116**, 370, (1940) and ref. [1]
[6] L. MAYER, *J. Appl. Phys.*, **24**, 105, (1953)
    G. BARTZ, G. WEISSENBERG and D. WISKOTT, *Proc. Third International Conference on Electron Microscopy London*, 1954 and ref. [1]
[7] M. KNOLL, *Z. Tech. Phys.*, **16**, 467, (1935)
[8] M. VON ARDENNE, *Z. Phys.*, **109**, 553, (1938)
[9] V. K. ZWORYKIN, J. HILLIER and SNYDER, *A.S.T.M. Bull.*, **117**, 15, (1942)
[10] C. W. OATLEY, W. C. NIXON and R. F. W. PEASE, *Advances in Electronics and Electron Physics*, **21**, 181, (1965)
[11] The Cambridge Instrument Company, *Scanning Electron Microscope*
[12] D. MCMULLAN, Ph.D. Thesis, Cambridge, (1952) and *Proc. I.E.E.*, **B100**, 245, (1953)
[13] A. S. BAXTER, Ph.D. Dissertation, Cambridge, (1949)
[14] K. C. A. SMITH, Ph.D. Dissertation, Cambridge, (1956)
[15] K. C. A. SMITH and C. W. OATLEY, *Brit. J. Appl. Phys.*, **6**, 391, (1955)
[16] O. C. WELLS, Ph.D. Thesis, Cambridge, (1957)
[17] C. W. OATLEY and T. E. EVERHART, *J. Electron*, **2**, 568, (1957)
[18] T. E. EVERHART and R. F. M. THORNLEY, *J. Sci. Inst.*, **37**, 246, (1960)
[19] A. N. BROERS, Ph.D. Thesis, Cambridge, (1965)
[20] T. H. P. CHANG, Ph.D. Thesis, Cambridge, (1967)
[21] R. F. W. PEASE and W. C. NIXON, *J. Sci. Instr.*, **42**, 81 (1965)

CHAPTER 2

The Scanning Electron
Microscope

2.1 Introduction

In this chapter a general and somewhat simplified description of the structure of a SEM is given which is then used as a basis for more detailed discussion in later chapters. The basic ideas and the structure of a scanning electron microscope can be described in terms of figure 2.1. Briefly, there are three groups of components. First there is the electron-optical column together with the associated electronics. Secondly there is the vacuum system including the specimen chamber and stage. The final group consists of the signal detection and display systems.

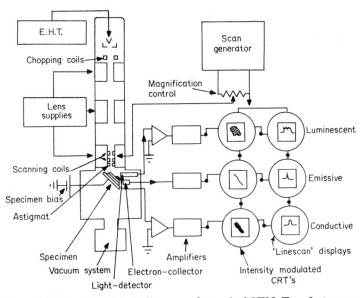

Figure 2.1. Simplified block-diagram of a typical SEM. Two features are not shown: (*i*) the degrees of freedom inherent in the specimen stage; (*ii*) the CRT with a short-persistance phosphor for photography.

13

The electron column consists of an electron gun and two, three or four electron lenses, depending on the design. An electron beam from the electron source flows through the lenses, which all serve the same function—to demagnify the beam diameter. As a result of this demagnification the spot-size at the specimen is 250 Å or less. Incorporated in the final lens assembly are two sets of magnetic scanning coils which, when energized by a suitable scan generator, cause the beam to be deflected in a raster-like pattern over the specimen surface in much the same manner as in a television tube. Three other elements are included in the electron column: (*i*) A set of apertures to help define the angular aperture subtended by the beam at the specimen and to avoid contamination of the lens surfaces. (*ii*) An 'astigmat', i.e. a specially designed set of coils to eliminate any small astigmatism that may be introduced into the system. (*iii*) A set of 'chopping' coils or plates so that a modulation can be superimposed on the electron beam.

A suitable pumping system provides the necessary vacuum both in the electron column and in the specimen chamber. An important part of the specimen chamber is the specimen stage which allows the specimen to be moved about under the electron beam and to be examined at the required angle relative to the beam. The electron beam (the primary beam) interacts with the specimen to give, among other effects, secondary electron emission, a reflected electron current, beam-induced conduction and, often, cathodoluminescence. Each of these signals can be detected, amplified and used to control the brightness of one of a bank of cathode-ray tubes. The spot position in each of these CRT's is determined by the same scan generator which affixes the position of the primary beam on the specimen surface. In this way the secondary electron signal, for example, from a given surface element is used to control the brightness of a corresponding point on a CRT so that a 'map' of the secondary electron current can be obtained. Normally the relevant signal is fed to the brightness control of a cathode-ray tube with a long-persistence phosphor which can be observed visually. In addition, arrangements are made for the signal to be displayed on a tube with a short-persistence phosphor so that the signal can be photographed. The magnification is controlled by the scan generator which ensures that the cathode-ray tubes are scanned in synchronism with the primary beam. The output from this scan generator is fed straight to the deflection coils of the CRT so that the raster size on the tube is kept constant with a size of approximately 10 × 10 cm, i.e. it fills the useful area of the CRT. By way of contrast only a variable fraction of the output is used to energize the primary beam scanning coils. The primary beam is therefore deflected less, i.e. the raster size on the specimen surface is smaller. If the voltage applied is such that the specimen raster is $10\mu \times 10\mu$, in one case, and 1×1 mm, in another, then the effective linear magnification is $\times 10^4$ in the first case and $\times 10^2$ in the second example.

In addition to the scan generator the essential electronic equipment includes the high-stability EHT supply for the electron gun, the high-stability current supplies for the magnetic lenses, the control systems for the cathode-ray tubes, the ancillary equipment associated with the various signal detection systems and monitoring systems. We shall, in due course, discuss these components where special or non-standard features are involved; for the present we shall consider the nature of the interaction between the primary beam and the specimen, as this topic is central to our whole theme.

2.2 The nature of the interaction between an electron beam and solid specimens

We are concerned with the electron beams which have been accelerated through a voltage, V_0, which, for most applications, lies between 1 and 50 kV. When an electron beam of this energy penetrates into a solid, most of the energy is intially lost by ionizing the atoms of the specimen. The more important interactions are shown, in general terms, in figure 2.2. In the first diagram a primary electron interacts elastically with one of the uppermost atoms of the surface. There is no interchange of energy between the incident electron and the host atom, but the fields inherent in the atom cause a change in momentum so that the electron is scattered through a large angle and is effectively reflected out of the specimen. This type of collision represents one end of a spectrum of collision behaviour. In figure 2.2(b) another process is illustrated in which the primary electron is again deflected out of the specimen but only after it has interacted in-elastically with a host atom. Finally in figure 2.2(c) the electron interacts with the host atoms in such a way that it is deflected down into the specimen losing more and more energy at each collision until it can no longer take part in the process of 'impact ionization', as this ejection of electrons from host atoms is called. The ejected electrons can have a kinetic energy of the order of the incident primary electron and so

Scanning Electron Microscopy

can cause the ejection of further electrons which can repeat the process until the kinetic energy is insufficient to cause further ionization. The ionization energy is, typically, 3 to 8 eV. The nett result is that within, say, 10^{-10} seconds a cascade of ejected or secondary electrons has been formed which is centred roughly on the path of the initial primary electron and which is intermingled with the stationary ions left behind by the impact ionization. The secondary

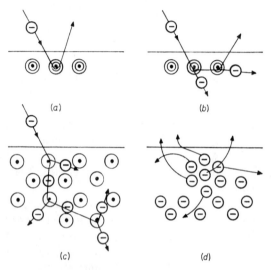

Figure 2.2. Schematic drawings of electron-solid interactions: (*a*) elastic reflection; (*b*) near-elastic reflection; (*c*) secondary electron formation by impact ionization; (*d*) secondary electron emission (only beam-induced electrons shown).

electrons diffuse outwards and gradually lose the remaining kinetic energy mainly by heating up the lattice (i.e. phonon production). There is obviously a near-continuum of processes between the one shown in figure 2.2(*b*) in which the primary electron is reflected with a slight loss and that shown in figure 2.2(*c*) where the primary electron (which is conventionally taken to be the most energetic one emerging from an impact ionization) is not reflected from the specimen at all. Let us now consider the ways in which this excitation caused by the primary beam can decay.

Table 2.1 lists the more important phenomena which result from electron beam bombardment. We have already mentioned primary electron reflection in figure 2.2(*a*). Secondary electron emission is the process shown schematically in figure 2.2(*d*). Consider the secondary electrons formed relatively near to the surface. Some of these will diffuse towards the surface losing energy by ionizing the host atoms. If, by the time such electrons reach the surface, they still retain kinetic energy in excess of the surface barrier energy, which is typically 2 to 6 eV, they have a high probability to escape from the specimen.

Table 2.1. Phenomena resulting from electron-beam bombardment

Reflection of primary electrons
Secondary electron emission
Cathodoluminescence
X-ray excitation
Beam-induced conductivity
Radiation damage

If a suitably placed electrode is charged to a positive potential these secondary electrons will be drawn to this 'collector' to give an emission current, which can be used, after amplification, to intensity modulate a scanned CRT. The bulk of the secondary electrons do not escape from the specimen but diffuse through the bulk. Some of them diffuse through the region containing the ions of the initial plasma. Recombinations can occur between the electrons and these ions; that is to say the excess free electrons can fall back into the unoccupied states in these ions. The energy so released will be emitted as a quantum of radiant energy. If the free electron drops into one of the outer states, a photon of energy corresponding to the visible or near infrared will be emitted. Should the electron subsequently drop into an inner state a characteristic x-ray emission results. This latter process, which forms the basis of the x-ray microanalyser, will not concern us here. When the light quanta so created excape from the specimen the phenomenon is called cathodoluminescence (the creation of light by cathode-ray, i.e. electron, bombardment). The exploitation of this effect to the study of a wide range of materials constitutes one major use of the SEM.

A process which competes with the processes described above is illustrated in figure 2.3. The specimen in this case is imagined to be a short length of some relatively resistive semiconductor with a small

c

bias across it so that an electric field exists in the specimen. The electron beam creates a large number of electrons and ions or 'electron-hole pairs', to adopt the standard semiconductor description. The field will separate these charges; the electrons will flow towards the anode while the holes drift towards the cathode. Every electron-hole pair which separates out as far as the electrodes is equivalent to a nett transfer of one electron from the negative to the positive

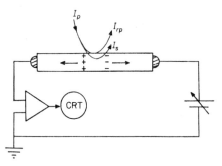

Figure 2.3. Circuit illustrating the idea of internal charge collection by an applied field.

electrode. In the circuit shown in figure 2.3 this internal current flow will be balanced by an external current flow which can be amplified and studied as a function of the position of the exciting beam on the surface. This effect can described as a 'charge-collection' current because the internal mechanism can be represented as a collection of charge of opposite sign by the two end-contacts. We shall see that a single primary electron can create several thousand electron-hole pairs. As a result a primary beam current, I_p, can cause a charge collection current $\gtrsim 10^3 I_p$ in the specimen circuit.

There is another, quite different cause of current flow under beam excitation. In figure 2.3 three currents are indicated, I_p is the primary beam current hitting the specimen, I_{rp} is the current 'leaving' the specimen due to reflection of primary electrons while I_s is the corresponding secondary electron emission current. In general $I_p - I_{rp} - I_s \neq 0$ so that the specimen tends to charge up. This tendency is balanced by current flow in the external circuit. So that a current of $I_p - I_{rp} - I_s$ flows in the specimen circuit to maintain the specimen electrically neutral. This is quite distinct from the charge-collection current described above. This 'neutrality flow', or 'specimen-absorbed current' as it is called, ceases when the specimen reaches neutrality. As, in general terms, a primary beam current, I_p, will produce a specimen current $\sim I_p/2$, the charge-collection current will greatly exceed the 'specimen current' if significant charge collection occurs. In addition the charge-collection current can persist after neutrality is reached. Both types of current flow play important roles in the application of the SEM.

These preliminary comments introduce the three main types of signal used in the SEM: emitted electrons, cathodoluminescence and electron-beam induced conduction. We will complete these comments on the interaction between an electron beam and a solid by mentioning radiation damage. All the effects that have been introduced so far are temporary in the sense that once the excitation is removed the effect decays rapidly (< a second). There are additional effects which are permanent as they remain in the specimen for days, months or years unless removed by high-temperature annealing. These permanent effects, which are largely detrimental, are known under the collective name of radiation damage. Radiation damage does not, at present, form the basis of any mode of operation of the SEM but is relevant to any discussion of the detrimental effects that can result from the examination of specimens in the SEM and we shall have to return to this topic in Chapter 6. However, we can describe here the type of detection systems used in the SEM, but this initial discussion will be at an elementary level. More detailed consideration is given to each system in turn at a later stage.

2.3 SEM detector systems

There is no standard set of detector systems used in scanning electron microscopes; each developer tends to prefer his own system. In spite of this diversity the underlying physical ideas are quite general and can be quickly described. Most of the salient ideas can be depicted in terms of figure 2.4 which illustrates a versatile system used for studying semiconductor materials and devices. This system can be used to study four sets of data simultaneously. The secondary electron emission is detected by the system marked A (figure 2.4). A metal cup with a metal gauze over the opening is held at, say, 200 volts positive, relative to earth. Secondary electrons emitted by the specimen (usually at earth potential) are attracted towards this collector. Some of these electrons penetrate through the gauze and are accelerated towards a scintillator crystal on top of which is a thin aluminium film maintained at, say, 10 to 12 kV. The energy acquired by the secondary electrons in reaching 12 kV is then converted into light by the processes of impact ionization followed by radiative recombination. A large fraction of this light is guided by a light-pipe into a photomultiplier and so gives a pulse of electrical current at the photomultiplier output. Such a collector system will also register

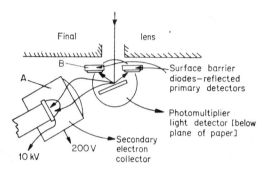

Figure 2.4. Typical array of detectors used in multi-mode operation of SEM.

signals from the primary electrons which are reflected directly into the scintillator. The relative fractions of the total signal due to secondary electron emission and to reflected primary electrons depend on the collector aperture, its position, the collector voltage, the specimen inclination relative to the beam and on the atomic number of the specimen. The system is most useful when a high proportion of the current is due to secondary electrons. A detector designed for reflected primary electrons is marked B in figure 2.4. Readers familiar with semiconductor nuclear particle detectors will recognize this type of detector. It consists of two silicon pn junction diodes made in high-resistivity ($\sim 1{,}000 \ \Omega$ cm) material so that the depletion layer is wide ($\geqslant 10\mu$). These junctions can be made very close to the surface so that when primary electrons are reflected from the specimen surface into the active junction areas they lose their energy by impact ionization in the depletion layer. The electrons and holes so formed are collected by the high electric field inherent in the depletion layer and therefore give rise to a current in an external circuit. This current is a measure of the reflected primary electron current incident on the particle counters. The output from the counters can be used individually, added or subtracted, depending on the information required, (see Chapter 8) and then fed, via an operational amplifier, to the brightness control (the grid of the electron gun) of a CRT.

Several systems have been used to detect the cathodoluminescence emitted from specimens. Figure 2.4 shows a simple yet versatile approach. A large-diameter photomultiplier is mounted at some distance from the specimen. In this way a reasonable collection can be retained by a detector which is remote from the specimen and which does not interfere with other detectors or the specimen stage movement. The photomultiplier can be chosen, within limits, so that the spectral sensitivity matches the spectral output from the specimen, i.e. an S11 or S20 photocathode can be used for specimens which give visible light whereas an S1 photocathode is more appropriate for specimens emitting in the near infrared ($\leqslant 1\mu$). The system can be made more selective by including filters in the path between the specimen and the photocathode.

Finally we have to detect the currents induced in the specimens by the primary beam. This is not difficult. The main requirement is the ability to mount the specimen so that contacts can be attached in order that an external bias can be applied and so that current continuity results. In order to achieve this the specimen stub, i.e. the housing in which the specimen sits, is designed to make the necessary contacts and to insulate those parts of the specimen which should not be in electrical contact. The current leads can be connected to external amplifiers and test equipment by the use of metal-to-ceramic vacuum seals. In one sense the measurement of beam-induced conduction just leads to additional specifications on the specimen stage. From the viewpoint of the amplifiers required the specification depends on the specimens being studied. Sometimes it is necessary to measure the short-circuit current flowing in the specimen circuit. In the case of a charge-collection current this involves using a low impedance (virtual earth) amplifier to measure 10^{-9} to 10^{-6} amps. In other situations it is required to measure the voltage generated in a 100 kΩ to 1 mΩ leakage resistor by a specimen current of 10^{-12} to 10^{-10} amps. Sometimes the voltage generated (10 to 100μV) by the beam has to be measured under open-circuit conditions, but usually there is no difficulty in making these measurements. The design problem in each case is to reach a suitable compromise between the noise and/or stability properties of the system and the bandwidth (speed of response) which determines the scanning speeds possible. It is convenient if line scans of the order of 0·001 seconds and frame scans of about 2 seconds can be used for visually observed data. The corresponding figures for photographically recorded rasters are, typically, ~ 0.02 sec and 100 sec, although considerable latitude is possible.

In each system, whatever the excitation, the resulting current flow is used to control the brightness of a scanned CRT. Any feature which causes a change in the local signal causes contrast on the screen or micrograph. We shall consider each cause of contrast in detail in Chapters 8, 9 and 10, where it will be seen that this topic can be clarified by understanding the basic processes occurring in each case and by noting how the detector system utilize these processes.

Another very useful way in which the signals can be exploited is shown in figure 2.1. Instead of feeding the signal to the grid of the CRT it is fed to the Y plates. In this way the signal can be studied as a function of position during every line scan of the specimen. Such 'line scan' observations are very effective in ensuring that the signals are used correctly and are useful in quantitative studies. Finally any initial description of detector systems must explain what is meant by 'back-off' and 'γ-correction'. These two terms can be explained by means of figure 2.5. Imagine that we have a charge-collection current which takes the form shown during a line scan and that we are interested in the details at A (figure 2.5(a)(i)). The two arrows indicate the working range of the system, for example they represent the range of voltages that can be usefully applied to the CRT grid. If we try to increase the detail observable at A by increasing I_{cc} or by increasing the transfer impedance, g, then the signal will move out of the working range. If, on the other hand, we reduce the total signal by subtracting a constant 'signal' I_d (see figure 2.5(a)(ii)) we can increase the gain, as in figure 2.5(a)(iii), so that the effective contrast at A is increased. Hence by 'backing-off' an arbitrary, but convenient current and by increasing the gain the contrast is increased. If we have a situation such as that depicted in figure 2.5(b)(i) and we wish to include the details at both B and C in the recorded data, the details at B will be difficult to observe so, if we incorporate a circuit which delivers not $g(I_{cc} - I_d)$ but $g(I_{cc} - I_d)^n$ to the grid where n is less than one, the high signals will be reduced at the expense of the low ones (figure 2.5(b)(ii)). The gain can now be increased and the signal at B is effectively increased and that at C is still within the working range (figure 2.5(b)(iii)).

2.4 The specimen environment

The environment in which the specimen is examined is important. There are two basic elements: the vacuum system employed and the specimen stage. The vacuum system should be designed for convenience – for a rapid changing of specimens and little maintenance – and, more important, it should not affect the specimen properties in any way. The specimen stage, or more truthfully, the range of stages needed must provide the necessary specimen movements and it must

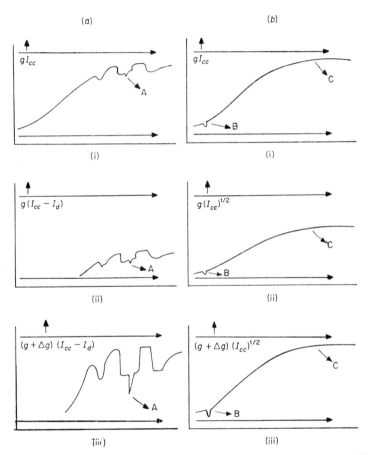

Figure 2.5. Control of signal fed to grid of CRT by (*a*) use of a 'back-off' current and (*b*) incorporation of sub-linear circuit element (γ – control). Note: the separation of the two horizontal arrows gives the useful working range of the system.

do so without introducing any unwanted movement or vibration of the specimen as this would degrade the resolution. In addition these movements have to be provided without causing vacuum leaks and without impeding the incorporation of the detector systems required. On occasion additional features such as heating and cooling have to be incorporated with fast response times and without introducing any degradation of the resolution. A variety of current and voltage supplies have to be incorporated in the stage reliably and conveniently. This list is a sufficient introduction to this important topic – and it is important because it is in stage design that the most variation and versatility are needed since users in different disciplines have widely differing needs.

We have given an elementary description of the SEM by introducing the component parts, the physical interactions involved and some of the terminology used. In order to simplify the examination in depth of these topics we must now introduce further notation to describe the ways in which the SEM can be used.

2.5 Terminology to describe the modes of operation of the SEM

There is no standardized notation to describe the modes of operation of the SEM. Most of the terms employed are reasonably self-explanatory to the experienced worker but tend to be 'jargonese' to the student or worker new to the field. The normally accepted criteria of any classification system are that they allow a division into major categories and a subsequent subdivision into sub-categories and so on as required. In an attempt to conform to this established pattern the following notation is adopted throughout this book.

(1) If the current of emitted electrons is being exploited to obtain information the SEM is being operated in the *emissive* mode. This notation is used whether secondary electrons or reflected primary electrons are being used and independently of the type of detector used.

(2) When the examination involves the use of any electric current created by the primary beam it is said that the *conductive* mode of operation is being used.

(3) When the light emitted from the specimen under electron-beam excitation is being used to diagnose specimen properties, the SEM is being used in the *luminescent* mode, irrespective of the exact mechanism whereby the light is created.

One point should be stressed about this notation: it has not been generally accepted to date. However, it does have the virtue of simplicity, is self-explanatory to the newcomer and is capable of further subdivision. It is a measure of the versatility of the scanning electron microscope that either this or a similar notation can be used. From this basis we can now examine the underlying origin of this versatility – the electron-optical column.

CHAPTER 3

The Electron-optical System

3.1 Introduction

We have only limited space available and must therefore confine discussion to the immediately relevant aspects of the electron-optical system. For more general study the reader is referred to the books and articles listed at the end of this chapter. No attempt will be made to describe in detail existing scanning electron columns; instead, the underlying ideas and the practical difficulties limiting performance will, it is hoped, be made clear. We have already seen in Chapter 2 that the basic elements of the electron column are the electron gun, the demagnifying lenses, the scanning coils, the astigmat, the apertures and, in general, some system of 'chopping' or modulating the electron beam. To this list we must add the need for some method of beam alignment and we have to incorporate sufficient magnetic shielding to avoid perturbation of the electron trajectories by stray magnetic fields. In this chapter we will examine the function of each component in turn with particular stress on the factors limiting the performance, and finally we will consider the performance of the integrated unit. The obvious point to start is with the electron source.

3.2 The electron gun

In general the electron source has the structure shown schematically in figure 3.1. A tungsten hairpin filament is mounted in a cylindrical shield which is closed except for a circular aperture (~ 2 mm diameter) immediately and centrally below the point of the tungsten filament. This assembly-filament and shield-forms the cathode assembly and at a high negative potential. The filament is directly heated by a high current (2·5 amp at ~ 1 volt) source. The anode (at earth potential) consists of an annular cylinder with coaxial aperture. The directly heated filament acts as the electron source while the anode provides the accelerating field. The shield (or Wenhalt cylinder) greatly contributes to the control of the system which can be used in two basic forms (figures 3.1 (a) and (b)). One is the 'diode' gun in which

26

the filament and the cylinder are at the same voltage. The second
form is the 'triode' gun in which the cylinder is biassed negative,
relative to the filament, and exerts the same kind of control function
as does the grid of a triode valve. We shall consider only the latter
as its ease of control and smaller, brighter spot-size makes it more
suitable for electron microscopes.

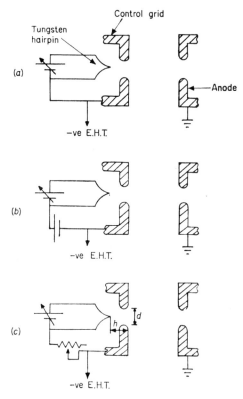

Figure 3.1. Electron sources based on thermionic emission from tungsten:
(a) a diode electron source; (b) a triode electron source and (c) a self-
biassing triode source.

The potential distribution in the neighbourhood of the filament is
determined by two main factors. One is the filament temperature
which determines the number of electrons emitted per second from
the filament and the second is the penetration of the anode field
through the grid aperture. The electrons leave the filament with a

kinetic energy determined by the temperature; they then diffuse until they reach the high fields in the neighbourhood of the aperture and are subsequently accelerated down the axis. The electron-optical operation of the system can be understood in terms of figure 3.2. Those electrons leaving the centre of the filament are accelerated through the anode aperture while those leaving the side of the filament are repelled by the shield and are forced towards the centre

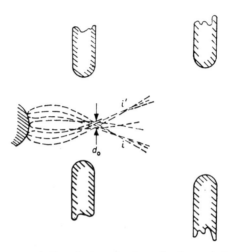

Figure 3.2. Representative electron trajectories in a triode source showing the formation of an image, ii', of the emission area and of a cross-over point of diameter d_0.

axis and are subsequently accelerated. As a result of this lens action there is an image of the filament in some position ii' and, more important, there is a cross-over point or disc of less confusion through which all the electrons pass and which acts as the virtual source. The cross-over diameter is less than the emitting area of the filament. As the bias voltage increases, the cross-over point moves towards the filament.

In the self-biassing triode gun, (figure 3.1(c)), the voltage difference between the filament and the cylinder is proportional to the current leaving the filament. Therefore, if this current increases, the cylinder voltage reacts to reduce the increase. This negative feedback tends to stabilize the emission. With a self-biassing system the exact geometry is not of paramount importance, but once the geometry is fixed it is necessary to obtain the correct biassing conditions. Figure 3.3 shows schematically the type of behaviour observed when the filament height, h, and the aperture diameter, d, are varied. These diagrams are indicative of the data obtained by Haine and Einstein [1]. Figure 3.3(a) shows how the brightness (which is defined

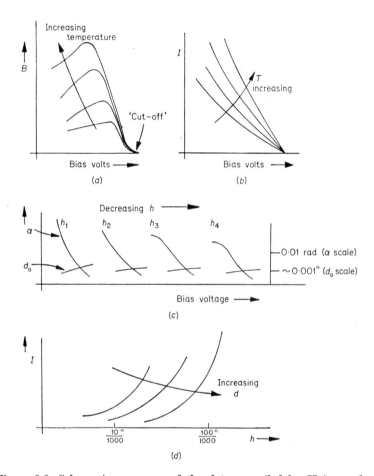

Figure 3.3. Schematic summary of the data compiled by Haine and Einstein [1]: (a) source brightness, B, as a function of bias voltage and filament temperature; (b) emission current, I, as a function of bias and filament temperature; (c) angular aperture, α, and cross-over diameter, d_0, as a function of filament height and bias voltage; (d) emission current as a function of filament height, h, and grid aperture diameter, d.

as the current density per unit solid angle) varies with temperature and bias. As the bias is decreased from the 'cut-off' value the brightness increases rapidly, reaches a maximum and then falls gradually. This behaviour is followed over a moderate range of h (0·015 in. $\leqslant h \leqslant$ 0·060 in.) the only change being that as h decreases the bias required increases. At the lower temperatures the brightness values approach the theoretical prediction. The implication is that geometrical factors rather than space-charge limitations determine the brightness. Only at the higher temperatures do the observed values fall below the theoretical values because of space-charge arising from the increased emission. Over the same range of bias the total current increases continuously as the bias is reduced. The angular aperture, α, and the spot diameter, d_0, vary, as shown in figure 3.3(c). The spot diameter remains effectively constant as the bias is reduced and the beam angle increases continuously. The rate of increase of beam angle decreases as h is reduced. Similar studies showed that the total beam current required to give maximum brightness decreases as h is decreased and d is increased. Therefore to obtain a small beam angle and maximum brightness, a small value of h and large d will give the required results with a small beam current (figure 3.3(d)). When operated near maximum brightness the energy distribution takes a Gaussian distribution when plotted against distance from the spot centre.

It should be remembered that the useful life of a filament is affected by gas attack and by thermal evaporation. Provided the backing pressure is below 10^{-4} torr there is little loss of life by gas attack. However, if the pressure is increased to 10^{-3} torr the lifetime is effectively reduced by a factor of ten (from 50 to 5 hours) [2]. The thermal evaporation obviously increases with temperature so that attempts to obtain increased brightness by running at high temperatures can only be made at the cost of a reduction in lifetime. The relationship between lifetime, τ, and the current density, j, can be written [2] $\tau \times j = 30$ implying that filaments can be expected to give 1 amp/cm² for about 30 hours. The total current delivered has to be variable from $\sim 10\mu\text{A}$ up to $\sim 250\mu\text{A}$.

Finally we should note that there are other kinds of filament that can be used. This point is discussed in Chapter 8. For the present we have seen that the electron gun provides an effective, stable, bright source of electrons in the form of a beam of small diameter contained in an angular distribution such that, when the source is

placed in the correct position relative to an electron lens, the lens
can demagnify or 'condense' the spot-size still further. We can now
examine how these lenses work.

3.3 The electron lens system

The scanning electron microscope employs either two, three or four
electron-optical lenses all performing the same function. That is to

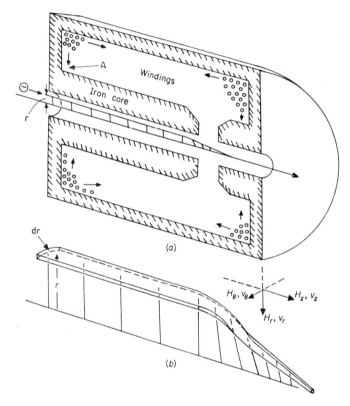

Figure 3.4. (a) Typical structure of a magnetic electron lens core;
(b) schematic representation of the effect of the fringing field at the gap
on a section of the electron beam contained between r and $r + dr$.

say each lens is used to demagnify the effective spot-size so that the
virtual source of diameter of $\sim 50\mu$ is reduced to a spot-size ~ 250 Å
to 100 Å by the time the beam reaches the specimen. Nowadays

magnetic lenses are generally used in electron microscopes and the scanning electron microscope is no exception. The reasons for this are mainly practical. Magnetic lenses have higher reliability because they are more robust, less likely to move out of alignment and are easier to clean than electrostatic systems. Much of the bulk of a magnetic lens can be located outside the vacuum and few EHT leads are required. Also magnetic lenses can be expected to give slightly better performance as regards lens aberrations. For the present we shall consider only magnetic lenses used as condenser lenses.

Figure 3.4 shows rather schematically the action of a fairly typical magnetic lens. A massive iron core of cylindrical symmetry is energized by a current-carrying coil in much the same way as a normal electromagnet. The focussing action occurs in the gap between the two poles of the 'electromagnet' where the magnetic lines of force take up the usual 'fringing' configuration. We know that the force on an electron in a magnetic field comes from the field component at right angles to the instantaneous velocity and is directed at right angles to the velocity and the operative field component. Therefore an electron travelling along the z direction parallel to the column axis and a distance r from it will 'feel' the presence of the H_r component (see figure 3.4) and so acquire a tangential velocity v_θ which in turn will interact with the H_z component leading to an inwards radial velocity v_r (see figure 3.4). Thus the electron is deflected sideways and inwards towards the column axis. As the electron *leaves* the gap region similar but opposite deflections will occur. But, because the electron is nearer the column axis where the effective fields are smaller, these opposing deflections are smaller. The nett result is a focussing action and some rotation. These processes of focussing action and rotation are shown, again rather schematically, in figure 3.4(*b*) where the behaviour of a section of the beam between r and $r + dr$ in the region remote from the pole pieces is illustrated as it passes through the region of the pole pieces. The focussing action has to be made as efficient and as aberration-free as possible. We cannot consider here the design aspects of this topic in any detail but can only indicate the significant parameters. Much of the notation of physical optics is applicable; focal length, principal plane, thick and thin lenses have the same significance here as in light optics, and can be used without further introduction. The obvious starting point is to enquire into the causes of lens aberations.

3.4 Lens aberrations

The function of the lens system is to demagnify the spot-size. The system parameters can be summed up in terms of the quantities shown in figure 3.5. The principal plane of the first lens of focal length f_1 is positioned a distance L_1 from a source of diameter d_0. Subsequent lenses are positioned at distances of L_2 and $L_2 + L_3$ from the first lens and have focal lenths f_2 and f_3 respectively. We wish to know the

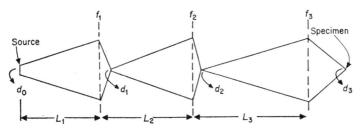

Figure 3.5. Ray-diagram showing the operation of a SEM electron-optical column.

final spot-diameter, d_3. We lose little in generality if we take $L_1 = L_2$ and $f_1 = f_2$. In this case we obtain the final spot-diameter as

$$d_3 = d_0 f_1^2 f_3 [\{(L_1 - f_1)^2 - L_1 f_1\}(L_3 - f_3) - L_1 f_1 (L_1 - 2f_1)]^{-1}$$

(3.1)

Equation (3.1) is valid provided the value of d_3 given does not fall below the theoretical limit imposed by the aberrations inherent in electron-lens systems. In order to estimate this theoretical limit may proceed as follows.

(1) In section 8.3 we shall see that a certain threshold beam current, I_{th}, has to be exceeded so that small changes in contrast can be observed against the noise background in an acceptable time. We first calculate the minimum spot-size, d_0, that can pass this current, using some suitable definition of the spot-diameter.

(2) We can then determine the effects of the various aberrations on a spot of d_0 and so determine the effective minimum spot-size at the specimen. In the absence of any degradation of the resolution as a result of the interaction between the electron beam and the specimen this minimum spot-size can be taken as a measure of the best resolution available with a given current I_{th}. In particular the theoretical best resolution can be estimated by taking the limit $I_{th} \to 0$.

In order to make these estimates we have to determine the relative importance of the various aberrations. Table 3.1 lists the aberrations observed in electron-optical systems. Of these faults the four that are important in the scanning electron microscope are shown in terms of the electron trajectories in figure 3.6. The first fault – 'chromatic' aberration' – arises because there is, in the electron beam, a

Table 3.1. Aberrations observed in electron-optical lens

Aberrations	Comments
Astigmatism	Can be designed out.
Chromatic aberration	Due in part to instability of EHT and lens supplies (can be reduced to acceptable level) and in part to spread of thermal velocities of emitted electrons.
Spherical aberration	Important in the SEM.
Diffraction	Fundamental limit
Coma	⎫ Not important in the scanning electron micro-
Distortion	⎭ scope.

spread $e\Delta V$ of electron energies about the mean energy eV_0. As a result, instead of obtaining a point focus, a disc of least confusion results with a diameter, d_c. Glaser [3] has shown that d_c can be written as:

$$d_c = C_c \frac{\Delta V}{V_0} \alpha \qquad (3.2)$$

where α is the semi-angular aperture at the image and C_c is the chromomatic aberration constant. C_c is determined by the nature of the focussing field. In eqn. (3.2) $\Delta V/V_0$ is the total fractional spread in electron voltage. Part of this arises from possible fluctuations ΔV_0 and ΔH in the cathode EHT and the lens field due to lens current instabilities. If these are the major cause then

$$\frac{\Delta V}{V_0} \sim \left\{ \left(\frac{\Delta V_0}{V_0} \right)^2 + \left(\frac{2\Delta H}{H} \right)^2 \right\}^{1/2}$$

If the fluctuations in the power supplies are reduced to $\leqslant 1$ part in 10^5 the residual chromatic aberration arises from the energy spread due to the finite emission velocities of the thermionic electrons. In this case

$$\frac{\Delta V}{V_0} \sim \frac{2KT_c}{eV_0}$$

where T_c is the filament temperature.

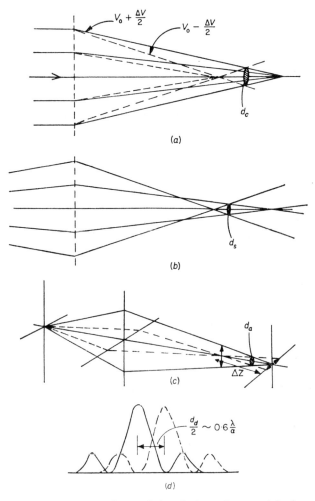

(a)

(b)

(c)

(d)

Figure 3.6. Aberrations observed in electron lenses; (a) chromatic aberration; (b) spherical aberration; (c) astigmatism and (d) a reminder of the resolution limit imposed by diffraction effects.

The second fault – astigmatism – arises when the lens does not possess perfect rotational symmetry about its axis, i.e. the focussing action depends on the plane with which we are concerned (See figure 3.6(c)). In particular there are two planes at right angles in which the difference in focal length is a maximum and which give line foci of a point object. Between these extremes there is a disk of least confusion the diameter, d_a, of which is given by [4].

$$d_a \approx \Delta z. \, \alpha. \qquad (3.3)$$

We shall see below that this astigmatism error can be corrected. The third fault cannot be completely removed because it is bound to occur even with a perfectly symmetrical lens and a completely monochromatic beam.

Spherical aberration arises from the use of finite numerical apertures because the electrons moving on trajectories which are more inclined to the lens axis experience stronger fields and are more deflected. In this case the diameter for the disc of least confusion is written as, d_s, and is given by [3]

$$d_s \sim C_s \, \alpha^3 \qquad (3.3)$$

where C_s, the spherical aberration, is a function of the focussing field, its strength and distribution, and is a function of the beam voltage. Finally there is the fundamental limit set by diffraction. In this case we can take the diameter, d_d, of the Airy disc as the disc of least confusion where

$$d_d \sim 1.22 \, \lambda/\alpha \qquad (3.4)$$

In the general case all these aberrations can occur concurrently and it is necessary to add the quantitative estimates of the individual errors together. The procedure usually followed [5] is to regard the individual estimates as error functions and regard the effective spot-size, $d_{\text{eff}}^{\text{th}}$, as the square root of the sum of the squares of the separate diameters, i.e.

$$d_{\text{eff}}^{0} = \{d_c{}^2 + d_s{}^2 + d_d{}^2 + d_a{}^2\}^{1/2} \qquad (3.5a)$$

when $I_{\text{th}} \to 0$ and

$$d_{\text{eff}} = \{d_0{}^2 + d_c{}^2 + d_s{}^2 + d_d{}^2 + d_a{}^2\}^{1/2} \qquad (3.5b)$$

for finite values of I_{th}.

It remains to estimate d_0. This can be done by following the procedure adopted by Smith [6]. Langmuir [7] gave the current density

J_A at the image of an electron source as

$$J_A = J_c \left(\frac{eV}{KT} + 1\right) \sin^2 \alpha \simeq J_c \frac{eV}{KT} \alpha^2$$

where J_c is the cathode emission current density, V is the image potential relative to the cathode $(eV \gg kT)$ and α is the semi-angular aperture at the image. J_A is the axial or maximum emission in the Gaussian distribution. The diameter, d_0, that would contain a total current I_{th} is given by

$$I_{th} = J_A k\frac{\pi}{4}. d_0^2 \qquad (3.6)$$

where $k \sim 0.62$ if the full Gaussian distribution is used out to a point where the current density has fallen to $\sim \frac{1}{5}$ of J_A and where $k = 1$ if the effective source is limited by an aperture. Taking $k = 1$ we get

$$d_0 = \frac{I_{th}}{\left(\frac{\pi}{4} . \frac{eV}{kT} J_c\right)} . \frac{1}{\alpha} = C_0/\alpha \qquad (3.7)$$

From eqns. (3.2) to (3.7) we obtain

$$(d_{\text{eff}})^2 = \left\{C_0^2 + (1 \cdot 22\lambda)^2\right\} \frac{1}{\alpha^2} + C_s^2\alpha^6 + \left[\left(\frac{C_c\Delta V}{V}\right)^2 + \Delta z\right]\alpha^2 \qquad (3.8)$$

Independent of the absolute magnitude of C_s, C_c, etc. there is, for a given current, an optimum value of α, i.e. a value of α which gives a minimum value of d_{eff}. The type of prediction made is shown very schematically in figure 3.7 [12]. These curves are indicative rather than quantitative because the behaviour depends on the values of C_s, C_c etc. In the best case, d_{eff} approaches 50 Å with beam currents of 10^{-12} at 20 kV with low values of C_s and C_c etc. The range of α employed is 0·0024 to 0·010. Figure 3.7 establishes a design situation at which to aim and indicates the significant parameters. The data indicate the importance of using low beam currents. This requirement conflicts with the needs arising from noise problems, which are reduced with increasing current. The figure also stresses the importance of using lenses with low values of C_s and C_c. This is another reason for preferring magnetic lenses which have lower spherical and chromatic constants than electrostatic lenses. We can now see briefly how these parameters vary with lens design.

Mainly as a result of Liebmann's work [8] it has been established that the important properties of a magnetic lens system, such as f, C_s/f, C_c/f, etc. can be expressed to a first approximation in terms of the quantities defined in figure 3.8(a). Figure 3.8(b) shows schematically the way in which the focal length and aberration constants

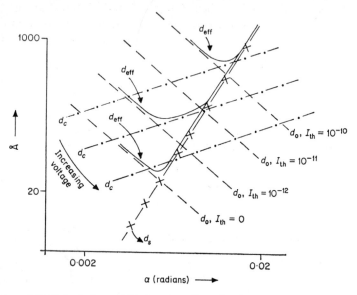

Figure 3.7. Calculations [12] showing the effective spot diameter, d_{eff} as a function of angular aperture, beam current and lens constants $·—·—·—·— = d_c$ (chromatic effects); $———— = d_0$ (current carrying ability) and $— × — × — × = d_s$ (spherical aberration).

vary with excitation. Here the excitation is expressed in terms of NI, the number of ampere-turns applied to the iron yoke. Obviously from the aberration viewpoint it is best to work at high excitations, i.e. high gapfields. If, however, we try to run at very high field strengths we reach a stage at which the iron saturates and there is no further

---

(*Opposite*)
Figure 3.8. (a) Definition of bore diameter, D, and pole-piece separation, S, as used by Liebermann [8]; (b) schematic curves showing dependence of focal length, f, spherical aberration constant, C_s, and chromatic aberration constant, C_c, on excitation level; (c) a means of obtaining low aberrations and long focal lengths by reducing the bore-diameter to obtain high excitations over short distances.

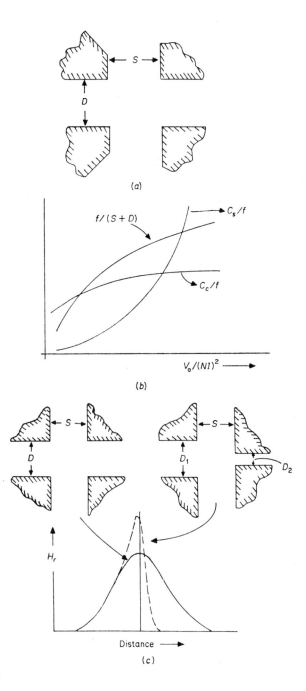

(a)

$f/(S+D)$

C_s/f

C_c/f

$V_o/(NI)^2$

(b)

S

D

S

D_1

D_2

H_r

Distance

(c)

increase in field strength with increase in excitation. This saturation effect obviously produces inefficiencies and it is detrimental to the lens properties. The whole iron yoke has to be designed so that the local flux density does not exceed a chosen critical value. Since we require a high flux in the gap and therefore in the iron in the immediate neighbourhood of the gap, this means in practice that the 'iron circuit' is designed so that the maximum flux occurs at the gap. To avoid excess flux flow in the core (at point A in figure 3.4 for example) the pole-pieces are tapered as in figure 3.8(a). Excess flux in the remainder of the loop can be avoided by keeping the relevant cross-sectional area large enough.

In the SEM the fact that, in general, we wish the specimen to be located below the bottom of the final lens by a 'working distance' of about a centimetre or more presents additional difficulties as this implies the use of a lens with a relatively long focal length. If the working distance is increased by dropping the excitation levels then the aberrations increase rather rapidly. The method usually adopted to obtain the required combination of high flux and long focal length is to use a high flux for a short distance. This is done by altering the bore in the manner indicated in figure 3.8(c).

In this way the longer working distance can be obtained with a $C_s \sim 2 \cdot 0$ cm compared with the $C_s \sim 0 \cdot 3$ cm typical of objective lenses in the TEM.

Finally we have to consider correction for astigmatism.

3.5 Astigmatism

The implicit assumption has been made throughout that the whole electron column has perfect cylindrical symmetry about a geometrical line through the lens centres. In practice there are departures from this idealized situation. These departures can arise in three ways: (*i*) from the presence of stray magnetic fields not having cylindrical symmetry, (*ii*) from mechanical asymmetries built-in during the manufacture and (*iii*) from asymmetric fields due to contamination on the bore walls and/or at the apertures becoming charged up by the beam.

The built-in faults can arise from four causes: (*i*) departures from roundness of the pole-piece central holes or 'bores', (*ii*) departures from flatness of the faces of the pole-pices, (*iii*) an imperfect parallelism between the pole faces and (*iv*) a lateral error between the bore axes of the two pole-pieces. Calculations [9] and general experience

indicate that (*i*) and (*ii*) are the major causes of astigmatism that can
be built into the lens. With care and by pushing the available manufacturing methods to the limit, lenses can be made in which these
causes of astigmatism can be reduced to an acceptable level. But it
is useful to incorporate a correction for astigmatism into the column
because of astigmatism introduced by contamination (see below).
This correction can be achieved by having a facility for including a

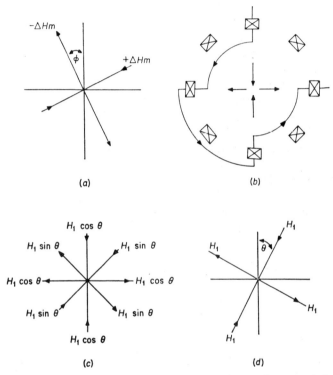

Figure 3.9. Astigmatism correction: (*a*) situation to be corrected; (*b*)
system used by Stewart [10] to provide compensating field, the second
four coils are wired in the same manner; (*c*) components of field produced by coil system with cos, sin and linear potentiometers; (*d*) nett
effective field produced by (*c*).

variable asymmetric field component. There are several ways in
which this can be achieved; one of the most convenient [10] is illustrated in figure 3.9. The situation to be corrected is shown in figure
3.9(*a*). In two perpendicular planes inclined at some unknown angle

ϕ to the reference axes, the inwards radial magnetic field differs from the mean value by $\pm \Delta H_{max}$. This can be corrected by one set of four magnetic coils wired in the manner shown in figure 3.9(b). If this set of coils can be mechanically rotated and the current through them varied then the correction can be made. A more elegant way [10] of making this correction is to include a second identical set of coils, similarly wired but rotated through 45°. If the voltage to one set of coils is taken from a cosine potentiometer in parallel with a further linear potentiometer and the voltage to the second set from the corresponding sine potentiometer in parallel with an identical linear potentiometer then the field distribution has the form given in figure 3.9(c). Both the control of magnitude and rotation are electrical and independent, the linear potentiometer is varied until $H_1 = \Delta H_{max}$ and the 'angle' potentiometer changed until, in the notation of figure 3.9, $\theta = -\phi$.

Having obtained a focussed beam as free of aberrations as possible it still has to be scanned across the specimen surface.

3.6 The scanning coils
We have already made the point that an increase in working distance can only be obtained at the expense of some loss of performance. It is therefore important to avoid all unnecessary components between the bottom of the final lens and the specimen. As a result the scanning

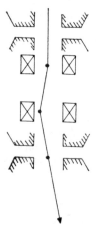

Figure 3.10. Double deflection system pioneered by Oatley and colleagues [11].

coils (or plates) are situated in the final lens housing or between the final two lenses (see figure 3.10). In this situation it is best [11] to provide a double deflection system in each dimension. In this way the beam passes through the centre of the final aperature and the maximum deflection obtainable is increased compared to a single deflection system. Again there is, in principle, the choice of using magnetic or electrostatic deflection. In this context it should be remembered that the beam has to be scanned in synchronism with the display cathode-ray tubes. Most commercial cathode-ray tubes are fitted with magnetic deflection coils, so it is more convenient to use these coils and run all of them from one drive unit or scan generator. Such generators are easier to provide for magnetic systems and, finally, as in the case of the lenses themselves, the coils can be placed outside the vacuum and will not be affected by contamination. The scan generator provides the necessary a.c. voltages for the beam to traverse the required raster, but it is also necessary to be able to displace the whole raster by a small amount. For example, when working at magnifications of the order of 20,000 to 30,000 it may be difficult to position the specimen exactly where required by means of mechanical movements alone. A more refined movement can be obtained by electrically deflecting the beam with a d.c. voltage applied to suitable coils. With a suitable coupling system this fine deflection d.c. voltage can also be applied to the scanning coils. It is often convenient if the raster directions can be altered on the specimen. This facility can be incorporated when the scanning coils are outside the vacuum by arranging that they can be mechanically rotated [12].

A related problem to the provision of the scanning facility is that of modulating or 'chopping' the electron beam. Two types of modulation are required. One is where the beam is turned 'on' and 'off' in a repeatable and controlled manner. Different workers have different needs, but a square-wave chopping at 1 kHz with a rise time of 1 microsecond covers many requirements. The second type of situation exists where the beam is continuously 'on' but it is required to turn it off very quickly (within 10 nanoseconds or better) in order to observe, for example, the decay of some excitation in a specimen and to keep the beam 'off' as long as required. Both of these types of control can be obtained by the use of suitable magnetic coils or electrostatic plates, which, together with suitable drive units, are used to deflect the beam back and forth across an aperture. Thus, on alternate parts of the cycle, the beam passes down the column or is 'fed to earth' by hitting the column wall. Such systems are usually inserted at the filament end of the column where there is more room and where they are less likely to degrade performance in any way. Although this is the usual way of modulating the beam, it can also be done by modulating the grid supply or, possibly, the cathode EHT.

3.7 Alignment, apertures and magnetic shielding

These features of the electron column are relatively straightforward, but very important. The methods of alignment of electron columns have become simplified when compared with those used in earlier models. Where possible, sections of the column are 'pre-aligned' by manufacturing to close tolerances and in a sufficiently robust form so that the alignment remains after many cleanings and much re-assembly. The extent to which this pre-alignment is made varies from instrument to instrument, but in all instruments it is necessary to move the filament relative to the grid cylinder or anode and to move the final apertures (see below). Filaments can only be made to a certain degree of accuracy which is not as good as the accuracy of the rest of the column. In addition, filaments are run at high temperatures and are cycled between the operating temperature and ambient temperature. There is no guarantee that the filament will remain in the same position. Thus mechanical movements in the plane at right angles to the column axis have to be provided. It is also increases the effectiveness of the gun if the filament can be moved along the axis relative to the Wehnalt cylinder (see section 3.2). Motions at right angles to the column axis can be provided by micrometer-type movements either through rotary seals or, better, through bellows seals. Similar movements have to be applied to the final aperture. This final aperture effectively defines the all important angle (2α in figure 3.7) subtended by the beam at the specimen. We may wish to vary this angle by altering the aperture size used. Larger apertures are often used to give higher beam currents (and in the initial lining up). The range of semi-angles required to cover the range of currents needed implies the use of apertures between 50 and 500μ in diameter. Thus the apertures have to be carefully positioned initially and need to be finally located by micrometer-type movements with good control. These final apertures are those requiring the most care and attention; other apertures included in the system are less critical. Often an aperture is inserted to define the diameter of the electron source. By arranging that only the centre part of the Gaussian distribution is used, a higher beam current density can be obtained. The remaining apertures are 'splash' apertures, so-called because their main function is to prevent stray electrons hitting the bore walls and contaminating them. The contamination falls instead on the apertures which can be easily cleaned or replaced.

Finally we have to consider magnetic shielding. The troublesome fields are stray a.c. magnetic fields from nearby apparatus and power supplies. These have frequencies of between 50 and 200 Hz and these have to be reduced below a total component of the order of 5 to 10 milligauss in the position of the electron column. This is not always easy to obtain without moving other apparatus. The difficulty of obtaining this low level can be realized when it is noted that the a.c. fields given off by many metal radiators, for example, are of the order of 100 milligauss at a distance of 1-2 ft from the radiator. Once the site for the column has been chosen it is still necessary to exclude these stray fields. This can be done by using Mu-metal screens around the lens in regions where the beam is sensitive to such fields, particularly in the region of the final lens.

With these precautions a finely focussed beam of uniform cross-section can be scanned across the specimen. We now have to consider the way in which this beam interacts with the specimen. In particular we have to establish how this interaction can degrade the resolution obtained.

REFERENCES

General References to Electron Optics

V. K. ZWORYKIN, G. A. MORTON, E. G. RAMBERG, J. HILLIER and A. W. VANCE, *Electron Optics and the Electron Microscope*, Wiley, New York, (1945)

V. E. COSSLETT, *Electron Optics* (2nd ed.), Clarendon Press, Oxford, (1950)

G. LIEBMANN, *Advances in Electronics*, **2**, 101, (1950)

L. M. MYERS, *Electron Optics*, Chapman and Hall, (1939)

O. KLEMPERER, *Electron Optics*, Camb. Univ. Press, (1939)

J. R. PIERCE, *Theory and Design of Electron Beams*, Van Nostrand, Princeton, (1954)

[1] M. E. HAINE and P. A. EINSTEIN, *Brit. J. Appl. Phys.*, **3**, 40, (1952)

[2] R. N. BLOOMER, *Brit. J. Appl. Phys.*, **8**, 83, (1957)

[3] W. GLASER, *Z. Phys.*, **117**, 285, (1941)

[4] V. K. ZWORYKIN, G. A. MORTON, E. G. RAMBERG, J. HILLIER and A. W. VANCE, *Electron Optics and the Electron Microscope*, (Chap. 16), Wiley, New York, (1945)

[5] V. E. COSSLETT, *Practical Electron Microscopy*, Butterworth's, (1951)

[6] K. C. A. SMITH, Ph.D. Dissertation, Cambridge, (1956)

[7] D. B. LANGMUIR, *Proc. I.R.E.*, **25**, 977, (1937)

[8] G. LIEBMANN, *Advances in Electronics*, **2**, 102, (1950)

[9] P. A. STURROCK, *Trans. Roy. Soc. Lond.*, **A243**, 387, (1951)

[10] A. D. G. STEWART, – see Cambridge Instrument Co. – SEM

[11] C. W. OATLEY, W. C. NIXON and R. F. W. PEASE, *Advances in Electronics and Electron Physics*, **21**, 181, (1965)

[12] T. E. EVERHART, R. F. W. PEASE and S. R. PEDERSON, *Electronic Research Laboratory Report:* ERL/66/11, Berkeley, (May 1966)

CHAPTER 4

Electron Beam Energy Losses in Solids (I)

4.1 Introduction

Our understanding of both secondary emission and of the back-scattering of electrons depends heavily on the knowledge we have of the interactions between the incident electrons and the atoms of the bombarded material. This knowledge depends in turn upon the expertise gained by atomic and nuclear physicists in the 1930's in studying the interactions between β-rays and individual atoms. Once we have understood the ways in which an electron beam can excite a specimen we can seek to understand how this excitation is used in the SEM. This interaction between β-rays and matter is central to all aspects of scanning electron microscopy. All the modes of operation depend on this interaction, particularly in the way in which the incident energy is absorbed as a function of depth. Because of space limitations we will restrict our topic to the range of primary election energies in use in practice, i.e. $\leqslant 100$ keV. In this energy range the energy loss due to the emission of radiation by an electron in the Coulomb field of a nucleus can be neglected. So, although this type of interaction can lead to considerable scattering of the incident

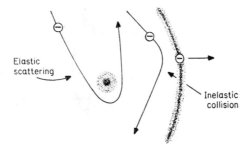

Figure 4.1. A reminder of the interactions between fast electrons and atoms that are important in the SEM: the elastic scattering by the nucleus and the inelastic interaction with the bound electrons.

47

electrons, this scattering may be regarded as elastic. The major energy loss is due to interactions between the incident fast electron and the bound electrons of the target material.

This electron-electron interaction is shown in figure 4.1. A fast electron approaches an electron which is bound to one of the host atoms. The Coulombic field between the two electrons leads to an interchange of energy as a result of which the bound electron is forced into an allowed excited state while the incident electron loses energy. The appropriate Schroeder equation is used to calculate the relative probabilities that each electron will end up in a particular state. Therefore the relative probabilities of an electron of energy, E_0, losing ΔE_{01}, ΔE_{02} . . . in a collision are known. So by multiplying the energy losses by these relative probabilities the average energy loss per unit distance of path can be determined. In the non-relativistic case [1] this rate of loss can be written as

$$dE/ds = (2\pi e^4 \, N\mathscr{Z}/E) \ln \{E/E_i \sqrt{e}/2\}$$

where N is the number of atoms/cm³, $\mathscr{Z}$ is the atomic number and E_i is the average excitation potential of the atom. This expression, which takes account of the ultimate indistinguishability of the two electrons emerging from the ionizing collision, gives very good agreement with experiments performed in gases. In trying to check this equation, in solid materials, we come up against the difficulty illustrated in figure 4.2, in which we have contrasted the behaviour in gases with that in solids. In gases the electron-electron interactions are relatively widely separated in space. Such interations are studied by the use of cloud chambers in which the actual paths of the electrons are made visible. In this way a direct comparison can be made between the experimental observations and the formula for the loss of energy per unit distance of the *electron path*. In solid materials where the distance between collisions is much less because of the much larger density of atoms available to take part in collisions, this technique is not possible. The most direct experimental study that can be made in solids is to study how the energy loss varies as a function of specimen *thickness*. But this is still somewhat indirect because, superimposed on the collisions at which a significant energy loss occurs, there are scattering events which are essentially elastic but which lead to significant changes in directions. A measurement of the energy loss as a function of foil thickness integrates over many scatterings or collisions. As a result a knowledge of the average distance of

penetration into the crystal compared to the total path length needed
to absorb the total primary electron energy is required before comparison can be made with the theoretical formula. We can express
this point more quantitatively. If l is the mean distance between
collisions and/or scatterings and if random walk statistics are
applicable, the electron will finish up at a distance $L = \sqrt{n}\, l$ from
the point of incidence where n is the average number of collisions

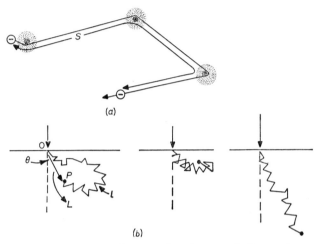

Figure 4.2. The problem of comparing data on bulk specimens with
theory: (*a*) gaseous case, ability to follow electron *path*; (*b*) solid case,
ability only to determine average *transverse range*, i.e. distance along
direction of incidence corresponding to complete energy loss.

experienced. The line $O\,P\ (= L)$ makes an angle θ with the surface
normal. If the distribution function $p(\theta)$ is known, the mean depth
of penetration can be estimated as a function of beam energy. From
this the mean loss of energy in a foil of given thickness can be calculated. We return to the details of such calculations in sections 4.4
and 4.5.

In discussing the physical ideas on which scanning electron
microscopy is based we need information about:

(1) The interaction between the primary beam and the specimen,
in particular about the way in which energy is absorbed as a
function of death.

(2) The way in which electron-beam excitation leads to secondary-

E

Scanning Electron Microscopy

electron emission and the manner in which such emission depends on temperature, specimen properties and beam energy, etc.

(3) The basic facts about the back-scattering of electrons.

(4) The use of electron-beam excitation to generate photon emission.

In this and the following chapter we consider the first three of these topics; the fourth is central to the cathodoluminescent mode of operation and is discussed in Chapter 10. The initial discussion here is limited to materials which are good or fair electrical conductors. Additional complications arising when insulator specimens are examined are discussed in Chapter 5.

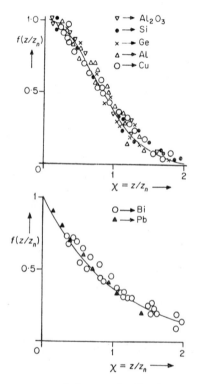

Figure 4.3. The success of the standardization process suggested by Makhov *et al.* [5–8]; (a) $f(z)$ as a function of z/z_n for low and medium atomic number materials; (b) as (a) but for heavy atomic number materials.

4.2 Treatments of the beam interaction problem

In discussing this very complex subject in a limited space the best an author can hope to do is to introduce the underlying ideas, the approximations employed, the shortcomings of the physical models, the discrepancies between theory and experiment and the difficulties facing further work. To the present author's way of thinking there are two current approaches which are relevant to scanning electron microscopy. The first is perhaps best exemplified by a series of papers by Cosslett and Thomas [2, 3, 4,] which seek a very detailed physical understanding of the phenomena which occur, under a wide range of experimental conditions. It is a fair but oversimplified statement to say that the relative merits of several, first-order models have been established but there is no generalized theory than can be used to predict the behaviour with certainty in a given situation. The second approach due to Vyatskin, Makhov, and collaborators [5, 6, 7 & 8] is more empirical in that it glosses over the details of the microscopic scattering mechanisms and seeks to establish a series of universal expressions (in closed form) giving the energy loss as a function of depth over a wide range of beam energy and atomic number. We have, therefore, a long-term approach which will in due course give us a satisfactory quantitative model and an empirical approach which we can use in the meantime to indicate the approximate behaviour. From the point of view of the SEM the position is unsatisfactory in that nearly all the work has considered only specimens which are normal to the beam. We will begin by summarizing Makhov's empirical approach.

4.3 Empirical analysis of electron-beam interactions

4.3.1 *Beam intensity as a function of depth*

This approach leans heavily on experimental studies of the relative number, f, of electrons of initial energy E_0 which penetrate to a given depth in the target material. It was established [6] that universal curves can be obtained, without recourse to theory, provided they are plotted in a standard form. If, instead of plotting f against the absolute depth z, f is plotted against z/z_n, where z_n is the depth at which $f = 1/e$, universal curves can be obtained. (See figure 4.3) Analytically these results can be expressed by

$$\frac{I(z)}{I(o)} = f(z/z_n) = \exp\left[-(z/z_n)^p\right].$$ (4.1)

Scanning Electron Microscopy

when p is a constant for a given material. The available values are given in table 4.1

Table 4.1 (a). *Experimental estimates of the parameter, p. [5]*

Material	Value of p
Al, Si, Cu, Ge & Al_2O_3	~ 2
Bi, Pb	~ 1

Table 4.1 (b). *Experimental estimates of C and n [6, 7]*

Material	$C \times 10^3$	n	E_0 (keV)
Al	3·8	1·68	2·5 to 27
Si	3·4	1·65	2 to 20
Cu	5·8	1·53	2 to 20
Ge	6·5	1·47	2 to 18
Bi	4·2	1·44	3 to 20
Al_2O_3	4·6	1·65	1 to 9

Later work [7] established that z_n could be written in the form $z_n = CE_0^n$ where C and n vary very little from one material to another. The actual experimental values are given in table 4.1 (b) with the range of E_0 over which this expression has been confirmed for each material.

The question arises as to why, when the curves are made to co-incide at one point, do they coincide over the whole range of f? Makhov considers this point. The arguments are complex and involve the use of the idea of the transverse path of an electron. Consider the situation shown in figure 4.4. The normal incidence of a narrow parallel beam leads to a statistically symmetrical scattering of the primary electrons of the type shown. These scattered electrons will, statistically, lose their energy after travelling a distance L from the point of incidence. If the angle of scatter is θ then the projected value of L in the z direction is $R = L \cos \theta$; R is termed the transverse range. It will be seen that a given depth z coincides with the transverse range of the group of electrons which are absorbed (i.e. lost to the transmitted beam) at this depth. Hence the above expression (eqn. 4.1) relating f to z can be expressed as

$$f(R, z_n) = \exp\left[R/z_n)^p\right] \text{ or } R = |\ln f|^{1/p} \qquad (4.2)$$

So that, if comparisons are made for various E_0 at constant f, R will vary linearly with z_n and the dependence of R on E_0 will be determined by the dependence of z_n on E_0. This dependence is the same for all values of R differing only by the constant $|\ln f|^{1/p}$. In particular the average value of R^p, which is given by

$$\overline{R^p} = \int_{R_{\min}\to 0}^{R_{\max}\to\infty} R^p \left(\frac{-df}{dR}\right) dR, \qquad (4.3)$$

can be shown (by integration by parts) to be equal to $z_n{}^p$.

The standardization properties of the intensity curves can now be understood. Because the ratio R/z_n is constant for all E_0 at constant f,

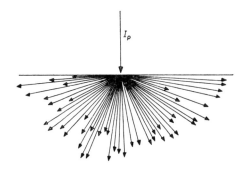

Figure 4.4. Scattering pattern assumed by Makhov *et al.* [5–8]; no division into loss by reflection or true absorbtion and statistical symmetry.

the enforced coincidence at one value of f say ($f = 1/e$) leads automatically to coincidence at all values of f. We can state this another way. The fact that the curves can be made to fall on a universal curve implies that, as E_0 is varied, the only factor which varies macroscopically is the scale of the phenomena, i.e. the average angular distribution of the scattering is, to this approximation, unchanged. Quantitatively the scale of the phenomena depends on E_0 as CE_{n0}.

Makhov [7] shows that a further corrollary of this standardization process is the fact that the relative number of electrons absorbed in a layer dz at a depth of z can be expressed in a standard form. If $g = (1 - f)$ is the relative number of electrons absorbed in a thickness, z, then the relative number dg/dz, absorbed in a unit thickness at dz is given by $dg/dz = - (df/dz)$.

From eqn. (4.1) we obtain

$$dg/dz = pz^{p-1}/(CE_0^n)^{-p} \exp - [z^p(CE_0^n)^p] = (p/z_n)\, \chi^{p-1} \exp(-X^p) \tag{4.4}$$

If $z_n(dg/dz)$ is plotted against $X(\ = z/z_n)$ we obtain universal curves over the appropriate range of E_0. Figure 4.5 shows the form of this expression for low atomic number $(p = 2)$, curve (a), and for high atomic number $(p = 1)$, curve (b).

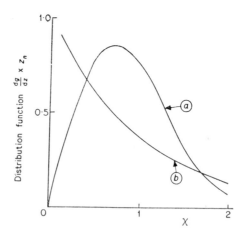

Figure 4.5. Distribution function of beam-induced electrons according to Makhov *et al.* [5–8], plotted in the form $(dg/dz)\, z_n$ against z/z_n. Curve (a) for Al, Si, Cu, Ge and Al_2O_3; Curve (b) for Bi.

4.3.2 *Beam energy as a function of depth*

So far the discussion has been solely concerned with the absorbtion of the *number of electrons* as a function of depth. No comment has been made about the manner in which the electron *energy* varies with depth. We wish to determine the number of electrons with energy between E_z and $E_z + dE_z$ at a depth z as a function of E_0 etc. If, following Makhov [7], we define $h\ (E_z, z, E_0)$ as the number of

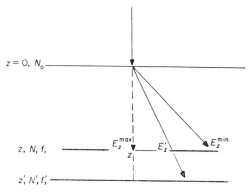

Figure 4.6. Definition of parameters used by the Russian workers to obtain energy loss as a function of depth.

electrons of energy E_z at a depth z then the total number of electrons in the beam at depth z is given by

$$N = N_0 f = \int_{E_z^{\min}}^{E_z^{\max}} h \, (E_z, z, E_0) \, dE_z \tag{4.5}$$

where $E_z^{\min}$ and $E_z^{\max}$ are the minimum and maximum of E_z at depth z, and where N_0 is the number of electrons in the beam at $z = 0$. If we consider only those electrons at depth z which can penetrate to some greater depth $z = z'$ we can write

$$N' = N_0 f' = \int_{E_z'}^{E_z^{\max}} h \, dE_z \tag{4.6}$$

where N' is the number of electrons which reach $z = z'$ and where E_z' ($< E_z^{\min}$) is the energy corresponding to a transverse range z' (see figure 4.6). We therefore obtain by differentiation of eqn. (4.6).

$$\frac{\partial N'}{\partial E_z'} = \frac{dN'}{dE_z} = h \tag{4.7}$$

Makhov then uses the formula given in eqn. (4.1) to obtain the relationship given in eqn. (4.8) between the minimum energy E_z' of those electrons at z which will reach z' and the residual range $(z' - z)$, i.e.

$$E_z' = \left(\frac{z' - z}{|\operatorname{em} f'|^{1/p} C} \right)^{1/n} \tag{4.8}$$

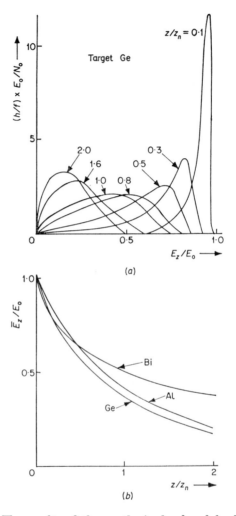

Figure 4.7. The results of the synthesis developed by Makhov *et al.* (*a*) standardized electron generation rate as function of number of electrons in beam plotted against E/E_0 i.e. ordinate is $(h/f) \times (E_0/N_0)$ for various values of z/z_n; (*b*) mean energy, $\bar{E}_z$, (relative to E_0) as a function of depth for Al, Ge and Bi; (*c*) absorbed energy as a function of depth for Al, Ge and Bi; (*d*) comparison with experiment. Curve (1) predicted; Curve (2) measurements by Young [9].

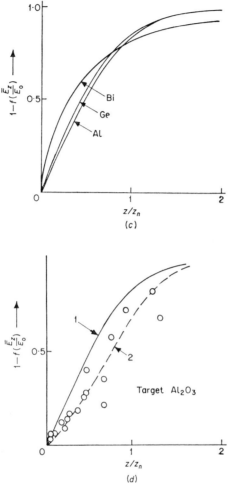

Figure 4.7. (*continued*)

That is to say, it is formally assumed that the relationship giving the transmitted fraction at various depths as a fraction of the *initial* energy and the *total* range is also applicable when the *residual* energy of a particular group of electrons at an arbitrary depth and the *residual* range at that depth are used instead.

We know from eqn. (4.1) that $f' = \exp\left(- [z'/CE_0^n]^p\right)$ and so from this relationship and eqn. (4.8) we derive

$$E_z' = E_0 \left(1 - \frac{z}{|\ln f'|^{1/p} CE_0^n}\right)1/n \qquad (4.9)$$

and

$$N' = N_0 f' = N_0 \exp\left(- \left[\frac{z}{CE_0^n \left(1 - (E_z'/E_0)^n\right)}\right]^p\right) \qquad (4.10)$$

This latter expression gives h by differentiation. With this result we can obtain four important quantities.

(1) The mean electron energy, $\bar{E}_z$, at a distance z. This quantity is usually given in relative form

$$\bar{\epsilon} = \frac{\bar{E}_z}{E_0} = \frac{1}{E_0} \int_0^{E_0} \frac{E_z h dE_z}{\int h dE_z}$$

(2) The rate of mean relative electron energy loss $= -\dfrac{1}{E_0}\dfrac{dE_z}{dz}$

(3) The mean beam energy $\overline{W} = f \times \bar{E}_z$.

(4) The rate of mean, relative beam energy loss:

$$\frac{d\bar{\omega}}{dz} = \frac{1}{E_0} \cdot \frac{d\overline{W}}{dz} = \frac{1}{E_0} \cdot \frac{d(f\bar{E}_z)}{dz}$$

Figure 4.7 compiled from Makhov's papers [7] shows the results obtained. Figure 4.7 (a) shows (hE_0/fN_0) plotted against (E_z/E_0) for various values of z/R. At low depths a narrow distribution at $E_z \sim E_0$ exists, but at greater depths the most probable energy decreases and the spread, i.e. the distribution width, increases rapidly. Figure 4.7 (b) shows how the mean electron energy $(\bar{E}_z/E_0)$ falls off with z/R for both low atomic number targets (Al, $p = 2$, $n = 1.68$ and Ge, $p = 2$, $n = 1.48$) and for a high atomic number target (Bi, $p = 1$, $n = 1.44$). Figure 4.7 (c) gives the absorbed beam energy as a function of depth for the same materials. Finally in figure 4.7(d) a comparison is made with experimental data obtained with an Al_2O_3 target by Young [9]. Although the experimental data are somewhat scattered it is fair to state that, in this case, the theory predicts an energy absorbtion which is too high by a factor which can be as high as two, but which is unlikely to be greater.

Obviously there are limitations to this approach. In addition to the limited agreement with observations, several simplifications have been made which are best discussed after a more physical model of the various contributing mechanism has been established. But briefly two points should be made. First, no division is made into electron loss by reflection or by true absorbtion. The whole approach is based on an empirical relationship derived from transmission studies in which the transmitted current is compared with the *incident* primary current. Both losses are added together to give an effective absorbtion coefficient. Secondly, the full implications of the assumption made in eqn. (4.8) need to be examined. However, even at the very worst, this step can be regarded as an arbitrary assumption which is justified as far as it is successful.

We shall return to this approximation in due course but we can now examine a more detailed approach.

4.4 Physical analysis of electron-beam interactions

4.4.1 *Introduction*

The semi-empirical approach discussed above has the advantage that solutions can be obtained in closed form even if the expressions are somewhat complex. The disadvantage is the approximate nature of the solutions so obtained, i.e. the very simplifications introduced in order to obtain analytic solutions lead, of necessity, to approximation. In order to obtain greater accuracy we have to go beyond the approximations used, in particular we have to examine the limitations of the assumption that only the scale of the observed phenomena changes as the beam energy is varied. This necessitates a detailed analysis of all the processes leading to energy loss and scattering, of the relative importance of each mechanism and of the manner in which they vary with beam voltage, foil thickness and atomic number. Here we can do little more than set the scene because of space limitations. The first point to establish is the nature of the physical interactions that occur.

We can first divide the loss mechanisms into those which result in the reflection or 'back-scattering' of the primary electrons and those which result in the absorption of the incident electrons relatively deep in the bulk of the target. To a first approximation the processes which lead to these two losses do not differ in principle but only in degree. That is to say, for both absorbed and back-scattered electrons, the scattering and loss processes are the same. But, as a result of the statistical nature of the scattering processes, they result in some electrons being scattered through an angle of greater than 90°, i.e. from the specimen, while others are scattered in the forward direction and so penetrate deeper into the specimen. In each case the scattering can be elastic or inelastic. We may divide the degrees of scattering into four groups. First there is single scattering which is self-explanatory. Secondly there are 'plural' and 'multiple' scattering. The first of these terms implies that the electrons undergo a few (~ 10) scattering events, for example, during the passage through a thin-foil target. The second term implies many scatterings, usually greater than 20 and less than some number which represents the onset of 'diffusion-like' scattering. Towards the end of the electron range the motion of the electrons becomes random, particularly with primary electrons of relatively high energy incident on targets of moderate to high atomic number. This is termed 'diffusion' scattering.

Later we shall be more specific in defining these terms. For the present we have established that the most probable scattering distribution depends on the interactions between the incident particle and the individual atoms, upon the statistics involved in such collisions and upon the number of collisions which occur. The general method of calculation followed in each case is first to calculate the differential cross-section for scattering on the model considered. By differential cross-section we mean the probability that, in any one collision, an electron will be scattered through an angle $\theta \rightarrow \theta + d\theta$. By integrating this quantity over the required angular range the total probability of scattering over this range can be determined. By estimating the number of scattering events per unit length of path we can determine the number of electrons which are deflected into a given angular range over a given path length. We then seek to relate this result to experimental data obtained by measuring the angular distribution of electrons scattered either from thin films or solid targets. Here we come up against the problem mentioned in section 4.1: what is the relationship between the behaviour as a function of path length and the behaviour as a function of depth? In addition to knowledge about the angular distributions we need information about the dependence of the electron range upon electron energy and target atomic number, and so have to estimate the probable energy loss at each collision. In the case of particular interest in scanning electron microscopy, i.e. a solid target as opposed to a foil, the particles can go through all types of scattering – single, plural, multiple and diffusion. We shall begin by stressing the processes leading to the absorbtion of electron energy. The back-scattering of electrons will be discussed in a later section.

Up to the present, the majority of the detailed work has centred on single and plural scattering into small scattering angles ($\leqslant 10^{-2}$ radians) at energies of the order of 30 to 100 kV. The reason for this emphasis is, of course, because these are the conditions (80 kV, thin films (~ 300 Å) and narrow angular apertures) which are exploited in the transmission electron microscope. Under these conditions the energy loss may, to a first approximation, be neglected. Below 30 kV, with solid targets and large-angle scattering the energy loss becomes important. A further complication arises under the relatively low beam voltage conditions appropriate to scanning electron microscopy, because the Born approximation will then require significant correction, if it is to give valid estimates (see below, section 4.4.3).

The following section gives some indication of the complexity involved in calculating scattering cross-sections and the definitions of plural, multiple and diffusion scattering are put on a firmer basis. A subsequent section discusses the angular distribution of the scattered electrons, while the final section deals with energy-range relationships.

4.4.2 *The elastic and inelastic scattering of electrons by target atoms*
The elastic scattering of an incident electron by a nucleus is more likely than the inelastic electron-electron collision. This is because of the small electron mass which allows it to be deflected through large angles without approaching close to the nucleus. Obviously 'screening', i.e. the shielding of the nuclear Coulombic field by the electrons, is very important. In the absence of screening the scattering of an electron by the nuclear field is given by the Rutherford formula. Within the limitations of the Born approximation the differential cross-section for scattering by the whole atom is given by [10]:

$$d\sigma(\theta) = \frac{2\pi e^4}{4p^2v^2}\left[\mathscr{Z} - F \right]^2 \cdot \frac{\sin\theta d\theta}{\sin^4(\theta/2)} \qquad (4.11)$$

where p and v are the electron momentum and velocity respectively at low energies ($v \ll c$). F is the atomic form factor and is probably best obtained on the Fermi-Thomas model of the atom. On this model $F/\mathscr{Z}$ is a function only of the parameter $(\lambda \mathscr{Z}^{1/3})^{-1} \sin\theta/2$, where λ is the De Broglie wavelength of the incident electron. At low energies the use of the Born approximation is invalid. In this approximation the wave functions of incident and 'struck' particles are taken as plane waves and the approximation is valid provided that the amplitude of the wave scattered by the atomic field is small compared to that of the incident wave. In quantitative terms this requires that

$$\alpha = \frac{\mathscr{Z}e^2}{\hbar v} \ll 1. \ (v \text{ is the particle velocity.})$$

This is not true for electrons in the 5 to 40 keV energy range of interest to us. Molière [11] has taken the problem beyond this limitation and by using the WKB approach (see Mott [12]) has derived the scattering for all values of the parameter α. For $\alpha \ll 1$ Molière's formula agrees with the Born approximation and, for $\alpha \sim 1$, gives a smaller scattering cross-section than the Born approximation.

With regard to inelastic scattering, Mott has shown [13] that, on the quantum theory, taking due regard of the indistinguishability of the scattered and 'struck' electron, the electron scattering cross-section is given by

$$d\sigma(\theta) = \frac{2\pi \mathscr{Z}^2 e^4 \cos\theta \sin\theta d\theta}{E^2} \left[\frac{1}{\sin^4\theta} + \frac{1}{\cos^4\theta} - \frac{1}{\sin^2\theta \cos^2\theta} \times \cos \right.$$
$$\left. \left\{ \frac{\mathscr{Z}^2 c^2 \log\tan\theta}{\hbar v} \right\} \right] \qquad (4.12)$$

This expression, which gives the angular distribution, can be related to the corresponding energy changes by the use of the energy-momentum relationship. If one electron is scattered through θ its energy is given by $W = E \cos^2\theta$, while the second will be scattered through $(\pi/2) - \theta$, with energy $E \sin^2\theta$. Therefore eqn. (4.12) can be transformed to

$$d\sigma(EW) = \frac{\pi e^4 \, dW}{E} \left\{ \frac{1}{W^2} + \frac{1}{(E-W)^2} - \frac{1}{W(E-W)} \times \cos \right.$$
$$\left. \frac{e^2}{\hbar v} \log \frac{(E-W)}{W} \right\} \qquad (4.13)$$

and the number of secondary electrons of energy W to $W + dW$ created in a path-length ds is $\mathscr{Z}Nds \, d\sigma \, (EW)$ where $\mathscr{Z}N$ is the number of electrons/cm^3. From the estimates of the differential scattering cross-section it is possible to obtain the Bethe loss expression [14] which gives the change in the *mean* electron energy, E_m, in a mass thickness ρds, by

$$\frac{dE_m}{d(\rho s)} = \frac{2\pi\, e^4\, Na}{AE}\, \mathscr{L}\, \ln\left(\frac{2E}{I}\right) \qquad (4.14)$$

where Na is Avogadro's number, A is the atomic weight, ρ the density and I is the mean excitation potential of the target atoms. The mean energy E_m is given by

$$E_m = \int_0^{E_0} N(E)\, E\, dE \Big/ \int_0^{E_0} N(E)\, dE.$$

Equation (4.14) is the non-relativistic form and is a good approximation even for low values of E_0 except for targets of very low atomic number. This equation can be integrated to give a relation between E_m and the mass thickness traversed

$$(\rho s)\bar{E}_m = \frac{I^2}{8\pi\, e^4\, Na} \cdot \frac{A}{\mathscr{L}} \left[\bar{E}_i\{2\ln(2E_0/I)\} - \bar{E}i\{2\ln(2\,E_m/I)\}\right] \quad (4.15)$$

where $\bar{E}_i$ is the exponential integral (see Jahnke and Emde [15]). A Bethe range, ρR_b, can be obtained by setting $E_m = I/2$ which, after scaling down by the ratio of the specimen thickness to actual path length can, in principle, be compared with experimental estimates of the range as measured in terms of foil thickness (see section 4.5.4).

4.4.3 *Multiple and plural scattering*
In the case where the foil is sufficiently thick for the electrons to make many scatterings, but not thick enough for energy losses to be significant, the theory of errors can be applied. It is found [16] that the probability, $P(\theta)d\theta$, of an electron emerging at a scattering angle θ is given by

$$P(\theta)d\theta = [2\theta/\langle\theta^2\rangle]\exp\left(-\,\theta^2/\langle\theta^2\rangle\,d\theta\right) \qquad (4.16)$$

where $\langle\theta^2\rangle$ is the mean-square scattering angle. Equation (4.16) is taken as a definition of multiple scattering, i.e. if the angular distribution is Gaussian the scattering is termed multiple scattering. $\langle\theta^2\rangle$ is estimated by using a formula, derived by Mott [17], which gives the probability of deflection between θ & $\theta + d\theta$ in a layer dz of foil in the absence of screening as

$$[f(\theta)d\theta]_{dz} = \frac{8\pi N\,\mathscr{L}\,(\mathscr{L}+1)e^4}{p^2\,v^2}\,\frac{d\theta}{\theta^3}\,dz. \qquad (4.17)$$

$\langle \theta^2 \rangle$ is obtained by integrating $\theta^2 f(\theta) d\theta$ between two limits θ_{min} and θ_{max}. The lower limit, θ_{min} arises because the electrons shield the nucleus at very small angles and greatly reduce the scattering probability below that given by eqn. (4.17). Usually θ_{min} is taken as $\theta_{min} = (\hbar/p\mathscr{Z}^{-1/3}a_0)$ (where a_0 is the Bohr radius) provided that the Born approximation is valid. If this is not so,

$$\theta_{min} \approx \left(\frac{\mathscr{Z}e^2}{\hbar v} \right) \times \left(\frac{\hbar}{p\mathscr{Z}^{-1/3}} \right) \frac{1}{a_0}$$

is a more appropriate value [18]. The choice of θ_{max} is more arbitrary. θ_{max} is chosen by the statistics so that there will be many collisions in the foil with $\theta < \theta_{max}$, but not many with $\theta > \theta_{max}$. Usually θ_{max} is taken as that angle for which there is, on the average, only one collision during the passage through the foil of thickness, t, in which $\theta > \theta_{max}$. On this basis $\theta^2_{max} = 4\pi N\mathscr{Z}(\mathscr{Z} + 1)e^4 t/(pv)^2$. Finally $\langle \theta^2 \rangle$ is calculated to be equal to $\theta^2_{max} \ln (\theta_{max}/\theta_{min})$. The fraction of the beam $f(\theta)$ collected in a cone of semi-angle θ is equal to

$$\int_0^\theta P(\theta) \, 2\pi \, \theta d\theta = 1 - \exp\left(-\theta^2/\langle \theta^2 \rangle \right)$$

So comparison with experimental data leads to estimates of $\langle \theta^2 \rangle$.

This relatively simple theory is only one of several which differ in detail, in the model assumed for the electron distribution, in the angular range considered and in the degree of correction for the failure of the Born approximation. For example, another approach by Bethe, Rose and Smith [19] based on transport theory is valid in the multiple and diffusion scattering situations. It predicts that the transmission is given by $f = 0 \cdot 862/(z/\lambda_r + 0 \cdot 719)$ where λ_r is the transport mean free path which is equal to the mean free path for elastic scattering divided by $\overline{(1 - \cos \theta)}$. Neglecting the contribution from large-angle single scattering and ignoring the energy loss, the Bethe, Rose and Smith theory gives

$$1/\lambda_r = 4 \cdot 5 \, \frac{\rho \mathscr{Z}^2}{A E_0^2} \log_{10} \left(\frac{E_0^{1/2}}{2 \, \mathscr{Z}^{1/3}} \right) \times 10^{10}. \tag{4.18}$$

λ_r has also been estimated allowing for screening. The result is to increase the dependence of λ_r on $\mathscr{Z}$.

The multiple-scattering theories have certain features in common. The assumption that successive scattering events are independent is common to all as is the neglect of large-angle scattering. This latter assumption becomes increasingly less valid as E_0 is decreased. Cosslett and Thomas [3] have stressed that the proportion of elementary scattering events leading to $\theta > 90°$ is inversely proportional to E_0 because of the energy dependence of the screening constant. (See definition of θ_{min} above.) In addition, the chance of a large-angle scattering event will vary in proportion to the film thickness, but, for multiple scattering producing a similar deflection, the deflection will increase as the square root of the number of events and hence on the square root of the thickness. Therefore the small-angle theories can be expected to show increasing discrepancies at low beam energies in thick films.

The first theory outlined above is unsatisfactory in that there is some arbitrariness in the definition of θ_{max} and there is no consideration of the transition from single to multiple scattering. Molière [20] has given a treatment of the scattering problem which is applicable to both the plural and multiple scattering cases and which has certain advantages, i.e. it is analytic in form until at a late stage in the development, it uses the more correct Fermi-Thomas electron distribution, and it takes account of deviations from the Born approximation. On this model the scattering into an angular interval $d\theta$ at θ is given by a power series in

$$\delta = (\theta/\theta_{max}\sqrt{B}) \tag{4.19}$$

where B is given by $B - \ln B = b$ and b is a parameter related to the number of collisions by

$$b = 2\ln\left(\frac{\theta_{max}}{\theta_a}\right) - 0.154. \tag{4.20}$$

The parameter θ_a is a lower 'cut-off' or 'screening' angle similar to θ_{min}. On the Fermi-Thomas model Molière estimate that

$$\theta_a{}^2 = \left(\frac{\hbar/p}{0.865\,a_0\,\mathscr{Z}^{-1/3}}\right)^2\left[1.13 + 3.76\left(\frac{\mathscr{Z}e^2}{\hbar v}\right)^2\right] \tag{4.21}$$

The second term in brackets on the right-hand side in eqn. (4.21) represents a correction term to the Born approximation. By expanding the distribution $P(\theta)\theta d\theta$ as a power series it is found that the first term gives a Gaussian distribution while the second term gives $\sim 10\%$ correction. At small angles the correct distribution lies above the Gaussian distribution, whereas at moderate angles it lies below.

F

Finally, in the single scattering region it lies considerably above it. The width of the distribution as defined by the $1/e$ point is $\theta_w = \theta_{max} \times (B - 1\cdot2)^{1/2}$ where B is given by eqn. (4.19).

The complexity of this situation is now apparent. No matter what approximations are made, the resulting distribution is complicated and depends on a number of parameters which are in themselves difficult to calculate. Obviously considerable care and critical assessment is needed at each stage. This comment is also true for diffusion scattering.

4.4.4 *Diffusion scattering*

We define the 'diffusion' depth as that depth at which the electron motion is completely random. There are, in fact, several definitions of the diffusion depth:

(1) It is identified with the depth at which the most probable scattering angle reaches its maximum value which is subsequently constant at greater depths.

(2) It is equated to the depth from which Lenard's law [25], which predicts an exponential fall-off in beam intensity, is obeyed.

(3) As, on the average, the electrons cease to penetrate further into the target once the flow has become diffusive, the diffusion depth can be equated to the foil thickness which gives 50% transmission.

(4) For mathematical convenience the diffusion depth has been defined as the depth at which the most probable scattering angle becomes equal to $\cos^{-1}(1/e)$. Cosslett [21] has compared these definitions and commented on the way in which they have been applied.

Table 4.2. *Comparison between experimental and theoretical estimates of the diffusion depth*

Material	Cosslett [21] (in units of $\mu g/cm^2$)			
	(ρz_D)	$(\rho z_{av})_A$	$(\rho z_{av})_m$	$\rho<z>_s$
Al	455	350	780	460
Cu	390	240	430	400
Ag	275	150	250	270
Au	220	85	120	165

In table 4·2 the experimental observations of the diffusion depth expressed in $\mu g/cm^2$ are compared with theoretical estimates due to Archard [22]. The experimental observations (ρz_d) represent the mean value obtained by using the first three definitions listed above. The values obtained using these definitions agreed to within the experimental error of $\pm 10\%$. The values, (ρz_{av}), given in the second column were derived from a formula, $z_{av} = 40R/7\mathscr{Z}$, given by Archard [22]. Here R is the range calculated on the Bethe loss law. It is apparent that there is some disagreement with experimental observation both in magnitude and dependence on $\mathscr{Z}$. The model used by Archard calculates the mean free path for elastic scattering based on the Rutherford scattering formula in its low-angle limit and uncorrected for screening. If these limitations are removed it is found that (z_{av}) is given by $(z_{av}) \sim 8R/(\mathscr{Z} - 5)$. Using this formula the values, $(\rho z_{av})_M$, given in the third column are obtained. Once again the theoretical prediction can be criticized in that it predicts a greater dependence on $\mathscr{Z}$ than is observed experimentally. To obtain reasonable agreement it is necessary to resort to Monte-Carlo calculations to estimate the diffusion depth. In the final column of table 4.2 the results of such a calculation are represented. It is seen that good agreement is obtained. As the final column can be written as $\langle z \rangle_s \simeq 12 R/(\mathscr{Z} + 8)$ it can be concluded that a reasonably accurate estimate of the diffusion distance can be obtained from the formula $z_D \simeq 12R/(\mathscr{Z} + 8)$.

The initial theoretical treatment of diffusion scattering was made by Bothe [23] using transport theory. The theory predicted the Lenard transmission law $f = \exp[-(\mu/\rho)\,\rho z]$ with $\mu/\rho = (2\rho\mathscr{Z}^2/AE_0^2) \times 10^{11}$. This expression for μ/ρ predicts values that are too high and a dependence of μ/ρ on both $\mathscr{Z}$ and E_0 which is greater than that observed experimentally. Molière [20], by correcting for the Born approximation and allowing for increasing film thickness, obtains values which agree more closely with the experimental observations both as regards magnitude and dependence on E_0 and $\mathscr{Z}$. Bethe, Rose and Smith [19] have extended their treatment of multiple scattering to include the diffusion case by considering the energy loss. Probably as a result of oversimplifying assumptions (see section 4.5) their theory gives estimates of the diffusion depths which are about half those observed in practice and gives a predicted dependence on E_0 less than that obtained experimentally. The theory also predicts an angular distribution which can be described as a modified cosine

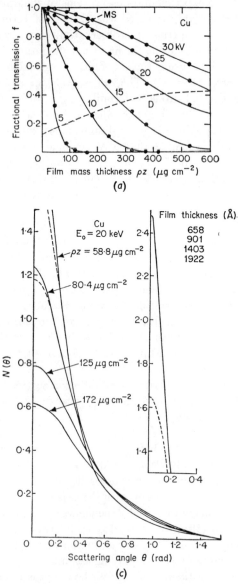

Figure 4.8. Data due to Cosslett and Thomas [3]; (a) transmitted fraction as a function of beam voltage and film thickness for Cu; ---- (MS) denotes transition between plural and multiple scattering;

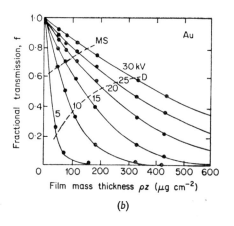

(b)

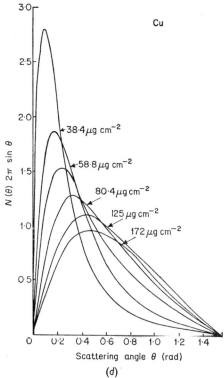

(d)

— — — — (D) denotes transition between multiple and diffusion scattering; (b) similar to (a) for Au; (c) and (d) angular distributions as a function of film thickness (ρz) for Cu bombarded by 20 kV electrons.

69

distribution with a most probable angle of scatter = 45°, whereas the experimental observations are closer to the cos² distribution (most probable angle $\simeq$ 35°) predicted by Molière. We shall reconsider these and other points when we have presented a cross-section of the detailed data.

4.5 Experimental observations

4.5.1 *Transmission and angular distribution studies*

We shall rely heavily here on the work of Cosslett and Thomas. Observations obtained by these workers [3] of the fractional transmission for Cu and Au are shown in figure 4.8. The results obtained by the same workers on Al resemble the Cu data and for Ag the results are intermediate between those for Cu and Au. These curves can be idealized to some extent into three regions corresponding to plural, multiple and diffusion scattering. In the same figure we have illustrated the angular distributions observed. For the thinner films the agreement with the Gaussian curve can be assessed by comparing the dotted curves with the experimental data. At higher film thicknesses the curve is Gaussian in shape up to $\theta = 0{\cdot}4$ radians with a longer 'tail' than predicted at high θ. This 'tail' becomes more pronounced as the scattering becomes more diffusion-like. One important parameter is the value of angle corresponding to the peak in the angular distribution as it gives information about the onset of both multiple and diffusion scattering. This is the type of data available and is best discussed in detail in terms of the three regions indicated in figure 4.8. For space reasons we have omitted a detailed discussion of plural scattering and we will therefore first consider multiple scattering.

4.5.2. *Comparison with theory – multiple scattering*

(1) *Transmitted fraction.* Figure 4.9 makes a comparison between theory and experiment. The general form of the predicted curve fits the experimental observations of the transmitted fraction. Quantitatively the fit is reasonable in view of the complexity of the problem. The fit worsens as the energy is reduced. Discrepancies in detail must be expected because the theories were developed for the high-energy region and so neglect the energy loss and are not concerned with the invalidity of the Born approximation. The main ways in which the theories need modification may be summarized as follows:

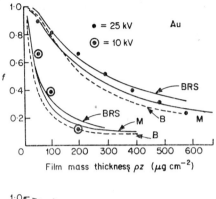

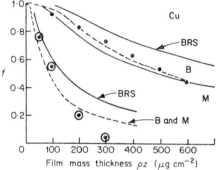

Figure 4.9. Comparison between experimental estimates ($\bullet + \odot$) of transmitted fraction in Au and Cu as function of (ρz) with theory. BRS denotes prediction on Bethe-Rose-Smith theory while B and M denote those on the Bothe and Molière approaches (After Coslett and Thomas [3]).

(1) With regard to the mean-square scattering angle $\langle \theta_0{}^2 \rangle$, it has been found that the experimental determinations of this quantity are smaller than those predicted by Bothe's theory. In addition, this parameter is found to vary with E_0. For example, see table 4.3.

Table 4.3. *The variation of* $\langle \theta_0 \rangle^2_{expt}$ *with* E_0 *for Cu and Au* [3]

$E_0(\text{keV})$	Cu	Au
25	$\langle \theta_0 \rangle^2_{expt} = 0 \cdot 77 \langle \theta_0 \rangle^2_{th}$	$\langle \theta_0 \rangle^2_{expt} = 0 \cdot 60 \langle \theta_0 \rangle^2_{th}$
10	$\langle \theta_0 \rangle^2_{expt} = 0 \cdot 55 \langle \theta_0 \rangle^2_{th}$	$\langle \theta_0 \rangle^2_{expt} = 0 \cdot 35 \langle \theta_0 \rangle^2_{th}$

(2) Correction for the failure of the Born approximation reduces the scattering cross-section and so increases the transmitted fraction. This effect would be more noticeable for high atomic-number targets as E_0 is reduced. This factor would explain the greater divergence between the results for Au compared to those obtained for Cu.

(3) The attempts made by Molière [11] and Lenz [24] to correct for the Born approximation and the energy loss need re-examining.

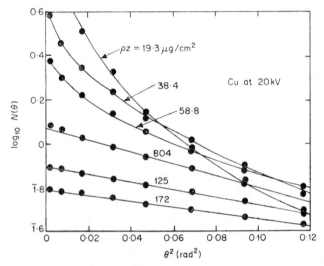

Figure 4.10. Replot of the angular distribution data to test the fit to a Gaussian distribution [3].

Briefly $\langle\theta_0\rangle^2$ is replaced by $B \times \langle\theta_0\rangle^2$ and the estimates of B are in doubt. In particular B as calculated varies too rapidly with (ρz).

(4) The Bethe, Rose and Smith theory is possibly limited by the simplifying assumptions made (see section 4.5). Cosslett and Thomas have suggested that an interesting modification of the starting equations of this theory would be to include both the energy loss and the screening factor.

(2) *Angular distribution.* Figure 4.10 shows a more rigorous test of the agreement between the predicted Gaussian distribution and the observations. A straight line exists for $\rho z > 125\mu g/cm^2$. A compilation of similar data from a variety of targets is given in table 4.4.

Table 4.4. The number of scattering events, p(ms), corresponding to the onset of multiple scattering together with the corresponding most probable angle of scattering [3]

Material	$E_0 = 10$ keV		$E_0 = 20$ keV	
	p(ms)	θ_0	p(ms)	θ_0
Al	17 to 32	16 to 24	26	19
Cu	25	22	28	20
Ag	23 to 35	18 to 29	26	19
Au	26	18	20 to 31	18 to 21

In this table the number of scattering events corresponding to the onset of multiple scattering is given together with the corresponding value of the most probable scattering angle. Within the rather large

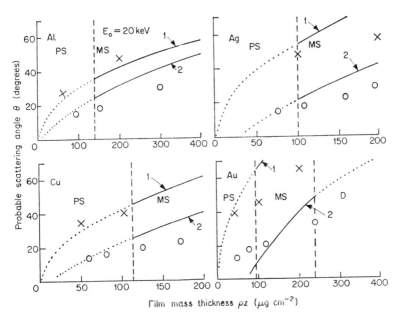

Figure 4.11. Estimates of the most probable scattering angle as a function of film thickness in Al, Ag, Cu and Au at 20 kV; O denotes experimental estimates on Molière-Lenz theory; X denotes experimental estimates on Bothe theory, Curves (1) and (2) represent theoretical predictions on B and ML theories respectively.

experimental error there is no dependence of either parameter on the atomic number. The implication is that a minimum number of scattering acts is needed to produce a Gaussian distribution irrespective of the magnitude of each deflection. If we accept that $p(ms)$ is constant then, using the approximate expression

$$\langle\theta_0\rangle^2/p(ms) \approx \frac{160}{3}\,\mathscr{Z}^{2/3}/E_0\,, \qquad (4.22)$$

We would expect θ_0 to vary as $\mathscr{Z}^{1/3}$. The experimental observations show a smaller dependence on $\mathscr{Z}$ than this. Equation (4.22) implies a strong dependence of $\langle\theta_0\rangle^2$ upon E_0 but this dependence is not observed in practice. The discrepancy may arise because the screening factor used to obtain eqn. (4.22) may be in error. In particular it is possible that the effective atomic radius, which is used to calculate the screening factor, may not depend on $\mathscr{Z}$ as rapidly as $\mathscr{Z}^{-1/3}$ as hitherto assumed. (See section 4.5.) In addition, the effective atomic radius may not in fact be a constant as assumed but may well be a function of E_0. Plots of $\langle\theta_0\rangle^2$ against (ρz) do not fit Bothe's theory (See figure 4.11), even when corrected for energy loss and the failure of the Born approximation. It is not clear why this divergence arises. The major success of the Bothe theory is that it gives the correct prediction for the angular distribution as a function of (ρz).

4.5.3 *Comparison with theory – diffusion scattering*

(1) *Transmitted fraction.* Here we are concerned with determinations of the mass absorbtion coefficient in the Lenard law [25] which

Table 4.5. *Mass absorbtion coefficients; (μ/ρ). e = experimental estimates due to Cosslett and Thomas [4]; $(\mu/\rho)_B$ = theoretical prediction on original Bothe theory; $(\mu/\rho)_{ML}$ = theoretical prediction on Bothe theory after correction by Molière and Lenz*

Material	$E_0 = 5\text{keV}$			$E_0 = 15\text{keV}$			$E_0 = 25\text{keV}$		
	$(\mu/\rho)_e$	$(\mu/\rho)_B$	$(\mu/\rho)_{ML}$	$(\mu/\rho)_e$	$(\mu/\rho)_B$	$(\mu/\rho)_{ML}$	$(\mu/\rho)_e$	$(\mu/\rho)_B$	$(\mu/\rho)_{ML}$
Cu	4·0	10	6·5	0·78	1·1	1·3	0·16	0·40	0·53
Ag	4·0	15	—	0·73	1·5	1·4	0·21	0·60	0·69
Au	4·0	24	—	0·72	2·6	1·7	0·25	0·95	0·84

expresses the transmitted fraction as $f = \exp - (\mu/\rho)\rho z$. The important features of the experimental determination of μ/ρ are shown in table 4.5 which also compares the data with theoretical estimates.

The experimental determinations are smaller than the values predicted by the Bothe theory even after correction for energy loss and the failure of the Born approximation. The discrepancy increases with increase in $\mathscr{Z}$. Quantitively $(\mu/\rho)_e$ can be written:

$$(\mu/\rho)_e = 1\cdot4 \times 10^{10}\, E_0^{-3/2}\quad 5 \leqslant E_0 \leqslant 15\ \text{keV}$$

$$= 1\cdot9 \times 10^{11}\, \mathscr{Z}^{1/2}/E_0^2\ 15 \leqslant E_0 \leqslant 25\ \text{keV}$$

This dependence of the exponent of E_0 on E_0 is reflected in a similar dependence of the energy-range relation (see below). The dependence of $(\mu/\rho)_e$ on $\mathscr{Z}$ must be verified before it can be accepted completely because of the variation of the difficulty in determining the onset of diffusion scattering as the atomic number is varied. After correction in the manner suggested by Molière and Lenz the agreement between theory and experiment improves but is still not too good, probably because of the exclusion of the higher-order terms in Molière's theory. These higher-order terms contain the contributions to the scattering from high-angle scattering events. A discussion

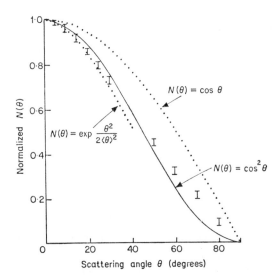

Figure 4.12. Comparisons between the experimental angular distributions and the theoretical predictions discussed in the text [4].

of the onset of diffusion scattering has already been given in section 4.4.4.

(2) *Angular distribution.* The experimentally determined angular distribution from thick films agrees well with the $\cos^2\theta$ dependence predicted by Bothe's theory except at high angles where a divergence arises due to the neglect of large-angle scattering events (see figure 4.12). At small angles a Gaussian distribution fits the data satisfactorily as well. The $\cos\theta$ prediction of the Bethe, Rose, Smith theory is not nearly so good a fit. Also shown, in figure 4.13, are

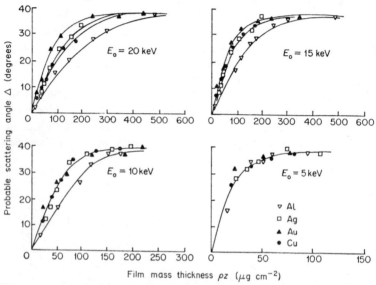

Figure 4.13. Experiment estimates of most probable scattering angles showing the increased dependence on $\mathscr{Z}$ at higher beam energies [4].

experimental observations [4] of the most probable scattering angle as a function of E_0, in Au, Ag, Cu and Al. The maximum value is found to be 38° independent of $\mathscr{Z}$ and E_0 as compared with 35° as predicted by Bothe. The number of scattering events required to give diffusion scattering is 100 ± 10 independent of atomic number and electron energy. Except at the lowest energy the distance (ρz) required to reach diffusion scattering is a function of atomic number. The dependence on $\mathscr{Z}$ increases as E_0 increases.

4.5.4 *Energy-range relationships*

(1) *General.* There are four definitions of the electron range used in the literature. The maximum range is defined as the film thickness required to reduce the transmitted flux to zero. Since such range estimates are made by extrapolating the transmission against film thickness curve to $f = 0$, they are difficult to make because of the 'tail' to the curve (see figure 4.14(*a*)). A more accurate method is to

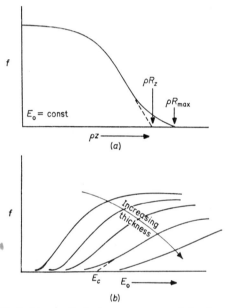

Figure 4.14. Definitions of electron range used in the literature; (*a*) extrapolated range ρR_z, maximum range, ρR_{max}; (*b*) extrapolated range by alternative method.

define an extrapolated range, R_z, obtained either by extrapolating the linear part of this curve to $f = 0$ or by extrapolating the curves shown in figure 4.14(*b*) to $f = 0$ to obtain the value (E_c) of E_0 for which the film thickness is equal to the extrapolated range. There are, in addition, two definitions of the range which depend on the electron energy. The first, sometimes referred to as the Thomson-Whiddington range, is the thickness required to reduce the *most probable* energy to zero. The second, called the mean range by Cosslett and Thomas [4], is the specimen thickness required to make the *mean* electron energy equal to zero. Above $E_0 = 10$ keV the ranges determined by these different definitions are simply related to each other and to the range, R_B, found by integrating the Bethe energy loss law, but below $E_0 = 10$ keV the relationships become more complex. Cosslett and Thomas [4] argue that the extrapolated range, R_z, is the more significant quantity to work with as it is easier to determine experimentally; it can be compared directly (except for 'straggling' complications) with that predicted by the Bethe loss law which deals with the mean energy loss; finally R_z can be related to the absorbtion coefficient as given by the Lenard law. Cosslett and Thomas give a very detailed discussion of the relationships between the various ranges, of the agreement between the various experimental estimates and of the validity of some currently made assumptions. The salient features of this discussion of relevance to scanning electron microscopy are discussed below.

(2) *The ranges based on transmission flux studies.* Usually the extrapolated range can be expressed as a function of the electron energy by

$$R_z = kE_c{}^n \equiv kE_0{}^n \qquad (4.23)$$

where k and n are numerical constants for the element and E_c is the extrapolated energy for which a given specimen thickness represents R_z (see figure 4.14(b)). The value of n is somewhat dependent on E_0. The values quoted in table 4.6 illustrate this dependence.

These values are in satisfactory agreement with other estimates,

Table 4.6. *The dependence of R_z on E_c ($= E_0$)*

Material	k	n	range of keV	Reference
Cu	103	1·5	5 to 15	[4]
	125	1·37	2 to 5	,,
Ag	82	1·5	5 to 15	,,
Au	45	1·5	2 to 15	,,
Al	390	1·34	2 to 5	,,
	274	1·50	5 to 15	,,
	270	1·54	5 to 11	[9]

[*Note:* The units of k are such that if E_0 is expressed in keV, then R_z is given in Å]

particularly those obtained by Holliday and Sternglass [26]. These authors suggested that, when plotted in terms of mass-thickness, the extrapolated range appeared to be independent of $\mathscr{Z}$. The validity of this suggestion can be seen from table 4.7, in which the values

Table 4.7. The constancy of ρR_z as $\mathscr{Z}$ is varied

E_0(keV)	2·5	5	10	15
Al	36 (27·5)	90 (86)	230 (300)	— (600)
Cu	43 (38)	102 (120)	305 (375)	530 (760)
Ag	42 (49)	96 (140)	280 (450)	510 (850)
Au	40 (72)	97 (192)	280 (600)	510 (1150)

[*Note:* The figures given in parenthesis are the corresponding values of ρR_B. Both values given in $\mu g/cm^2$]

obtained by Cosslett and Thomas are given as a function of E_0. With the exception of the data for Al, and ρR_z is essentially independent of $\mathscr{Z}$.

Lenard's law, $f = \exp [- \mu/\rho) \rho z]$, relating the transmission to the film thickness, is valid under the conditions in which the extrapolated range is determined. If f_c is the value of the transmission when $E_0 = E_c$ and $\rho z = \rho R_z$, then $\rho R_z = - \ln f_c/(\mu/\rho)$. This expression is obeyed well in practice. The dependence of (μ/ρ) on $\mathscr{Z}$ and E_0 is also in accord with the observations of ρR_z. Over the energy range 5 to 15 keV, (μ/ρ) is independent of $\mathscr{Z}$ and is given by $\mu/\rho = 1·4 \times 10^{10} E_0^{-1·5}$ (E_0 in eV).

The increased difficulty in making observations of the maximum range, R_{max}, means that there is less agreement between the reported observations, which are therefore of less use both practically and for comparison with theory. In general, the values of R_{max} are 1·4 to 1·6 greater than R_z. For $R_{max} \propto E_0^n$ Cosslett and Thomas find that for Cu, Ag and Au n has values 1·2 for $1 < E_0 < 5$ keV, 1·4 for $5 < E_0 < 10$ keV and 1·7 for $10 < E_0 < 15$ keV.

(3) *The ranges related to energy loss.* The classical measurements of Whiddington [27] related the *most probable* electron energy, E_p, after transmission through a film of thickness z by

$$E_0^2 - E_p^2(z) = bz \qquad (4.24)$$

Subsequent studies revealed that b is not a true constant for a given element but varies somewhat with the energy range employed. If b/ρ is studied for a given range of energy it is found to vary by a factor of two over the range of atomic number $\mathscr{Z} = 13$ (Al) to $\mathscr{Z} = 79$ (Au). The data compiled by Cosslett and Thomas are shown in figure 4.15 and appear to be at variance with the Whiddington

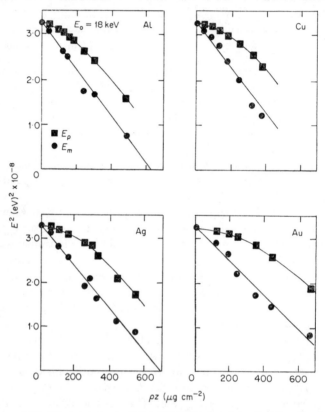

Figure 4.15. Rigorous test of the Whiddington law showing the better agreement obtained by relating the square of the mean energy, E_m, (as opposed to the most probable energy, E_p) to the depth [4].

law as the E_p against ρz curve is by no means a straight line. It must be realized that the films used by Whiddington did not cover such a large range of film thickness as those used by Cosslett and Thomas. As a result the Whiddington law in the form implied by eqn. (4.24) must be regarded as an approximation valid over a limited range of pz. The various estimates of b/ρ are in reasonable agreement when it is recognized that this parameter is an increasing function of E_0. Comparison with theory is difficult. Landau [28] has given an expression for the most probable energy loss occurring in a film of thickness z which is valid, provided the energy loss is small compared to the initial energy. Unfortunately this limitation is not always observed at low initial energies and the theoretical and experimental estimates diverge. On the other hand the difficulties are significantly reduced if the measurements are made in terms of the mean energy, E_m.

From figure 4.15 it is apparent that a relationship of the form

$$E_0{}^2 - E_m(z)^2 = b'z \qquad (4.25)$$

is well obeyed. The parameter b'/ρ is not a constant but increases with increase in E_0 and with decrease in $\mathscr{Z}$. The values shown in table 4.8, which were taken from reference [4], illustrate this dependence. The mean range, R_m, found by extrapolation from data such as those depicted in figure 4.14, is related to the beam energy by $R_m = k'E_0{}^{1.5}$

Table 4.8. *Experimental determinations of the parameter* b'/ρ ($\times$ 10^{-11}) *as a function of* E_0 *and* $\mathscr{Z}$ *compared with those predicted by the Bethe loss law* (*In parentheses*)

Material	E_0(keV)		
	9	15	18
Al	4·0 (3·6)	4·6 (4·0)	5·2 (4·2)
Cu	3·4 (2·9)	3·9 (3·3)	4·9 (3·4)
Ag	3·0 (2·6)	3·8 (2·9)	4·6 (3·0)
Au	2·7 (2·0)	3·1 (2·3)	3·8 (2·5)

for Cu, Ag and Au with $k' = 96$, 90 and 58 respectively. For Al the index is 1·65 and $k' = 200$. For Al and Cu, $R_m/R_z - 1$ to within experimental error. For Ag, R_m/R_z is consistantly slightly larger than unity and for Au $R_m/R_z = 1·30$. Finally we can make a comparison with the Bethe mass-range, R_B, obtained by the integration of the Bethe law. This comparison is readily made in figure 4.16 [4]. R_B increases faster than R_z and E increase and from tables 4.6 to

G

4.8 it is apparent that R_B increases at a greater rate with increase in E_0 and $\mathscr{Z}$ than does R_z (or any of the experimental determinations). Just what fraction of the difference is due to an error in the Bethe value rather than to the 'detour factor', s/z (the ratio of the actual path length, s, to the foil thickness, z) is difficult to judge.

4.6 Comment

Although we have relied heavily on the work of Cosslett and Thomas, no loss in generality has resulted from this concentration of interest. The papers discussed represent not only new and extensive data but such a deep critique and synthesis of previous experience as to merit

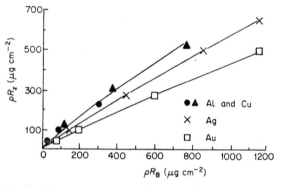

Figure 4.16. Relationship between the extrapolated range (ρR_z) and the Bethe range (ρR_B) for Al, Cu, Ag and Au [4].

this interest. In addition, there are no real points of controversy in the data, i.e. the information given is representative. Other data can be found in the papers listed at the end of this chapter.

This, then, is the background against which the contrast mechanisms in the conductive and cathodoluminescent modes have to be understood. Unless the absorption of beam energy as a function of depth can be predicted to within an accuracy of $\lesssim 20\%$, any attempt to use scanning electron microscopy to determine reliable quantitative estimates of significant parameters by these modes of operation is predestined to considerable uncertainty. The accurate prediction of the energy loss and the scattering behaviour is therefore central to our theme. This chapter shows the difficulties inherent in the solution of this problem. Until either by theory or by Monte-Carlo calculation we can make such predictions, we may use a more empirical approach of the type initiated by Makhov and his colleagues; but we have to accept its inherent limitations.

Having considered the complexities of the processes leading to electron energy absorption we can now tackle the processes leading to electron-beam induced emission.

REFERENCES

[1] H. A. BETHE, *Ann. Phys. Lpz.*, **5**, 325, (1930); see also [14]

[2] V. E. COSSLETT and R. N. THOMAS, *Brit. J. Appl. Phys.*, **15**, 235, (1964)

[3] V. E. COSSLETT and R. N. THOMAS, *Brit. J. Appl. Phys.*, **15**, 883, (1964)

[4] V. E. COSSLETT and R. N. THOMAS, *Brit. J. Appl. Phys.*, **15**, 1283, (1964)

[5] A. YA VYATSKIN and A. F. MAKHOV, *Soviet Physics – Tech. Phys.*, **3**, 690, (1958)

[6] A. YA VYATSKIN and A. F. MAKHOV, *Soviet Physics – Solid-State*, **2**, 810, (1960)

[7] A. F. MAKHOV, *Soviet Physics – Solid-State*, **2**, 1934, 1942, 1945, (1960)

[8] A. YA VYATSKIN and A. N. PILYANKEVICH, *Soviet Physics – Solid-State*, **5**, 1662, (1964) and with V. V. TRUNEV, ibid, **6**, 1230, (1964)

[9] J. R. YOUNG, *J. Appl. Phys.*, **28**, 524, (1957)

[10] See H. A. BETHE and J. ASHKIN, 'Passage of Radiations through Matter', *Experimental Nuclear Physics*, p. 1166, Wiley, New York, (1953)

[11] G. MOLIÈRE, W. *Naturf.*, **3a**, 78, (1948)

[12] See N. F. MOTT, *Elements of Wave Mechanics*, Cambridge Univ. Press, (1952)

[13] N. F. MOTT, *Proc. Roy. Soc. Lond.*, **A124**, 425, (1929); **A135**, 429, (1932)

[14] H. A. BETHE, *Handbuch d. Physik*, **24**, 519, Springer-Verlog, Berlin, (1933)

[15] J. JAHNKE and F. EMDE, *Tables of Functions*, Dover, New York, (1945)

[16] W. BOTHE, *Handbuch d. Physik*, **22/2**, 1, Springer-Verlag, Berlin, (1933), and *Z. Naturf.*, **4a**, 88, (1949)

[17] N. F. MOTT, *Proc. Roy. Soc. Lond.*, **A126**, 259, (1930), and see ref. [10]

[18] See ref. [10], p. 284

[19] H. A. BETHE, M. E. ROSE and L. P. SMITH, *Proc. Amer. Phil. Soc.*, **78**, 573, (1938)

[20] See ref. [11] and G. MOLIÈRE, W. *Phys.*, **156**, 318, (1959)

[21] V. E. COSSLETT, *Brit. J. Appl. Phys.*, **15**, 107, (1964)

[22] G. D. ARCHARD, *J. Appl. Phys.*, **32**, 1505, (1961)

[23] W. BOTHE, *Z. Phys.*, **54**, 161, (1929)

[24] F. LENZ, *Z. Naturf.*, **9a**, 185, (1954) and *Proc. Phys. Soc.*, **76**, 714, (1960)

[25] P. LENARD, *Ann. Phys. Lpz.*, **12**, 449, (1903)

[26] J. E. HOLLIDAY and E. J. STERNGLASS, *J. Appl. Phys.*, **28**, 1189, (1957)

[27] R. WHIDDINGTON, *Proc. Roy. Soc. Lond.*, **A86**, 365, (1912)

[28] L. LANDAU, *J. Phys.*, *Moscow*, **8**, 201, (1944)

CHAPTER 5

Electron Beam Energy Losses in Solids (II)

5.1 Introduction

So far we have stressed the absorption of energy and the scattering of electrons as a function of depth in the target. We have not divided the beam loss into its component parts of absorption loss, back-scattering loss and loss by secondary electron emission. In this chapter we shall first discuss the back-scattering of electrons and then the processes of secondary electron emission. In each case we shall present the main experimental facts and then discuss them against the existing theoretical background.

5.2 The back-scattering of electrons

5.2.1 *Experimental observations*

We start by defining the difference between back-scattered electrons and secondary electron emission. This will be on an energy basis by arbitrarily defining secondary electrons as those emitted from the specimen with energies $\leqslant 50$ eV. Electrons with greater energies are regarded as back-scattered (or reflected) electrons. The arbitrariness of this assumption does not complicate the topic. In what follows we shall deal only with back-scattered electrons, i.e. the data were obtained with systems which rejected the secondary electrons by, for example, incorporating a grid at ≈ -100 volts.

We need to know the way in which the following quantities depend on the atomic number of the target and on the primary beam energy:

(1) The total back-scattering coefficient, η, i.e. the total flow of back-scattered electrons per incident primary electron summed over all angles.

(2) The angular distribution of the back-scattered electrons.

(3) The mean energy of the reflected electrons.

(4) The most probable energy, i.e. the energy corresponding to the peak in the angular distribution curve.

Table 5.1. *Back-scattering coefficient as a function of atomic number and beam energy* [1]

				Material					
C.	Al	Ni	Cu	Ag	Pt	Au	U	E_0(keV)	Ref.
0·054	0·135	0·285		0·361			0·463	28	
0·059	0·143	0·300		0·365			0·455	11	[2]
0·083	0·186	0·347		0·420			0·482	4·5	
0·07	0·14		0·28	0·40		0·48		20	[41]
0·07	0·16	0·30		0·41	0·48			20	[42]
0·09	0·13			0·36		0·45		20	[43]
	0·17		0·32	0·45	0·53			20 to 40	[44]
	0·16		0·29	0·40	0·47			20 to 40	[45]
	0·16		0·31	0·43		0·48		10 to 70	[3]
	0·13		0·29	0·39		0·50		10 to 80	[46]

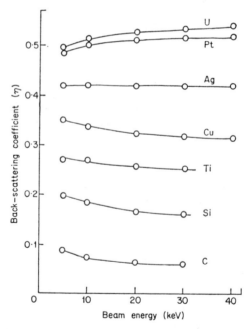

Figure 5.1. Variation of back-scattering coefficient as a function of beam voltage for various values of atomic number. After Bishop [1].

All of these parameters can be studied as a function of the angle of incidence of the primary beam. We will limit the discussion to data obtained with the beam normal to the specimen surface.

Table 5.1 shows a compilation of the reported work and was taken from reference [1]. This table, although the results are somewhat scattered in detail, shows two trends: (*i*) there is a gradual increase in the back-scattering coefficient with increase in target atomic number, (*ii*) there is a small variation of η with change in primary beam energy. These trends are seen more clearly in table 5.2 and in figure 5.1. These show Bishop's data [1] which are less scattered. The dependence on atomic number is apparent and the dependence on beam energy can be seen in detail over a range $5 \leqslant E_0 \leqslant 40$ keV. For low atomic number targets the back-scattering coefficient decreases gradually with increase in E_0. This trend decreases as $\mathscr{Z}$ increases until for Ag $(\mathscr{Z} = 47)$ η is independent of the beam energy. For high atomic number $(\mathscr{Z} \geqslant 74)$ η increases, albeit slowly, with increase in beam energy. A measure of the reliability of such studies can be seen from figure 5.2 which was taken from reference [1] and which compares Bishop's data with earlier work due to Weinryb and Philibert

Table 5.2. Values of back-scattering coefficient [1]

Material	$\mathscr{Z}$	Beam energy (keV)		
		5	10	30
Carbon	6	0·085	0·072	0·06
Aluminium	13	0·186	0·177	0·155
Silicon	14	0·197	0·186	0·162
Titanium	22	0·270	0·268	0·254
Chromium	24	0·285	0·283	0·270
Iron	26	0·300	0·296	0·288
Nickel	28	0·333	0·323	0·308
Copper	29	0·352	0·339	0·319
Zinc	30	0·352	0·342	0·330
Germanium	32	0·362	0·349	0·334
Molybdenum	42	0 367	0·381	0·385
Silver	47	0·418	0·420	0·420
Tungsten	74	0·472	0·483	0·501
Platinum	78	0·486	0·503	0·516
Gold	79	0·489	0·501	0·521
Uranium	92	0·495	0·513	0·534

[2]. The aspect of figure 5.2 that we shall exploit in due course to explain the contrast observed when particle-counters are used in the SEM is the near-monotonic increase in η with increase in $\mathscr{Z}$. It should [1] perhaps be stressed that the curve given in figure 5.2 is

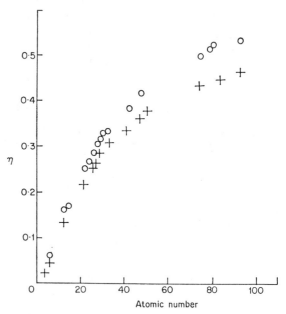

Figure 5.2. Variation of η with atomic number for $V_0 = 30$ kV. O $\equiv$ Bishop's data [1], $+$ $\equiv$ data due to Weinryb and Philibert [2].

not necessarily smooth but probably has two discontinuities at $\mathscr{Z} = 30$ and at $\mathscr{Z} \approx 60$. The increase in η with increase in $\mathscr{Z}$ is observed over a wide range of primary beam energy. In fact only at values of $E_0 \leqslant 1$ keV is this behaviour not observed. This lack of dependence on $\mathscr{Z}$ at low E_0 does not itself impede the use of particle counters. (See Chapter 8.)

In 1957 Kanter [3] reported that the angular distribution, $I(\theta)$, of the back-scattered electrons can be approximated by a Lambert cosine distribution, i.e.

$$I(\theta) = \frac{d\eta(\theta)}{d\Omega} \simeq (\eta/\pi) \mid \cos \theta \mid$$

Just how good an approximation this is can be seen from figure 5.3

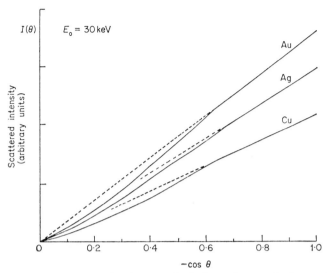

Figure 5.3. Showing the 'near-cosine' dependence of the scattered intensity for Au, Ag and Cu [1].

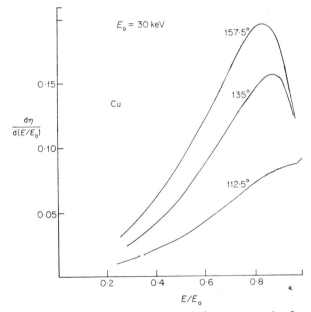

Figure 5.4. Distribution of back-scattered electron energies for various angles of scattering [1].

which shows confirmatory observations [1] for elements of medium to large atomic number. Only at low angles do the experimental observations deviate from the cosine law. The deviation is usually less than 25%. Finally we have illustrated the way in which the energy of the reflected electrons varies with angle. In figure 5.4 curves of $d\eta/d(E/E_0)$ are shown for Cu subjected to bombardment by 30-keV electrons. The distributions are asymmetric and are peaked at values

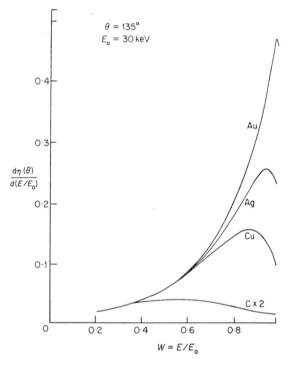

Figure 5.5. Distribution of back-scattered electron energies at $\theta = 135°$ for various atomic numbers [1].

of E/E_0 approaching unity. The total number of reflected electrons increases as the scattering angle is increased. By plotting $d\eta/d(E/E_0)$ as a function of atomic number (figure 5.5) we see that the distribution becomes increasingly narrow as $\mathcal{Z}$ increases, i.e. an increasing proportion of the back-scattered electrons have an energy near to the most probable energy. In addition, the value of the most probable energy increases with increase in atomic number. Finally, in figure 5.6 we illustrate how the most probable and mean energy losses increase with scattering angle. In particular we see how, at high scattering angles, the difference in behaviour between elements of low and high atomic number is accentuated. We shall use these data in Chapter 8,

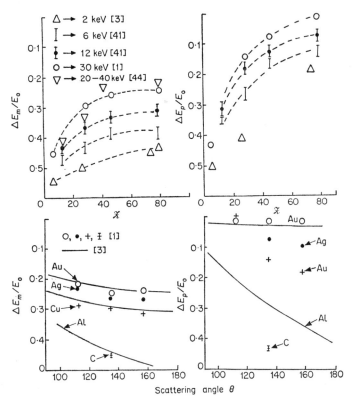

Figure 5.6. Variation of mean energy loss, $\Delta E_m/E_0$, and most probable energy loss, $\Delta E_p/E_0$; (a) as function of target atomic number and (b) as function scattering angle [1], [3], [41] + [44].

in particular the dependence of η on $\mathscr{Z}$, in interpreting emissive micrographs. For the present we need to examine the theoretical analysis of these observations.

5.2.2 Physical models of the back-scattering process
Among the approaches to this problem which illustrate the ideas

involved are two complementary approaches due to Everhart [4] and Archard [5]. Everhart assumed that for low atomic-number elements the back-scattered electrons undergo mostly single, large-angle elastic scattering and estimated that the number of electrons reaching the surface after scattering from a relative depth z', is given by

$$dN(z') = N_0\alpha(1 - z')^{\alpha-1} (1 - 2z')dz'$$

where $z' = z/R$ is the depth relative to the range, α is given by $\alpha = \mathscr{Z}^2 e^4 N/m^2 CA$, where A is the gram atomic weight, C is defined below and the other symbols have their usual meaning. Everhart assumed that the energy loss is given by the Thomson Whiddington law in the form $v^4 = v_0{}^4 - c\rho z$ and obtained a back-scattering coefficient on this model, η_1, given by

$$\eta_1 = [\alpha - 1 + (\tfrac{1}{2})^\alpha]/(1 + \alpha) \tag{5.1}$$

In general the value predicted by eqn. (5.1) is too low. Everhart obtained agreement by assuming an increased value of C (see below). Body [6] has sought to reduce the discrepancy by including two-fold scattering and has shown that two terms, η_2 and η_2', given by

$$\eta_2 = \tfrac{1}{2}[1 - 0{\cdot}7^{476}(1 + 1{\cdot}214\alpha)]; \text{ valid for } \frac{\pi}{4} \leqslant \theta \leqslant \frac{\pi}{2}$$

and

$$\eta_2' = 1 - \exp\left\{ - \frac{\alpha^2}{4(\alpha + 1)} + \frac{\alpha^3}{8(\alpha + 1)}\right\}; \text{ valid for } \frac{\pi}{2} \leqslant \theta \leqslant \pi$$

should be added to η_1 to obtain the total predicted back-scattered coefficient. The inclusion of these terms brings about closer agreement between theory and the experimental data, but the form of the predicted dependence on $\mathscr{Z}$ is not in very good agreement with observation. We return to this point after discussing the Archard model [5].

This worker applied the simplified Bethe, Rose, Smith model which argues as follows. For large atomic number specimens the back-scattering mechanism can be simplified into two processes: (*i*) The electrons penetrate along straight paths into the specimen until they reach a depth corresponding to the onset of diffusion. (*ii*) From this diffusion depth the electrons diffuse (again in straight lines) isotropically in all directions. This theory takes account of the fact that the electron progress eventually becomes random, but neglects the possibility that the electrons may undergo large single elastic scatterings between the surface and the 'depth of complete diffusion'; i.e. these assumptions represent the other extreme to the model adopted by Everhart. Archard used a definition of 'depth of complete diffusion' due to Bethe *et al* [7], which gives this depth, z_d, as that at which the average cosine of the angle between the primary beam direction and

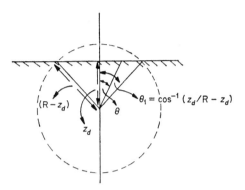

Figure 5.7. Definition of parameters used in Archard's model [5].

the actual direction of motion is equal to $1/e$. (See figure 5.7.) This is equivalent to a mean electron energy, E_d, given by

$$\int_{E_d}^{E_0} dE/\lambda \mid \partial E/\partial z \mid = \tfrac{1}{2}, \text{ with } \lambda = \frac{\pi N e^4 \mathscr{Z}^2}{2E^2} \ln \{2a_{\mathrm{H}} m(2E/m)^{1/2}/\hbar \mathscr{Z}^{1/3}\}$$

dE/dz can be obtained from Bethe's theory. A full development of this approach gives, to a fair approximation,

$$z_d/R \simeq 40/7\mathscr{Z} \quad \text{for} \quad 10 \leqslant \mathscr{Z} \leqslant 80 \tag{5.2}$$

From figure 5.7 we see that the fraction of the scattered electrons which leave the specimen is

$$\left.\begin{aligned} \eta &= \frac{1}{4\pi} \int_0^{\cos^{-1}(Z_d/R-Z_d)} 2\pi \sin\theta d\theta \\ &= \tfrac{1}{2}[1 - 2z_d/R]/[1 - z_d/R] \end{aligned}\right\} \tag{5.3}$$

Combining eqns. (5.2) and (5.3) we obtain

$$\eta = (7\mathscr{Z} - 80)/(14\mathscr{Z} - 80). \tag{5.4}$$

A measure of the success of this simple approach can be seen from figure 5.8. Archard points out that the model is oversimplified as in practice both the multiple and the single, large-angle mechanisms occur and he suggests that some weighted average of the multiple and single scattering back-scattered coefficients would be more realistic, the major problem being how to determine the relative weights. Archard also shows how the arbitary change in C, suggested by Everhart, can be justified. Everhart assumes that electrons scattered

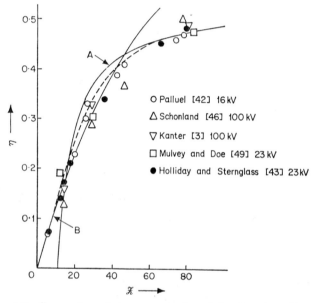

Figure 5.8. Comparison between experimental estimates of η as a function of atomic number and theoretical predictions. Curve (A) diffusion model, Curve (B) single, large-angle scattering model, dashed curve composite model [5].

through an angle of $\pi/2$ or greater are lost to subsequent deeper layers of the specimen while those scattered through $\pi/2$ or less are assumed not to be scattered at all. Archard argues that a second approximation to the Everhart model is adequately represented by assuming that half this second group are in fact lost to subsequent layers (by twofold scatterings of suitable directions). This has the effect of increasing $\alpha/\mathscr{Z}$ to 0·041. This is close to the arbitrary increase (from 0·012 to 0·045) assumed by Everhart by changing C. Thus the order of the adjustment made by Everhart is justified.

We can now sum up the position in terms of figure 5.8 which is taken from Archard's paper [5]. At high $\mathscr{Z}$ the electron motion quickly becomes diffuse (small z_d) so that there is little chance of a single, high-angle scattering. Therefore the diffusion expression gives a fair approximation to the observations. At low $\mathscr{Z}$ there is always sufficient time for a single-scattering event of high angle to occur, so this mechanism predominates and the second-order Everhart expression gives a reasonable fit. In the region of medium $\mathscr{Z}$ one mechanism gives way to the other, i.e. some $\mathscr{Z}$-dependent weighting (as yet undetermined) is required. It should be noted that curve B in figure 5.8 probably overestimates the 'single event' scattering as it is based on $\alpha/\mathscr{Z} = 0.047$ as opposed to 0.041 as indicated above. Finally there are indications from studies [8] of the back-scattering coefficient from thin films that there are also significant single, large-angle events in materials of high $\mathscr{Z}$ and measurable diffusion-like behaviour in materials of low $\mathscr{Z}$.

These are the basic ideas used to explain the magnitude of η and its dependence on $\mathscr{Z}$. There has been a wealth of more recent work which incorporates and extends these approaches, usually by incorporating elements of both models. Recent measurements of the back-scattering from thin films by Kanter [9] have proved the need to include elements of both models. In particular this worker concluded that, for thin foils at least, single elastic scattering events have little influence at low atomic number, but contributes significantly at high $\mathscr{Z}$. This view is contrary to the initial ideas in this field. Finally it should be recorded that Dashen [10] has established a general formal theory of back-scattering in terms of an exact integral equation and has discussed its solution in certain cases. Again the conclusion is reached that both single and diffusion scattering play a role.

5.3 Secondary electron emission

5.3.1 *Introduction*

Secondary electron emission leads to the most important, i.e. most generally useful, contrast mechanisms in the emissive mode of operation of the SEM so it is important to understand in detail the known properties of this phenomenon. For convenience we shall summarize the essential facts about secondary electron emission in two groups: (*i*) those pertaining to materials of high electrical conductivity and (*ii*) those obtained on semiconductors, and insulators, both amorphous and crystalline. Rather than represent a subsequent interpretation of the observations we have elected to interpret the observations as they are presented, relying on the previous discussion of electron-beam absorption to supply the necessary background.

Starting with conducting materials, the following topics are pertinent to scanning electron microscopy:

(*a*) The secondary electron yield as a function of the primary beam energy.

(*b*) The energy distribution of the emitted electrons.

(*c*) The angular distribution of the emitted electrons.

(*d*) The effect of varying the angle of incidence of the primary beam.

(*e*) The temperature dependence of secondary electron emission.

(*f*) The relationship between the secondary emission yield and other material properties such as the work-function, density and atomic number.

5.3.2 *Conducting materials*

(1) *The yield as a function of the primary beam energy.* If all the emitted electrons are collected irrespective of the angle of emission then the

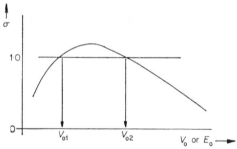

Figure 5.9. Emission yield as a function of beam voltage or beam energy, giving definition of first (V_{01}) and second (V_{02}) crossover points.

measured yield curve takes the form [11] shown in figure 5.9 for a wide range of materials. The salient features are the increase in σ with increase in beam energy, E_0, at low beam energies followed by a gradual decrease at high energies. Here σ is the number of emitted electrons per incident primary electron. Two parameters essentially define such curves; one is the energy, E_0^{max}, at which the yield is a maximum, the other is the value, σ_{max}, of the maximum yield. For a large variety of materials $100 < E_0{}^{max} < 800$ electron-volts, while $0.5 < \sigma_{max} < 2$ with the bulk of the values of σ_{max} lying between 1 and 1·4. If the yield curves are standardized, i.e. are plotted in the form $E_0/E_0{}^{max}$ against σ/σ_{max} then they fall on one universal curve to a fair approximation [12]. Such yield curves are not always straightforward to obtain as they can be affected by the presence of surface contamination and by the degree of roughness of the specimen surface. Yield curves are independent of the magnitude of the primary beam current, provided no heating occurs. The shape of the yield curves can be explained in qualitative terms by noting that two processes are occurring which vary with the primary beam voltage in different ways. As the beam voltage is increased, the number of secondary electrons created increases and the average depth at which they are formed also increases. Therefore the second process, the diffusion of 'hot' electrons to the surface, becomes more difficult. At $E_0 \leqslant E_0{}^{max}$ the first process is rate-determining but for $E_0 > E_0{}^{max}$ the second process predominates.

(2) *The energy distribution of the emitted electrons.* The energy distribution with the beam at normal incidence takes the form shown schematically in figure 5.10 [13]. There is a large peak at low energy

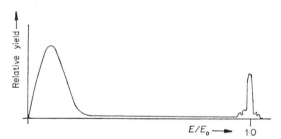

Figure 5.10. Relative yield as a function of energy of emitted electrons.

which represents 'true' secondary electrons. Most of these electrons have energies between 0 and 30 eV with the average value near to 5 eV. There is a sharply defined peak of reflected primary electrons at $E/E_0 = 1$. The tails to this peak often reveal considerable structure. Finally there is a third group of inelastically reflected electrons, sometimes called tertiary electrons, with energies extending from

H

30 eV up to E_0. Obviously the demarcation line between secondary and tertiary electrons is somewhat indefinite. The usual assumption is to define secondary electrons as those with energies less than 50 eV. As this energy is well into the 'tail' of the low-energy peak such a definition is satisfactory since the inherent arbitrariness affects only a very few electrons. Only at very low values of E_0 does this definition lose its significance. Figure 5.11 illustrates the behaviour observed [14]

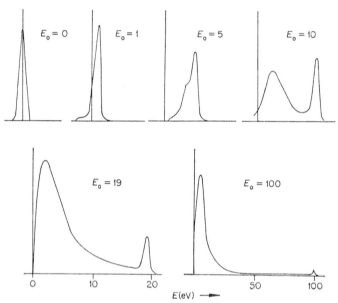

Figure 5.11. Data obtained by Harrower [14] showing yields obtained as a function of energy with very low beam energies.

with very low values of E_0. Only at values of $E_0 \geqslant 10$ volts can a clear demarcation be obtained between secondary and elastically reflected electrons.

In general the energy distribution is smoothly varying with the two major peaks already illustrated. There are two situations in which subsidiary maxima are observed: (*i*) On specimens that have been subjected to an extensive heat treatment [15] a series of minor peaks is sometimes observed on the upper slope of the secondary electron peak (see figure 5.12). (A first-order theory, suggesting that the peaks are due to Auger processes [16], has been advanced.) (*ii*) A series of minor peaks are observed [17, 18] just below the high-energy peak.

(3) *The angular distribution of the emitted secondary electrons.* Experiments have been performed [19] in which the angular distribution of a group of electrons with a selected energy was measured. By repeating such studies for three energy groups, namely 1·5, 10 and 20 eV, it was established that the angular distribution is cosine to a good approximation for each energy group, (see figure 5.13). Only at the very

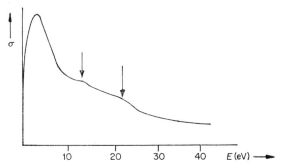

Figure 5.12. The occurrence of subsidiary peaks on the secondary emission yield curves of specimens that have been subjected to considerable heat treatment.

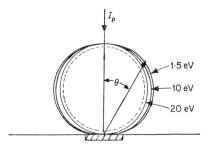

Figure 5.13. Polar diagram showing the near-perfect cosine distribution of emitted electrons as a function of electron energy [19].

lowest energy is a slight deviation (a slight 'flattening' of the polar diagram) observed. The cosine dependence of the number of emitted electrons is independent of the crystal, has no fine structure and is independent of the angle of incidence of the primary beam.

The fact that the distribution is cosine in nature over the entire energy range is an important result; it implies that the secondary electrons hitting the specimen surface from inside the specimen also have a cosine distribution, i.e. the angular distribution of secondary electrons in the specimen is isotropic.

(4) *Variations in secondary electron yield as function of angle of incidence.* Figure 5.14 shows an electron beam incident at an angle θ on a smooth surface. For the present we define the range, R, of the incident primary electrons as the average distance in the direction of

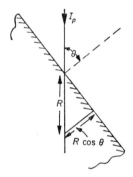

Figure 5.14. Showing the basic cause of the increase in secondary emission yield as the angle of incidence, θ, is increased, i.e. the secondary electrons are created closer to the surface.

the incident beam required to absorb all the primary electron energy. For a beam incident at an angle θ the primary electron energy will be all absorbed when the electron is, statistically, at a depth $R \cos \theta$ below the surface. If we define α as the coefficient of absorption of the secondary electrons and d_s as the mean depth of escape of these electrons, then, if the absorption is exponential, the yield at normal incidence $\sigma(0)$, will be proportional to $\exp(-d_s \alpha)$ and that at an angle θ, $\alpha(\theta)$, will be proportional to $\exp(-d_s \alpha \cos \theta)$. Therefore $\sigma(\theta) = \sigma(0) \exp[d_s\alpha(1 - \cos \theta)]$. This expression, due to Bruining [20], has been confirmed [21] for $0 < \theta < 80$ and is applicable for beam energies $\geqslant E_0^{max}$ where the yield is determined by the absorption of the secondary electrons. At $E_0 < E_0^{max}$ little variation with angle of incidence is to be expected. This result has been confirmed experimentally [2]. Another situation in which little variation with angle of incidence is expected is when the surface is rough. When the scale of the roughness is small compared to the beam diameter an integrated yield over many effective angles of incidence is obtained and this varies little with θ.

We can generalize these comments on the effect of surface inclination and roughness to include the case of importance in scanning electron microscopy in which a very fine and well focussed beam is scanned across the surface. The topography will, in principle, be revealed to a resolution of the order of the beam diameter (spot-size) at the surface because of the dependence of the secondary emission yield upon angle. As the beam inclination, defined in figure 5.14, increases so the yield increases with the result that inclined surfaces give a greater yield than those to which the beam is inclined more normally. There is another factor which can lead to 'topological' variations in yield. Consider figure 5.15. So far we have made the implicit assumption that secondary electrons created towards the end of a primary electron range have to diffuse a considerable distance to the surface and there-

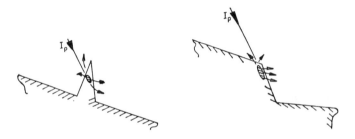

Figure 5.15. Enhanced emission of spikes at edges due to increased area with high probability of escape.

fore make relatively little contribution to the emissive yield. This assumption is valid if the surface is relatively smooth, but, when the surface has spikes or edges of the form shown in figure 5.15, the secondary electrons formed at the end of the range have only a short distance to diffuse to the surface and so contribute to the yield. We shall consider this situation again in Chapter 8.

(5) *The effect of specimen temperature on secondary emission.* Provided the surface is clean, i.e. free from absorbed surface films, the properties of which vary with the temperature, there is little or no variation of secondary electron emission with temperature. For example, no detectable change ($< 0.3\%$) was observed in σ from a Mo target over a temperature range of 20 to 1,100°C [23]. A change of only 0.01 to 0.02 in σ from a Ni specimen has been recorded [24] during a tempera-

ture increase from 20 to 840°C. Similarly the cooling of Zn or Sb from 300 to 77°K resulted in no change in the yield curves [25]. Only if the temperature range includes a transition temperature is there a significant change in the yield. The secondary emission yield from Sn changes [26] abruptly at the melting point and a temperature dependence observed between 120 to 180°C is associated with the transition from β- to γ-Sn. Almost invariably other forms of temperature

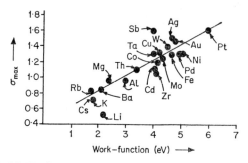

Figure 5.16. McKay's [27] empirical relationship between σ_{max} and surface work-function.

dependence are associated with temperature-dependent absorbed films. The reason for this general insensitivity to specimen temperature will be discussed below in relation to the results obtained with non-conducting materials which behave slightly differently.

(6) *The relationship between secondary electron emission and other material parameters.* There has been considerable experimentation to determine the way in which work-function changes affect the secondary-emission properties. These experiments are normally carried out by evaporating near-monoatomic layers of some reactive metal on the specimen surface so as to lower the work-function [27]. In contrast to thermionic and photo-emission, secondary electron emission is relatively insensitive to changes in work-function. A measure of this insensitivity can be seen from work by McKay [27] in which a Na film lowered the work-function of a tungsten specimen by a factor of two and yet increased the secondary emission by only 60%. The corresponding increase in thermionic emission would be of the order of 10^6. The reason for this relative lack of strong dependence is that, in secondary electron emission, we are mainly dealing with electrons

having a distribution of energies centred on a mean energy of about 5 eV. If this energy, which is supplied by the electron beam, had been supplied thermally the lattice temperature would have had to be $\geqslant 10^4 °$ K. Therefore changing the specimen temperature by 1,000° K or decreasing the barrier height only affects the emission behaviour of those electrons with energies near the barrier energy.

Although the dependence of the secondary electron yield on surface work-function is smaller than that observed with photo- and ther-mion-emission it is nevertheless significant. Figure 5.16 shows an empirical relation between the maximum yield and the work-function first drawn up by McKay [27]. McKay stressed that this figure is empirical and does not imply that an increase in work-function leads to an increase in yield, but rather that the work-function is related to some parameters which do determine the yield. For example, a similar plot relating σ_{max} to the density ρ can be drawn up. Other attempts have been made to establish connections between the yield and other quantities. Kollath [28] points out that the alkali and alkaline earth metals together with other light metals have a low maximum yield value of between 0·6 and 1 while the heavy metals of high atomic number have higher values of 1·1 to 1·7. Finally, Sternglass [29] has related σ_{max} to a position in the periodic table by noting that in each row the yield increases from left to right, i.e. from the alkali metal to the multivalent metal.

5.3.3 *Non-conducting materials.*

(1) *The yield as a function of E_0.* Neglecting for the present somewhat anomolous effects observed in composite layers, one of the major differences between good conductors and other materials is the magnitude of σ_{max}. For metals this parameter has a value between 0·6 and 1·7. For other materials [30] σ_{max} can vary from 1 to 20. Usually relative conductive semiconductors like Si and Ge give low values similar to those observed on metal targets. Intermetallic compounds (A_IB_V and A_IB_{IV}) and wide bandgap materials, such as CdS, have immediate values while the alkali halides and the alkaline earth oxides have the highest values, approaching 20. The exact value obtained from a given material depends on the specimen history, its crystal state, the imperfection content and on the surface structure. When we consider the shape of the yield curves themselves two differences arise when compared with metals. The value of E_0^{max} is

considerably increased from typically 200 to 800 for metals to 1,000
to 2,000 for many metallic oxides. If we attempt to fit the yield
curves for semi-insulating materials onto a universal curve we have
less success than we do with metallic materials. In particular the
'spread' of the high energy 'tails' is considerably greater.

It is obviously of considerable interest to ask why the yield is
higher in these materials and in particular why the yield apparently
increases with increase in resistivity. There are two factors which

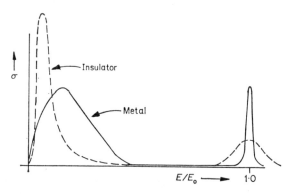

Figure 5.17. Schematic diagram showing the basic difference between
the energy distribution of emitted electrons from metals and from
insulators.

can lead to this change. These are the excitation of the secondary
electrons and the diffusion (and subsequent escape) of these electrons
to the surface. It is unlikely that an increase in the excitation of
secondary electrons is the cause, because it is more difficult to create
electron-hole pairs in materials of high bandgap, (compare table 9.1).
Therefore in terms of relative densities of excitation of secondary
electrons we would expect *a decrease* in yield as the intrinsic resistivity of the material increases. The more likely cause of the observed
increase is probably associated with the relative ease with which the
secondary electrons can diffuse to the specimen surface, i.e. on the
reduced degree of scattering experienced by the electrons. The
secondary electrons can be scattered by lattice vibrations (electron-
phonon interactions). They can be lost by recombination with holes,
either by direct recombination or by recombination via impurity
atoms (see Chapter 9). Finally they can be scattered, trapped or
caused to recombine by crystal imperfections. Often these processes

are specific to the material being examined and do not, necessarily, bear a simple relationship to the resistivity of the material. However, there is one scattering mechanism which is important in metals and which becomes increasingly less significant as the resistivity is increased. This scattering mechanism is free carrier scattering, i.e. electron-electron interactions. In this case we are concerned with interactions between 'hot' electrons (energy 5 to 10 eV) with thermal electrons (energy $\sim \dfrac{1}{40}$ eV). In these collisions the hot electrons must, statistically, lose energy. It is therefore probable that the increase in yield, with increase in resistivity, arises from a corresponding decrease in free carrier scattering. We shall see that other observations support this model.

(2) *The energy distribution of the emitted secondary electrons.* Figure 5.17 illustrates the essential difference between the energy distribution observed with metals compared to that with poorly conducting materials. The energy distribution of the emitted secondary electrons is narrower in insulators and the mean energy is reduced from typically 5 to 10 eV to 2·5 to 5 eV. It has been suggested [13] that the reduction of mean energy arises because of the increased depth from which the secondary electrons can reach the surface and still have sufficient energy to overcome the surface barrier. In other words, the arrival of electrons from relatively deep in the crystal at the surface with energies just sufficient to overcome the surface barrier lowers the mean energy of the emitted electrons compared to that observed with metal targets. This interpretation is consistent with the idea of a decreased scattering probability in resistive materials. As a result of the lowering of the mean energy of electrons arriving at the surface from within the crystal we would expect an increased dependence (*i*) on the temperature and (*ii*) on the surface work-function compared to the dependences observed with metals. This prediction is borne out by the experimental observations.

(3) *The effect of specimen temperature and surface work function.* The degree of temperature dependence varies considerably. Using Ge targets Johnson and McKay [31] found that the yield decreased by 5% for a temperature rise from 20 to 600°C. This change was found to be independent of the dopant employed. As the dopant levels used were $\leqslant 10^{18}/cm^3$ it is unlikely that free carrier scattering

is important. It is probable that the observed decrease is associated with increasing lattice scattering as the temperature is increased. Even for relatively unstable compounds such as Cs_3Sb a significant change in secondary electron emission is observed in going from -30 to $70°C$. Amorphous glass-like solids show no dependence of yield upon temperature, because the scattering is determined by the degree of disorder of the material. By way of contrast, in good single crystal

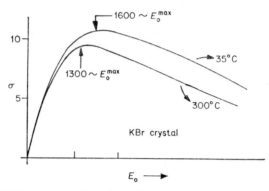

Figure 5.18. The temperature dependence of the yield curve from good single crystals of KBr [33].

specimens of the alkali halides and alkaline earth oxides the scattering is limited by lattice vibrations which increase with temperature. Then, provided the effective range of the incident primary electrons is greater than the effective 'escape' or diffusion distance of the secondary electrons, we would expect some temperature dependence. In fact, it has been calculated [32] that the escape distance should vary as $T^{-1/2}$. If sufficient care is taken on surface preparation the observed results can be fitted to a $T^{-1/2}$ law to a first approximation.

Table 5.3. The temperature dependence of the maximum yield σ_{max} and the mean energy of the emitted electrons $\overline{E}$, for oxide cathodes [34]

Specimen Temperature (°C)	σ_{max}	$\overline{E}$	$(\sigma_{max} \times \overline{E})$
300	2	11·7	23·4
470	3·1	8·5	26·3
615	5·3	3·7	19·6

In addition it was found [33] that the value of E_0^{max} was also temperature-dependent and varied in the manner shown in figure 5.18. This
variation of peak (or mean) energy with temperature is borne out by
Russian work [34] on oxide cathodes. Table 5.3 shows both the yield
and the mean energy as a function of temperature. Within the
limitations imposed by the sparseness of the data it can be seen that

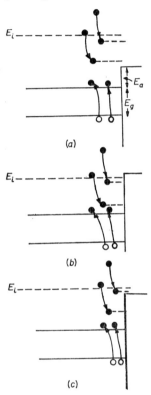

Figure 5.19. Dexter's argument [36] showing the effect of band
structure on the temperature dependence of secondary electron emission
(See text).

the product $(\sigma_{max} \times \bar{E})$ is approximately constant. One rather extreme form of temperature dependence has been reported for oxide
cathodes [35] in which the secondary electron current varied with
temperature according to $i_2 = B \exp(-A/KT)$; where the 'activation energy' A was of the order of 0.35 eV and was found to depend
on the processing used to form the specimen.

Obviously a wide range of behaviour is to be expected because of
the differing band structures. Here we can consider the points made by
Dexter [36] in differentiating between good and poor photo-emitting
materials. We are concerned with the behaviour of 'hot' electrons
with energies of the order of 10 eV. One of the factors determining the
energy with which such an electron reaches the surface is its ability
to impact ionize an atom before it reaches the surface. We can give

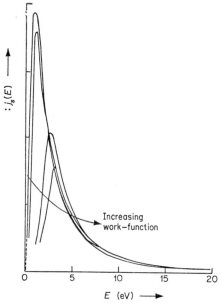

Figure 5.20. Energy distribution of electrons emitted from cesiated Ge.
(Appelt [37]).

an oversimplified picture by treating the three cases considered in
figure 5.19 which show the different behaviour which results as the
ratio of the ionization energy, E_i, and electron affinity, E_a, is varied.
In each case an electron with an energy in excess of E_i, is envisaged
as travelling towards the specimen surface losing small amounts of
energy by phonon emission and by subsequently ionizing an atom.
Figure 5.19(a) shows the case in which E_i is considerably greater than
E_a. Even after producing another electron-hole pair the hot electron
can escape without thermal aid. Figure 5.19(b) illustrates the case
where $E_i < E_a$. The hot electron has no significant chance of escaping

after pair production. Finally figure 5.19(c) shows the case in which E_i is slightly greater than E_a so that after pair production the electron has some chance of escape, particularly with thermal aid. Thus the details of the band structure play an important role. The importance of the relative values of E_i and E_a implies that under certain conditions a reduction in surface work-function should lead to an increase in yield. Information on cesiated Ge which corresponds to the case shown in figure 5.19(c) has been obtained by Appelt [37]. Figure 5.20 shows the variation of yield with change in work-function. As the work-function is reduced the yield is increased and the mean energy of the emitted electrons is decreased. The upper part of the curve with emitted electrons of energy $\geqslant$ 5eV is unaffected. These observations are again consistent with a distribution of secondary electrons arriving at the surface with electron energies covering a range from well above the value corresponding to the work-function to well below this value. As the work-function is reduced (or, to a lesser extent, as the temperature is increased) the lower energies electrons can escape into the vacuum, so the yield is increased and the mean energy of the emitted electrons reduced. In terms of the discussion centred on figure 5.19, lowering the work-function allows more electrons that have produced electron-hole pairs prior to reaching the surface, to escape.

This dependence of secondary-emission yield on the surface properties of a specimen is an example of the interaction of electron-beam induced phenomena with specimen surfaces and interfaces. This topic is discussed in Chapter 6. For the present we will extend our initial discussion by considering some usual effects obtained on composite specimens.

5.4 The Malter effect

So far we have considered only uniform specimens. The only comment we have made about composite specimens has been to stress that valid estimates of σ can only be obtained if sufficient care is taken to obtain clean surfaces, i.e. to remove surface contaminents. However, composite specimens are of interest for other reasons. For example, under certain conditions very high yields of σ_{max} can be obtained.

Malter [38] was the first to observe very high ($>$ 100) values of the secondary emission yield. The specimens used were thin ($\approx$ 2,000 Å) layers of Al_2O_3 that were first cesiated and then subsequently oxidized. The secondary emission current differed in several ways from the usual emission. In addition to its magnitude the shape of the yield curve differed somewhat from the usual form in that the high-voltage end of the curve fell off more rapidly. It was established that the secondary electron current, i_2, was very dependent on the collector voltage. Malter obtained the relationship

$$i_2 = Ai_1{}^\alpha \exp \beta V_0 \qquad (5.5)$$

where A, α and β are constants. The parameter α is found to be less than unity, i.e. σ is not a constant independent of i_1, but tends to fall off as i_1 is increased. Finally it was found that the effect is highly inertial in that a finite time is required to reach the high steady-state emission and that the emission can persist long after the primary beam excitation has been removed. The emission decays rapidly at first after the excitation is removed but then decays more slowly. So slowly in fact that one surface examined still gave detectable emission twenty-four hours after the cessation of the excitation. This decay can be accelerated by irradiation with visible light. The results from one specimen to another were not reproducible. Electron-microscope studies of the Malter effect showed the reason for this lack of reproducibility. It was found that the emission was irregularly distributed across the surface, being localized at 'centres of emission'. Under conditions of heavy excitation, i.e. with high primary current and large electrode voltage, flashes of light – 'scintillations' – were observed. If the conditions resulted in many such scintillations the anomalous effect was destroyed. Subsequent studies [39] showed that the effect is not limited to Al_2O_3 films as it can be obtained with thin films of quartz, magnesium oxide and KCl. But Malter was unable to observe the effect with films of the oxides of Ta, Ca, Ag Cu (CuO), Ni, W and Zr, possibly because the heat treatment used in the film preparation reduced the film resistance to low values. Possibly related to this observation is the fact that the effect is strongly temperature-dependent. As the temperature is increased the emission falls off rapidly and the decay rates increase rapidly. The Malter electrons have energies of the order of tens of volts corresponding to the order of the voltage drop across the insulator. The effect can be obtained with accelerating voltages of between 15 and 1,000 volts. Finally it should be recorded that the effect could also be observed by the use of negative ion bombardment as well as by electron bombardment.

The interpretation of the Malter effect can be stated as follows. The initial bombardment with $\sigma > 1$ leads to the surface becoming positively charged. The resultant field is thought to cause the field emission of electrons from the underlying substrate into the insulating layer. These electrons are subsequently accelerated through the insulator towards the surface, passing throught the surface without neutralizing the surface charge. The initial inertia is caused by the time required to establish the necessary density of surface charge. During the bombardment one function of the primary electrons is to maintain this surface charge. The magnitudes of the field strengths in the films have been measured and found to be of the right order of magnitude, i.e. $\approx 10^6$ volts/cm. The question arises as to how the emission is sustained after the excitation is removed. It has been suggested that the accelerated electrons during the passage of the surface barrier cause the ionization of surface atoms by impact ionization. Thus the process is self-sustaining or at least only very slow in decay. There are other indications of the validity of this or a closely related model. If the film is made too thick the effect is not observed. This observation is consistent with the above model if it is assumed that the increasing width results in an increased energy loss and therefore in a decreased emission current, because electrons with these lower energies are unable to escape from the surface but tend to neutralize the positive surface charge. If the foil is too thin, electrons from the substrate can neutralize the surface charge; it is therefore to be expected that thin films would not give a Malter effect. This is the observed behaviour. The localized nature of the effect is to indicate the variation of the field-emission properties across the film.

In this and the previous sections we have been concerned with variations of secondary electron yield as a function of the primary electron beam voltage, i.e. as a function of the kinetic energy of the incident electrons as they hit the surface. The implicit assumption has been made that this energy corresponds to that gained by an electron in dropping down a voltage equal to the difference between the cathode potential and that of the underlying stage on which the specimen is held. The following sections outline situations in which this assumption is not valid.

5.5 Effects due to voltage drops across insulator specimens

5.5.1 *The effect of surface voltage*
Consider the situation shown in figure 5.21. An insulator specimen of a width which is considerably greater than the range of the

incident electrons is bombarded by a current I_1 of electrons from a filament at a voltage of V_0 compared to earth potential. The rear surface of the specimen is held at earth potential. At the onset of the bombardment the electrons reach the surface with an energy eV_0 and the instantaneous value of the yield will be that appropriate to this energy. In general this instantaneous value is not equal to unity so that the specimen surface tends to become charged. The sign and

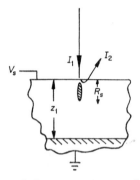

Figure 5.21. Definition of the parameters used to discuss charge-up effects.

magnitude of the charge depends on a variety of factors which we shall consider below. The important point at present is that there is now (after a short time of bombardment) a voltage drop across the specimen as a result of which the incident electrons reach the specimen surface with an energy which is no longer equal to eV_0. Since σ is energy-dependent, the yield will change as a function of time until a state of quasi-equilibrium is reached. The manner in which this state of equilibrium is reached can be seen from figure 5.22. The yield is plotted against the effective primary electron energy, V_{eff}. If, at some incident of time, the surface voltage is V_s then the effective electron energy is $V_0 + |V_s|$, if $V_s > 0$ and is given by $V_0 - |V_s|$ for $V_s < 0$. Consider the case where the insulator is not perfect but is capable of passing a small, but finite, current under the field resulting from the surface charge and the image charge created at the lower face. The equilibrium state will be reached when the excess charge

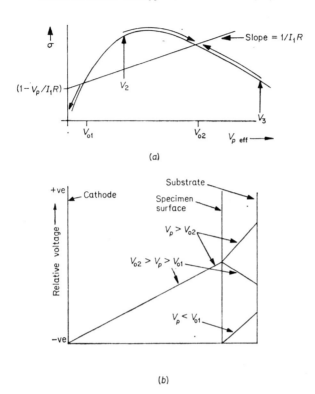

Figure 5.22. (*a*) Schematic diagram of the way in which the equilibrium state in an insulator layer is attained under electron bombardment. (*b*) Equilibrium voltage distributions obtained under bombardment with varying beam energies.

delivered per second to the specimen surface is balanced by an equal but opposite charge flow through the insulator. Consider also the case where the surface charges up positively, i.e. $I_2 > I_1$; then provided that the specimen obeys Ohm's law we can write.

$$V_s - R[I_2 - I_1] = (V_{\text{eff}} - V_0) \qquad (5.6)$$

where R is the effective resistance to earth. From eqn. (5.6) and the definition of σ we obtain

$$\sigma = V_{\text{eff}}/I_1 R - (V_0/I_1 R - 1) \qquad (5.7)$$

I

The equilibrium positions occur at the points of intersection of eqn. (5.7) with the yield curve (see figure 5.22). Imagine that we initiate a bombardment with an effective beam voltage corresponding to V_2. At this point the yield is high and the surface charges positive as the insulator cannot pass the necessary current to neutralize the surface charge. As a result V_s increases and the operating point moves towards $V_{\text{eff}} = V_{02}$ at which the excess surface charge can be neutralized by internal current flow. Similar arguments show that, for various starting conditions, the movements occurring during the attainment of equilibrium are those shown in figure 5.22. There are two points of stable equilibrium; one at $V_{\text{eff}} = V_{02}$ which represents a finite emission yield and the second at $V_{\text{eff}} = 0$. In this latter case the surface reaches the cathode potential; all the potential drop occurs across the specimen and the yield is effectively zero. The corresponding voltage distributions are shown in figure 5.22(b). The equilibrium states can be summed up as follows:

(1) If the initial accelerating voltage V_0 is less than V_{01}, $\sigma = 0$ and the difference in potential between the cathode and the substrate all appears across the insulator specimen.

(2) If $V_0 > V_{01}$ the equilibrium value of σ will be that corresponding to an accelerating voltage equal to V_{02}. In this case the voltage distribution across the insulator depends on the magnitude of V_0 relative to V_{02}. If $V_0 < V_{02}$ the bombarded surface will charge up positively. If $V_0 > V_{02}$ this surface will attain a negative charge.

The rate at which these equilibrium states are reached depends on a variety of material properties which are discussed in Chapters 6 and 12. From the macroscopic viewpoint the rate at which the equilibrium is reached increases with the primary beam current as the ratio of the primary current to the instantaneous current flowing through the specimen determines the rate at which the surface voltage builds up. The subsequent decay of the surface voltage after the excitation has been removed depends mainly on the insulator resistance, except in the case of virtually perfect insulators. In this case, which is represented by the limit $R \to \infty$ and $\sigma = 1$ at both V_{01} and V_{02}, the arrival of charge either in the form of electrons or ions through the vacuum can make a significant contribution [47].

The above discussion is somewhat limited because of the restrictions made and the assumptions made in order to introduce the phenomena.

These limitations, which can easily be removed, are listed below:

(1) The insulator specimens need not obey Ohm's law over the complete range of voltages effectively applied across the specimen.

(2) We have limited the discussion to cases where the film thickness is much greater than the penetration distance of the primary electrons. We shall see that this point is related to a need to examine what factors determine R as defined above.

(3) We have neglected the existence of any electrode effects, i.e. it has been assumed that all the emitted electrons are collected by suitably placed electrodes at potentials which do not interfere with the emission.

(4) The possibility that permanent damage can be done to insulator specimens as a result of the high field built up in the specimen by the bombardment has not been considered.

(5) We have not considered specimens with variations in microscopic properties across the specimen surface and we have assumed that the field distribution across the insulator specimen is uniform.

In the following sections we discuss the first four of these limitations. The final limitation is considered in Chapter 6, which describes the surface and interface physics aspects of the interaction between electron beams and solids.

5.5.2 *The effect of secondary electron collector electrodes*

If a collector electrode at a variable potential is included in the experimental set-up the results get a little more complex, as the resulting equilibrium state depends on the voltage of this electrode. We can understand these important ideas by treating the case of a perfect insulator. We have to consider three cases:

(1) If the electrode potential is greater than V_{02} the final equilibrium state is that depicted above, i.e. the steady-state yield is that corresponding to $V_0 = V_{02}$ as the collector gathers all the emitted electrons.

(2) When the collector potential, V_c, lies between V_{01} and V_{02} another situation develops. Consider the case where $V_{01} < V_c < V_{02}$ and where the effective accelerating voltage is greater than V_{01}. For the sake of conciseness take $V_0 = V_{03} > V_{02}$. In this case there will be a field between the specimen surface and the collector electrode which repels most of the emitted secondary electrons. Under the primary beam excitation the surface will charge up

negatively and so reduce the impeding field between surface and collector. As a result more secondary electrons are collected. Equilibrium results when the surface voltage is such that a fraction, f, of the emitted electrons is collected so that this emission current just balances the primary current. A similar argument applies to the case in which the initial surface potential is below that of the collector and this leads to the establishment of the same equilibrium position (so long as V_c is kept constant) which is therefore stable, with the surface potential slightly higher than the collector potential.

(3) When the collector potential is well below V_{01} the only stable state which can exist is for $\sigma = 0$ as all the emitted electrons are returned to the target surface, which therefore attains the cathode potential, and primary electrons cease to strike the target.

These simple examples illustrate the role played by the collector potential in the case of a target which is perfectly insulating. Many readers will recognize that these ideas are a simplified form of those exploited in storage cathode-ray tubes. For further details in a concise and easily understood form readers are referred to the standard work by Knoll and Kazan [40].

5.5.3 *Electron-beam induced conductivity*

We are familiar with the impact ionization created in the specimen by the primary beam. It is of interest to do a rough calculation to estimate the density of free carriers introduced into the surface layer of a specimen by this mechanism. If a beam density of j amp/cm^2 of electrons of energy E_0 is incident on a semi-insulator of ionization energy E_i then the number of electron-hole pairs created per unit area is $(j/e)(E_0/E_i)$. By defining R as the effective range of the primary electrons we can also define an average density of induced electrons and holes as

$$\Delta n = \Delta p = (j/eR)(E_0/E_i) \qquad (5.8)$$

Taking as typical values $j = 1$ amp/cm^2, $E_0 = 20$ keV with $R \sim 2\mu$ and $E_i = 10$ eV we obtain $\Delta n = \Delta p \geqslant 10^{19}$/cm^3. When this figure is compared with the 10^8/cm^3 free carriers needed to give a resistivity of $10^8 \Omega$ cm in GaAs, it is apparent that considerable modulation of the conductivity is possible. Obviously the above calculation is naive as there is a variety of factors not considered.

For example, no allowance has been made for, the excess surface conductivity already existing in the region where the beam-induced carriers are formed, nor has the diffusion of these carriers into the bulk been considered. Nevertheless the modulation can be considerable. This modulation may have an effect on the surface voltage effects discussed in section 5.5.1 as it effectively reduces the resistance

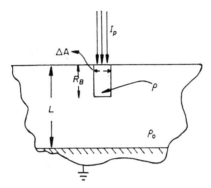

Figure 5.23. Definition of parameters used to describe beam-induced conductivity modulation.

to the carrier flow required to neutralize the surface charge. If, as in figure 5.23, the bulk resistivity of an insulator film of thickness L is ρ_0 then the effective resistance of an area ΔA is given by

$$dR_{\text{eff}} \approx \left(\frac{\rho R_B + \rho_0 (L - R_B)}{\Delta A} \right) \tag{5.9}$$

In the case where $\rho \ll \rho_0$, eqn. (5.9) reduces to $dR_{\text{eff}} \sim [\rho_0(L - R_B)]/ \Delta A$. When the penetration distance is of the order of the film thickness the effective resistance is greatly reduced, leading to much lower values for the voltage drops induced across the specimen by the electron-beam bombardment. This electron-beam induced conductivity has been used to make experimental determination of the secondary electron yield from highly resistive specimens since the use of thin films effectively removes the uncertainty between the values of V_0 and V_{eff}. We shall meet this effect in later discussions of contrast mechanisms in the scanning electron microscope. The effect is reversible, The next section considers effects which can be both reversible and irreversible.

5.5.4 *Irreversible effects due to electron-beam irradiation*

Imagine the situation in which a thin layer ($\sim 2\mu$) of a very good insulator is bombarded by a low-energy beam so that the primary electrons do not penetrate far into the layer. If, as a result of the film resistivity, the magnitude of the beam current and of the secondary emission, the voltage across the layer of thickness, L, reaches a value ΔV, then the electric field (assumed uniform) is $\sim \Delta V/L$. If this field

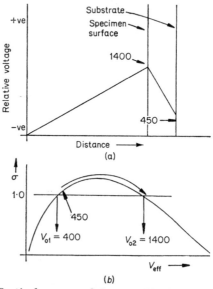

Figure 5.24. Particular case of figure 5.22 showing how a SiO_2 or Si_3N_4 layer can be broken down by electron-beam bombardment.

exceeds the breakdown field of the dielectric the possibility exists that some form of damage may be done to the film. Taking as an example the breakdown strength of Si_3N_4 as 4×10^6 volts/cm we see that a voltage drop of 800 volts across a 2μ-thick film would cause breakdown. Bearing in mind the existence of material inhomogeneties and localized enhancements of electric field, the necessary voltage may be considerably lower. That this type of situation can be realized in principle can be seen from figure 5.24(a). An idealized but realistic insulator film is imagined to have first and second cross-over points at 400 and 1,400 volts respectively. If a 2μ thick film were bombarded by primary electrons of 450 volts, the penetration distance would be minimal and the final potential distribution would be that shown in the figure 5.24(*b*) with about 1,000 volts across the specimen film.

The nature of the breakdown depends on a variety of factors both in the material itself and the macroscopic experimental arrangement. The breakdown can vary from a reversible breakdown to a completely destructive mode. This mechanism is one way in which the situation analysed in figure 5.22 can be generalized to include departures from Ohm's law. The ideas given in that section are still valid, but the straight line in the figure is replaced by a curve implying a voltage-dependent resistance.

With this description of insulator effects we conclude our discussion of electron-beam solids interactions. It is well to summarize the situation in general terms.

We have already underlined the difficulties facing the formulation of a general theory of electron-beam absorption. The main factors to be considered are the need to correct for the failure of the Born approximation at low beam energy and the neglect of large-angle single scattering and of the energy loss. Probably the best theory to date is that due to Bothe [48] after correction for the Born approximation and for the neglect of high-angle scattering which effectively violates the initial postulate of a constant incident flux. The theories of back-scattering and secondary electron emission suffer from the difficulties referred to above and from some oversimplifications introduced to increase the tractability of the problem. The major difficulties centre on the correct treatment of the relative importance of single and diffusion scattering and on the nature of the dependence of the primary electron range on the initial energy E_0 and on the atomic number. With metallic specimens the significant parameters in general have a dependence on E_0 and $\mathscr{Z}$ which is less than that predicted by theory. The formalism for theories of back-scattering and secondary electron emission are available but have not been fully developed in detail. The use of Monte-Carlo methods to calculate the significant parameters is on the increase with good success. This trend is probably indicative of the way in which the subject will develop, i.e. the parameters in the existing theoretical framework which cannot be calculated with good results on a purely theoretical basis will be estimated on a statistical basis, compared with experiment, and, where satisfactory, used in practical applications. Until these estimates are available we have to reply on a simplified, more empirical approach to obtain the energy absorption characteristic which may be in error by a factor of 2.

REFERENCES

[1] H. E. BISHOP, Ph.D. Dissertation, Cambridge, (1966)
[2] E. WEINRYB and J. PHILIBERT, *Compt. Rend.*, **258**, 4535, (1964)
[3] H. KANTER, *Ann. Phys. Lpz.*, **20**, 144, (1957), *Phys. Rev.*, **121**, 461, (1961)
[4] T. E. EVERHART, *J. Appl. Phys.*, **31**, 1483, (1960)
[5] G. D. ARCHARD, *J. Appl. Phys.*, **32**, 1505, (1961)
[6] Z. T. BODY, *Brit. J. Appl. Phys.*, **13**, 483, (1962)
[7] H. A. BETHE, M. E. ROSE and L. P. SMITH, *Proc. Amer. Phil. Soc.*, **78**, 573, (1938)

[8] H. FRANK, *Z. Naturf.*, **14a**, 247, (1959)
[9] H. KANTER, *Brit. J. Appl. Phys.*, **15**, 555, (1964)
[10] R. F. DASHEN, *Phys. Rev.*, **134**, A1025, (1964)
[11] R. KOLLATH, *Z. Phys.*, **38**, 202, (1937)
[12] R. KOLLATH, *Ann. Physik* (6), **1**, 357, (1947)
[13] See O. HACHENBERG and W. BRAUER, *Advances in Electrons and Electron Physics*, **11**, 413, (1959)

[14] G. A. HARROWER, *Phys. Rev.*, **104**, 52, (1956)
[15] G. A. HARROWER, *Phys. Rev.*, **102**, 340, (1956)
[16] J. J. LANDER, *Phys. Rev.*, **91**, 1382, (1953)
[17] E. RUDBERG, *Phys. Rev.*, **50**, 138, (1936)
[18] W. REICHERT and H. E. FARNSWORTH, *Phys. Rev.*, **75**, 1902, (1949)
[19] J. L. H. JONKER, *Philips Res. Rep.*, **12**, 249, (1957)
[20] H. BRUINING, *Physica*, **5**, 901, (1938)
[21] S. J. LUKJANOV, *Physik. Z. Sowjet union*, **13**, 123, (1938)
[22] H. BRUINING, *Physica*, **3**, 1046, (1936)
[23] P. M. MOROZOV, *Zh.E.T.F.*, **11**, 402, (1941)
[24] P. M. MOROZOV, *Zh.E.T.F.*, **11**, 410, (1941)
[25] A. I. FRIMER, *Zh.E.T.F.*, **17**, 71, (1947)
[26] See references [23] and [24]
[27] K. G. MCKAY, *Advances in Electronics*, **1**, 65, (1948)
[28] R. KOLLACH, *Handbuch d. Physik*, **21**, 232, (1956)
[29] E. J. STERNGLASS, *Phys. Rev.*, **80**, 925, (1950)
[30] H. BRUINING and J. H. DE BOER, *Physica*, **6**, 823, (1939)
[31] J. B. JOHNSON and K. G. MCKAY, *Phys. Rev.*, **93**, 668, (1953)
[32] A. J. DEKKER, *Phys. Rev.*, **94**, 1179, (1954)
[33] B. PETZEL, Doctorate Thesis, Dresden, (1958)
[34] POMERANTZ, *J. Frankl. Inst.*, **41**, 242, (1947)
[35] N. D. MORGULIS and A. A. NAGORSKIY, *Zh.E.T.F.*, **8**, 59, (1938)

[36] D. L. DEXTER, *Proc. Inter. Conf. on Semiconductor Physics*, Prague, (Czech. Acad. of Science), 122, (1961)
[37] G. APPELT, Doctorate Thesis, Dresden, (1958)
[38] L. MALTER, *Phys. Rev.*, **49**, 378, (1936)
[39] A. S. KORSHUNOVA and N. S. KHLEPNIKOV, *Zh.E.T.F.*, **9**, 860, (1939)

[40] M. KNOLL and B. KAZAN, *Storage Tubes*, Wiley, New York, (1952)

[41] R. N. THOMAS, Ph.D. Thesis, Cambridge, (1961)

[42] P. PALLUEL, *Compt. Rend.*, **224**, 1492 and 1551, (1947)

[43] J. E. HOLLIDAY and E. J. STERNGLASS, *J. Appl. Phys.*, **28**, 1189, (1957)

[44] H. KULENKAMPFF and K. RUTTIGER, *Z. Phys.*, **137**, 426, (1954), ibid **152**, 249

[45] H. KULENKAMPFF and W. SPYRA, *Z. Phys.*, **137**, 416, (1954)

[46] B. F. J. SCHONLAND, *Proc. Roy. Soc.*, **A104**, 235, (1923)

[47] D. S. PECK, R. R. BLAIR, W. L. BROWN and F. M. SMITS, *B.S. Tech. J.*, **42**, 95, (1963)

[48] W. BOTHE, *Z. Phys.*, **54**, 161, (1929)

[49] T. MULVEY and N. DOE, Private Communication to G. D. Archard, see ref. [5]

CHAPTER 6

Interactions between Electron Beams and Specimen Surfaces

6.1 Introduction

Ideally we wish to examine specimens, particularly semiconductor devices, without damaging or even altering the specimen characteristics in any way. At present this is not always possible. It is therefore necessary to know what detrimental effects can occur, how they can be eliminated or how experimental procedures can be devised to minimize adverse changes. There are several aspects to this problem. First, and perhaps foremost, the semiconductor device manufacturer needs to know whether inspection in the SEM does or does not degrade saleable devices. The surface physicist has to avoid inspection and examination techniques which impede the observation of phenomena of interest or which complicate the interpretation of surface data. The metallurgist, zoologist and medical researcher need to examine specimen topography with high resolution unimpaired by contamination effects. This, then, is a problem of some generality. A convenient way of listing these effects is given in table 6.1. Each of the possibilities is discussed in turn in the following sections. The effects listed are not always detrimental but can be used to investigate material and device properties, i.e. they provide, on occasion, an additional experimental tool. These effects can only be understood against some knowledge of the properties of material surfaces. To this end we begin by reviewing at a relatively simple level the ideas currently used to explain the surface properties of materials. Although the discussion is carried out in terms of semiconductor and insulator solid specimens many of the ideas can be extrapolated to solid-electrolyte or solid-liquid insulator systems.

In this chapter we shall mainly consider the final effect listed in table 6.1 and we shall consider it in some detail. The beam-induced contamination effect, which is really an experimental limitation arising from the use of oil vapours and insufficient attention to cleanliness, is discussed in Chapter 7 together with other essentially experimental problems. The degradation of insulator specimens is a topic which has been introduced in Chapter 5 and is referred to again in Chapter 12 which deals with applications of the SEM. The final effect is more fundamental in nature as it is inherent in the physical mechanisms exploited in the SEM and is therefore unlikely to be removed entirely by improvements in experimental techniques, although methods are being found to minimize such effects. This

Table 6.1. Possible adverse effects observed during SEM examination

Effect	Type of Specimen	Comment
Beam-induced contamination	Quite general, but depends on specimen nature	Can be largely eliminated by use of hygienic vacuum systems
Beam-induced voltage across specimen leading to dielectric breakdown	Limited to insulator specimens. May be of importance in bio-medical field as well as in physical science	Can be largely reduced by care and can be used as a diagnostic tool
Beam-induced changes in surface conductivity	Significant in the semiconductor field and in semi-insulator and insulator studies. Particularly important in devices which depend on surface conduction for operation	Still actively investigated to minimize adverse effects. Can be used as diagnostic tool

chapter is also used to emphasize the aspects of surface physics required in Chapters 11 and 12 which deal with the application of the SEM to the study of electronic materials and solid-state devices. Although the treatment in this chapter is largely concerned with actual devices, the ideas used can be transposed to bulk semiconductor and insulator specimens without difficulty.

6.2 The properties of 'real' surfaces

6.2.1 *Introduction*
Workers in the field differentiate between 'real' surfaces and 'clean'

surfaces. Real surface is the name given to a surface prepared by the usual etching and degreasing treatment followed by mild heat treatment. Such surfaces, when examined by low-energy electron diffraction, reveal the presence of contamination films, absorbed water, etc. Clean surfaces, on the other hand, have been subjected to long treatments [1, 2,] in various ambients over a range of temperatures until the low-energy electron diffraction patterns [3] are characteristic

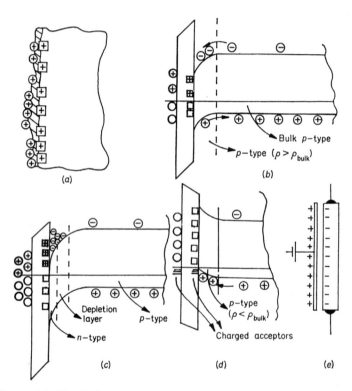

Figure 6.1. Reminder of the idea of 'band-bending': (*a*) the underlying cause – the presence of fixed surface charge in slow states (⊕) and in fast states ([+]), (*b*) the 'depletion' of the surface of a *p*-type layer by positive surface charge; (*c*) the 'inversion' of a *p*-type layer by a higher density of positive surface charge; (*d*) the 'accumulation' or increased surface conductivity induced by negative surface charge on a *p*-type substrate; (*e*) the creation of a surface charge by use of a charged metal plate – 'the field effect'.

only of the bulk material. Our preoccupation here will be with real surfaces.

In figure 6.1(*a*) we have illustrated the situation which exists on most Ge surfaces. On the surface of the Ge itself is an oxide film which is thin, of variable thickness ($\sim 10 \rightarrow 2,000$ Å) and which depends to a very great extent for its properties on the previous history of the specimen treatment. On the outer surface of this oxide layer there are surface states which can trap electrons, or holes, just as localized traps in the bulk of the material can immobilize the charge. Similar states exist at the interface between the oxide and the Ge. We usually distinguish [4] between the outer and inner states by calling them 'slow' and 'fast' respectively. This term refers to the ability of the charge in the traps to follow and electrical excitation that is quickly applied to (or removed from) the semiconductor circuit. The inner traps which are in good electrical contact with the free carriers in the semiconductor can follow such changes fairly fast (say, typically, in a microsecond) whereas the outer states are relatively isolated and therefore take longer (from 10^{-3}s to $\gg 1$ hour) to respond to the excitation. This situation is restated in figure 6.1(*b*) in terms of a band diagram. In the case illustrated the existence of fixed positive charge at the surface means that free carriers of opposite sign (electrons) will be attracted towards the surface while holes will be repelled into the bulk. In this way the bulk of the specimen is screened from the field of trapped positive surface charge. As a result of this tendency to produce electrical neutrality over as big a volume as possible, two things result. The first of these is that, associated with the 'dipole' formed by the trapped positive charge and the adjacent free electrons, there is an electric field, i.e. a voltage drop exists between the surface and the bulk. Secondly, the presence of the excess of electrons in the surface layer compared to the bulk means that the surface layer is more *n*-type than the bulk (see figure 6.1(*b*)). In fact, if there is a high density of positive charge in surface states, it is possible that an *n*-type layer of relatively high conductivity exists on the surface. Figure 6.1(*c*) shows how, in terms of the band diagram, the presence of more and more fixed positive charge can lead first to the depletion of majority carriers at the surface to give a surface depletion layer then secondly to the increase in minority carriers so that the conductivity type changes or an 'inversion' layer is formed. Figure 6.1(*d*) also defines, for completeness, what is meant by an accummulation layer. In this case the fixed charge distribution in the surface states is of such a sign as to lead to an increase in majority carrier density at the surface. One way of bringing about changes in surface conductivity experimentally is shown in figure 6.1(e). A metal plate placed close to the surface is positively charged. The semiconductor 'sees' an increase in fixed surface charge and more electrons are

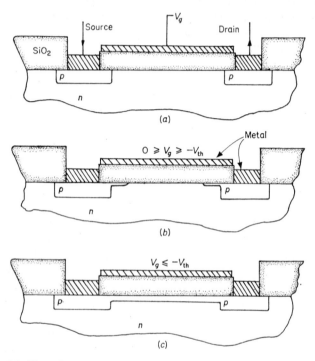

Figure 6.2. Use of control of surface conductance for device operation: the MOST; (a) high impedence path between source and drain, no inversion in absence of gate voltage; (b) inversion of part of the n-type region by application of a gate voltage $< |V_{th}|$; (c) complete inversion case $V_g > |V_{th}|$, channel current can flow between source and drain via p-type 'skin'.

attracted towards the surface. Thus, as the voltage on the plate is increased, the surface layer goes from p-type, through intrinsic to n-type. If a negative voltage is applied to the electrode the surface layer becomes increasingly p-type, i.e. the majority carrier concentration is increased. This control of surface conductivity by the field from a near-by plate is exploited in field-effect transistors. For completeness such a transistor is illustrated in figure 6.2. In this example the application of a negative voltage to the centre, insulated electrode (the 'gate') gradually opens up a p-type channel between the other electrodes (the 'source' and 'drain') so that these contacts become connected by a highly conductive layer. In the absence of a negative 'gate' voltage these contacts are connected by a path which includes the impedance of two reversed-biassed pn junctions.

This section introduces the ideas of surface states, surface conductivity and indicates how these ideas can be exploited to make devices. The importance of these ideas is self-evident when it is realized that the bulk of the information obtained in the scanning electron microscope is derived from the surface layer of the specimen being examined. For example, various estimates put the escape depth of secondary electrons between 100 and 500 Å; reflected electrons escape from approximately 1 to 2μ deep in the specimen while the total range of a 20-kV electron in silicon is approximately 4μ.

In one sense scanning electron microscopy is concerned solely with specimen surfaces. In view of this dependence on the surface properties it is important to enquire a little deeper into surface effects. A good point at which to start this enquiry is with surface-trapping phenomena.

6.2.2 Surface trapping

The division of surface states into fast and slow states is convenient but is often something of an oversimplification, as it implies that the surface insulator layer is perfect in character and is uniform in thickness. In practice this is often not the case. In addition to having a charge in surface states at the vacuum insulator and at the insulator-semiconductor interfaces it is possible that there exists a distribution of traps throughout the bulk of the insulator layer. This distribution need not be uniform either across the surface of the specimen or in depth throughout the width of the layer. Thus a whole distribution of traps can exist which are separated from the semiconductor by varying thicknesses of insulator. The response time of these traps can vary with distance from the semiconductor and with applied bias. Consider a simple case of a single set of traps of a discrete energy uniformly distributed throughout the insulator layer. (See figure 6.3(a).) The occupancy of this set of traps will be determined by the value of the Fermi level at the surface. Under an external excitation the quasi-Fermi level will move and the trap occupancy will not be in equilibrium. Equilibrium can be restored by a movement of charge from the traps. This movement can be brought about in two ways: by thermal activation or by tunnelling. In the present case where we are dealing with high, but localized barriers, particularly at high biasses, tunnelling is likely to prevail. In this case the tunnelling probability and therefore the response time will be a function of the trap distance from the semiconductor. Thus what is in fact a single discrete set of traps in the oxide, will appear from the viewpoint of

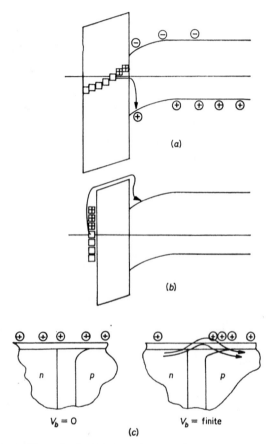

Figure 6.3. (*a*) Traps in 'bulk' of surface insulator layer, communicating with the semiconductor by tunnelling; (*b*) thermal activation of 'slow' surface states; (*c*) re-arrangement of surface charge by application of junction bias.

the semiconductor as a distribution of traps of varying response times and, therefore, if the assumption is made that the traps are all situated at a fixed distance from the semiconductor, of differing energy levels.

This discussion shows that a whole range of response times from the fast to the very slow can exist which is both field and temperature dependent. It also illustrates a complicating factor arising, on occasion, from the inability to give an unambiguous interpretation to the observed data. For example, if the measurements indicate a distribution of response times, the two distributions of states shown in figures 6.3(a) and (b) can fit the observations. Further experiments are then needed to clarify the situation. This interpretative difficulty has been stressed by Zaininger and Warfield [5, 6]. An additional complication can arise because of ionic mobility particularly at elevated temperatures, say 100°C.

We have so far regarded the charge in the surface states as being completely immobile. This is not necessarily true, some of the surface states (usually most of them) arise because the presence of surface impurity atoms gives rise to additional allowed electron states. Some of these impurity atoms will be ionized and will move, albeit slowly, over the surface. Thus, in certain situations such as that shown in figure 6.3(c), the supposedly fixed charge can in fact have a slight degree of mobility. There is another situation in which ionic mobility can lead to changes of local field by the creation of a space charge. If a silica layer which has been contaminated by ions of a reactive element is heated at, say, $\gtrsim$ 100°C with a suitable bias applied, the ions can move through the insulator layer thus leading to the formation of a positive space charge near the semiconductor, provided compensating electrons cannot be introduced from the semiconductor. Cooling the polarized oxide will 'freeze in' this space charge which will therefore affect the surface conductivity in the same manner as a charge in surface states [7, 8]. Even if the insulator films are not contaminated they can be polarized by a suitable combination of bias and external excitation. This situation possibly arises because the transition between the Si and SiO_2 does not occur abruptly but goes through a finite thickness of SiO_x ($x < 2$). Associated with the oxygen vacancies in this transition layer there may be traps (in general, hole traps) which can lead to space-charge and therefore polarization effects. For example, if electrons are knocked out of such traps by ionizing radiation and are swept away by an electric field, the nett effect is a positive charge layer in or very near to the

K

SiO_x layer. No matter how this positive charge comes about in detail it can persist for a long time after the excitation is removed, due to the absence of carriers in the oxide, the low mobility of such carriers as are present and the inability of carriers in the Si to enter far into the SiO_2 layer [9, 10, 11]. Related to this topic of surface trapping is the idea of surface recombination.

6.2.6 *Surface recombination*

Let us imagine that a surface state at the semiconductor-insulator interface captures an electron. If, before this electron is released by thermal excitation, the surface state now captures a hole an electron-hole pair will have been annihilated and the surface state will be free to take part in this recombination process again. The ability of a surface state to act as a recombination centre as opposed to a trap depends on the position of the state in the forbidden band, on the temperature on the local position of the quasi-Fermi level and on the relative ability of the centre to capture electrons and holes (i.e. on the relative capture cross-sections). It is well established that fast surface states do indeed act in this manner [12, 13, 14] in a wide range of materials. When this is the case the surface acts as a 'drain' for carriers of both sign and there is a nett movement of both electrons and holes towards the surface. This surface recombination current can compete with other processes, such as the movement of minority carriers across a transistor base-region to give transistor action, or with the radiative recombination of carriers in the bulk. Therefore, in practical terms, a large surface recombination current can represent a reduction in transistor gain or a decrease in radiative efficiency. A convenient measure of surface recombination effects is called the surface recombination velocity. This quantity is defined as

$$S = \frac{U}{\Delta n_{z=0}} \tag{6.1}$$

where U is the rate of loss of carriers at the surface due to recombination and $\Delta n_{z=0}$ is the excess density of free carriers at the surface. The surface recombination velocity depends strongly on the degree of band-bending existing at the surface.

Figure 6.4 shows schematically the behaviour often observed [25]. Here the relative recombination velocity is plotted against the surface voltage. The surface voltage is a formal measurement of the degree of band-bending and is usually taken as the difference in energy (or voltage) between the intrinsic level in the bulk and the same level at the surface (see figure 6.4(b)). At a particular value of the surface voltage, V_s^{max}, (see figure 6.4(a)), the surface recombination velocity is a maximum. Increasing or decreasing V_s about this value leads to a reduction in S by a factor of ten for changes of several kT/q in V_s.

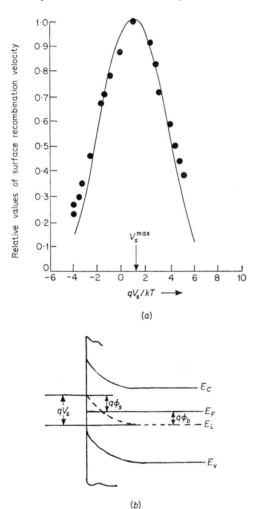

Figure 6.4. (a) Typical manner in which the surface recombination velocity varies as a function of surface voltage [25]; (b) definition of the surface voltage, V_s.

We can understand this behaviour by noting that the recombination rate will be a maximum when the surface density of electrons and holes are about equal. If the surface voltage departs from the value required to bring about this equality then one or other of the electron or hole recombination rates decreases and the slower rate will determine the overall speed. The magnitude and sign of V_s^{max} is an indication of the nature and density of the fixed charge at the surface. We

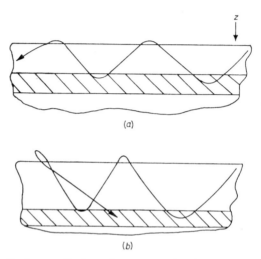

Figure 6.5. Surface-scattering phenomena: (*a*) Specular reflection, no additional scattering at surface; (*b*) diffuse or random scattering leading to reduced surface mobility of free carriers.

shall see below that surface recombination plays an important role in device behaviour. For the present we have to finish this discussion of surface effects by considering the question of free carrier mobility at the surface.

6.2.4 *Surface carrier mobility*

Take as an example the device shown in figure 6.2. When the device is conducting, the channel connecting the source and the drain will be passing milliamps yet the channel thickness may be only 1,000 Å wide. So the carriers are in a sense confined to the surface and bulk mobilities are not the appropriate values to use for the mobilities. The important point is that the surface presents an additional source of scattering compared with the bulk. A calculation of the surface mobility can be made, as in the case of bulk mobility, by solving Boltzmann's equation with suitable boundary conditions. The boundary conditions in the surface problem can be expressed in similar terms to those used when an electron, for example, is reflected from the surface.

Consider figure 6.5 in which an electron drifts across the specimen surface due to a lateral field and is, at the same time, confined to a potential 'well' formed by the surface barrier on one side and by a confining transverse electric field on the other. When the electron is scattered from the surface one of three things can happen. First it can be specularly reflected, that is to say, it collides elastically with the surface and experiences no momentum change other than a reversal of the velocity in the z-direction (see figure 6.5(a)). On the other hand the collision with the surface can be such that the electron has an equal probability of being reflected back into any element of solid angle. This diffuse or random scattering (see figure 6.5(b)) obviously leads to a reduction in mobility whereas specular reflection does not. These two possibilities represent extreme cases. In practice, surfaces often reflect both randomly and specularly at the same time. This can be taken into account by introducing a parameter p which is the probability that an electron will be specularly reflected at a surface collision. The effective mobility μ_{eff} is then given by [15]

$$\mu_{\text{eff}} = p\mu_b + (1 - p)\mu_s \qquad (6.2)$$

where μ_b is the carrier mobility in the bulk, μ_s is the mobility which would be measured if the surface behaved as a purely diffuse scatterer. There is no reason why p should be independent of the transverse electric field. In fact there are possible indications [16] that p decreases as the surface field increases. There are two other factors which can complicate the issue. The surface can act not only as a scatterer but as a source of traps which can immobilize the carriers for a small but finite time thus leading to a further reduction in effective mobility. Finally, the implicit assumption that the interface between, say, the silicon layer and SiO_2 layer on a thermally oxidized **MOST** structure is abrupt, is not necessarily true. In fact, the transition region $Si \rightarrow SiO_x \rightarrow SiO_2$ may extend over a substantial distance comparable with the current-carrying, surface layer thickness. So even in the absence of effects due to the actual interface the mobility in the surface layer may well be different from the bulk as its chemical composition is different, i.e. there may be come uncertainty as to the correct value to take for μ_b. So far we have used the MOST structure as a background to establish the major ideas inherent in surface physics. It is now necessary to show how these ideas affect the behaviour of more conventional transistors, i.e. transistors which ideally do not depend on the control of surface conductivity for their mode of operation.

6.3 The effect of surface properties on transistor action

There are four properties of passivated transistors which depend in part on the behaviour of the surface in the regions where the emitter-base junction, the base and the base-collector junction come to the surface. These properties are:

(1) The forward characteristics of the junctions.
(2) The leakage current under reverse bias.
(3) Breakdown characteristics.
(4) The spectrum of the $1/f$ noise.

Consider first the forward characteristic. We can, following Mitchell and Wilson [17], divide the junction current up into five components:

(*a*) A bulk recombination-generation current due to recombination-generation in the bulk regions on either side of the junction. This is the normal diffusion current flow analysed in detail by Shockley [18] and others [19].

(*b*) A similar current due to recombination-generation via traps existing in the junction layer itself. This is the situation analysed in one particular case by Sah, Noyce and Shockley [20].

(*c*) Recombination-generation current due to recombination-generation at the surface on either side of the junction. This process is analogous to (*a*) but suitably modified by the surface field, surface mobility, etc.

(*d*) A current due to surface recombination-generation in the junction region; the surface equivalent of (*b*).

(*e*) A current being carried by a surface channel connecting emitter to collector.

In general the VI characteristic resulting from each of these processes can be written as

$$I = I_0 \exp (eV/\beta kT) \qquad \text{for } V > 4kT/q \qquad (6.3)$$

where I_0 and β vary with the mechanisms considered. In particular $\beta \approx 1$ for (*a*) and (*c*); $1 < \beta < 2$ for (*b*) and (*d*) and $2 < \beta < 4$ for (*e*).

In general the distortion of the surface-junction region will be greatest on the less conductive side. In figure 6.6, for example, the presence of positive charge in the oxide leads to a widening of the junction region for the emitter-base junction in an *npn* transistor as the emitter region will be more highly doped than the base. But the reverse is true for the collector-base junction. The interface between the depletion layer and the *n*-type collector will be distorted more

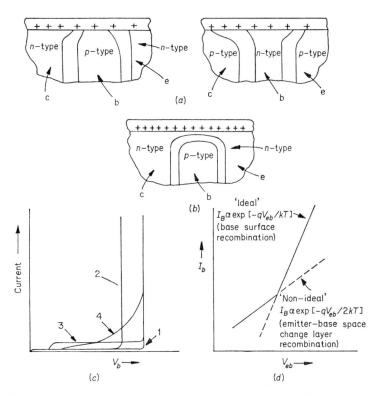

Figure 6.6. Effect of stored charge on junction configurations on *npn* and *pnp* transistors; (*a*) contrasting behaviour observed with positive charge in insulator on *npn* and *pnp* transistors; (*b*) complete inversion of base surface layer by positive stored charge in *npn* transistor; (*c*) *VI* curves observed in leaky junction structures: (1) ideal curve; (2) ideal curve but with reduced breakdown voltage; (3) diode with single 'channel' capable of carrying a limited current; (4) diode with voltage-dependent leakage paths; (*d*) causes of leakage current associated with surface recombination.

than that between the depletion layer and the p-type base so that the junction width will be less at the surface than in the bulk. So, in this example, the major contribution to surface current will come from the emitter-base region, but the base-collection junction will be important when the breakdown properties are considered.

If the breakdown is due to avalanche effects it occurs first in the regions where the electric field is highest. In the case considered and ignoring variations due to localized defects this will be at the surface. However, when a positively charged oxide exists on a *pnp* transistor (figure 6.7(*a*)) the surface field for the reversed-biassed, collector-base junction is less than the bulk field so that breakdown tends to be initiated in the bulk.

The reverse bias leakage at voltages well below that corresponding to breakdown arises from the generation of minority carriers in or near to the junction followed by their collection by the junction field. If the surface charge leads to an increase in surface junction area this increases the area that gives rise to a leakage current and so increases the leakage. If the surface charge is so great as to cause a channel to partially 'short circuit' the base (see figure 6.7(*b*)) the leakage current increases because (*a*) the effective junction area and hence the number of carriers collected by the junction, increase, (*b*) the surface layer represents a region with a high generation rate and (*c*) because of the conduction current carried by the channel. The behaviour as far as the reverse *VI* characteristic of the collector base junction is concerned can be summed up in terms of figure 6.7(*d*). The curve (1) represents the ideal characteristics with the small leakage current predicted by the bulk properties and a breakdown voltage determined by the bulk field. Curve (2) illustrates the case where there is no excess leakage but the breakage voltage is lowered by the high surface field. Curve (3) illustrates the situation where a source of excess surface leakage suddenly 'turns on' at a particular voltage and then gives a constant, voltage-independent leakage current. Finally curve (4) illustrates a very leaky curve arising either from an excess leakage source which increases in extent as the voltage is increased or from the existence of a series of such sources which be come operative at different voltages as the bias is increased.

Finally we have to consider the $1/f$ noise. This noise is known to be sensitive to surface conditions and McWhorter [21] has suggested that it arises from variations in the charge stored in slow states on the surface. These variations lead to corresponding changes in the surface conductivity. The $1/f$ noise increases greatly as the surface layer goes from accumulation to inversion and so depends on the oxide properties. In general, passivated devices have smaller $1/f$ components than non-passivated devices.

We can briefly sum-up the surface effects on transistor behaviour. Figure 6.6(d) summarizes the reverse bias junction characteristics while figure 6.6(e) shows how the recombination-generation currents in the space-charge region of the emitter-base junction predominate at low currents. It has been shown [22] experimentally that a major source of the excess base current arises from the surface of the emitter-base space-charge area. As a result the β value of the transistor is reduced and the base current is, of necessity, increased to provide the necessary majority carriers. The increase in I_B will be reflected in a drop in the common emitter gain $= (I_C - I_{CEO})/I_B$. Thus the surface properties affect the forward and reverse diode characteristics, the noise properties and the low current and high current gains.

6.4 Summary

At the risk of some tedium it is better to restate and summarize the ideas expressed above in view of their importance to SEM studies. Briefly we have arrived at the physical picture summarized in figure 6.2. The manufacturing processes used to make this structure can lead to the pressence of interface states, bulk traps in the insulator layer and slow states at the outer surface. These states arise from several causes. Even in the absence of impurities an interface represents a departure from the periodity of the bulk lattice and so Tamm-Shockley [23, 24] localized states exist at such interfaces in a density dependent on the crystal lattices involved, their degree of misfit, etc. Superimposed on these states are localized states due to impurities, departures from stochiometry either in the bulk of the insulator layer, or at the interfaces. These states can exhibit both donor-like and acceptor characteristics. In general, gases with strong electron affinities such as oxygen and ozone induce a negative surface charge, whereas water vapour and ammonia tend to cause a positively-charged surface. If voltage differences exist across the surface, the ionized impurities can drift in the associated field, i.e. the distribution is not necessarily static.

When a voltage increment is applied to the gate, i.e. an increment of charge delivered to the metal contact, a corresponding charge is developed on the oxide-semiconductor structure in order to terminate the lines of force. Part of this induced charge will be in bulk oxide traps and/or in surface states. The remainder will be free carrier charge in the surface layer and will represent a change in conductance. As the fraction of the applied voltage increment that is effective in changing the surface conductivity depends on the surface state density, so will the device characteristics. In addition the surface states will affect the surface recombination velocity and the free carrier mobilities. The surface properties are not necessarily time-independent, but can change under the effects of ambient changes, temperature variations, bias conditions and under external excitation such as electron-beam bombardment.

The surface properties exploited in the MOST structure, although they are not necessary to transistor operation in bipolar transistors, have to be carefully controlled in the manufacture of the latter. If this control is absent the surface properties can adversely affect the hardness of the reverse characteristic, the gain, and the transistor noise properties. The device manufacturer wants to know as precisely as possible the cause of the changes in characteristic from one device to another and with time in any one device. To obtain this information he has available the nornal macroscopic measurements such as CV plots [25] VI characteristics, field-effect studies [26] and the various methods [27] of determining the surface recombination velocity. In general these methods provide data which are averaged over the whole of the relevant area. It is often very useful to obtain localized information as well as the average value. This is where the SEM contributes. The approach is not always straightforward as the electron bombardment inherent in examination by the SEM can, itself, bring about changes in the surface properties that are being studies. Sometimes these changes are of use in diagnosing the surfaces properties. On other occasions they impede the observation of the relevant phenomena. What then are the changes induced in specimens by electron bombardment? They can be many and varied, but by way of introduction we will describe the general type of interaction that can occur under bombardment by high-energy particles.

6.5 Irradiation effects in solids

6.5.1 Introduction

There are two major ways in which high-energy electrons, protons, γ- and x-rays can affect solids. The first is the formation of a small region of intense ionization and this has already been discussed. Of immediate relevance is the fact that this ionization can alter the degree of occupancy of local states in the surface structure and so affect the conductivity of the underlying semiconductor, the noise properties, etc. If the ionization alters the occupancy of states in poor electrical communication with the semiconductor the change will be permanent, i.e. it can persist for months or until removed by annealing (usually in tens of hours at temperatures between 150 and 400°C). Even after annealing, some kind of change can persist. For, as we shall see below, although annealing will (often) restore the initial properties a 'memory' is sometimes induced in the specimen [28]. If the device is re-irradiated after annealing it is found that its sensitivity to the radiation has increased compared to the first irradiation, i.e. its properties change quicker with dose than initially.

The second way in which high-energy particles affect solids is by the creation of further defects. The defects most usually formed are vacancies and interstitials which then interact with existing defects to form new stable defects. In semiconductors and in insulators this can lead to an increase in the number and to a change in the nature of the existing traps and/or recombination centres. Further changes can be brought about by subsequent annealing. This may lead to a removal of the induced defects or the formation of more complex defects resulting from the amalgamation of several point, and other defects. The creation of additional defects in the bulk is usually only significant at particle energies in excess of say, typically, 100 keV and it can be neglected in the present context. It is often assumed that particles below this energy range do not significantly affect the number of effective defects in the surface region. The argument advanced is that the surface is a region of relatively poor material anyway and is therefore less susceptible to this kind of damage. What this argument does not consider is the fact that radiation-induced defects can interact with existing defects to form stable defects which differ in electrical behaviour from the initial defects. Thus the surface with its inherent greater density of defects may in fact be more susceptible to such effects. (See Mitchell and Wilson [17].) At present the bulk of the evidence on unpassivated devices at least suggests that the major effect of irradiation is to change the surface-charge density. Whether this change results from a change in occupancy of the original defect states or from a change in the nature of the states is not always clear. (Also see [51].)

Two other general points can be made about irradiation effects. To a first approximation the nature of the interaction with semi-conductor materials and devices is independent of the nature of the bombarding particles if impact ionization is the significant process. The important factor is the dose of radiation delivered, (see [17]). It is possible to predict with fair accuracy the behaviour under electron-beam bombardment by studying the results obtained with the experimentally very convenient, Co^{60} γ-radiation. Finally it should be stressed that, throughout the bombardment, recovery processes are occurring. Thus the observed changes arise from the nett difference between the excitation and the recovery processes. It is therefore possible that variations due to dose-rate may arise and that non-linear effects, such as saturation, may occur. In fact departures from reciprocity and saturation effects have both been observed [29, 30]. We shall study these effects in the next few sections which describe selected data relevant to scanning electron microscopy. For a fuller account the reader is referred to reference [17].

6.5.2 *Irradiation effects in semicondutor devices*: (*i*) MOST *structures*

Somewhat perversely we begin by describing irradiation effects due, not to electron-beam bombardment, but to x-ray irradiation. Grove and Snow [31] exposed MOST structures to 35-kV tungsten radiation ($\approx 5 \times 10^3$ rad/sec) with various values of the gate voltage during the exposure. After each exposure the C-V_g characteristic was determined and the increment in the charge introduced by the irradiation in the silicon was also found. The salient features are shown in figure 6.7. The increase in surface, free charge arising from a given exposure depends on the sign of V_g applied during the exposure. A greater increase occurs if $V_g > 0$. As the dosage increases, Q_s increases rapidly at first and then saturates. If the saturation value Q_s^∞ is plotted against $\sqrt{V_g}$ a straight line is obtained at small V_g.

To explain these results the authors apply the Von Hippel [32] model of space-charge formation in insulators. The underlying idea is that the irradiation-induced electrons and holes in the oxide nearly all recombine in the absence of a gate voltage, but, if the gate voltage is applied so as to carry the electrons away from the Si-SiO$_2$ interface, the holes can be trapped so that a positive space charge develops near this interface, provided, of course, that relatively few electrons can enter the oxide from the semiconductor. As the space-charge region grows the voltage across it increases until, ultimately, all the

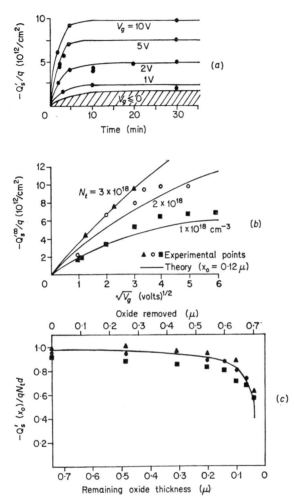

Figure 6.7. Data of Grove and Snow [31] showing irradiation effects in MOST structures; (a) surface, free-carrier density increase, Q_s, as function of time and gate voltage during exposure; (b) similar data compared with theoretical estimates as a function of trap density; (c) location of the origin of increased charge found by etching oxide away.

applied voltage is across it. In the case where we have a uniform density of hole traps N_t the final width, d, of the space charge region will be given by $d = (2\varepsilon\varepsilon_0 V_g/qN_t)^{1/2}$. The charge in this region is $qN_t d$ and will induce image charges at both the 'anode' and 'cathode' of the MOS capacitor. Gauss's theorem gives the charge in the silicon as

$$Q_s^\infty = qN_t d(1 - d/2x_0) \qquad d \leqslant z_0 \qquad (6.4)$$

so that $Q_s^\infty \propto \sqrt{V_g}$ at low V_g and approaches $qN_t x_0/2$ at high V_g. This variation agrees with that observed experimentally. Comparison between the theoretical expression and the experimental data yield values of N_t between 1 and 3 $\times$ 10^{18}/cm^3.

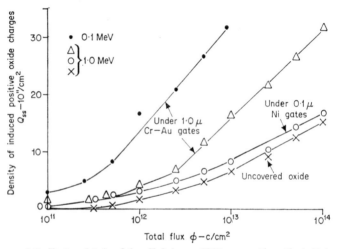

Figure 6.8. Data obtained by Zaininger [33] suggesting that it is the low-energy electrons which lead in irradiation effects in planar structures.

The localization of the space charge at the Si-SiO$_2$ interface was confirmed experimentally by etching off the metal, gate-contact and by measuring the surface conductance of the channel as the oxide was gradually etched off. Since the effective surface mobility was known from experimental measurements the charge stored in the Si as a function of oxide thickness can be determined. The results are shown in figure 6.7(c). For an oxide of thickness $\sim 0.75\mu$ irradiated with a voltage of $+ 4$ volts applied to the gate, d was found to be $< 1,000$ Å.

Zaininger [33] using relatively high energy electrons to bombard MOS structures made by thermal oxidation (dry oxygen) to give oxide layers 1,000 Å thick, obtained the data shown in figure 6.8. The dependence on gate voltage was very similar to that described under x-ray-irradiation. The bombarded specimens were very stable. Isochronal annealing at 150 to 300°C led to major reductions in Q_{ss}^{∞} which were largely independent on the sign and magnitude of V_g that was applied during annealing. All the effects annealed out at

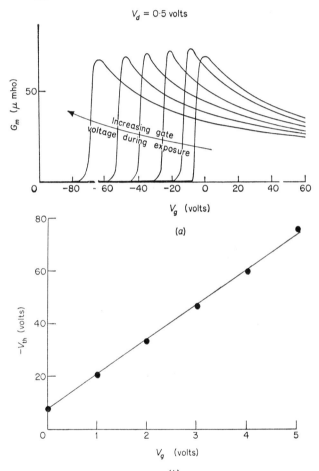

Figure 6.9. Variation of (a) transconductance and (b) threshold voltage, with the gate voltage applied during irradiation [34].

400°C. The significant feature of the data is the way in which the value of Q_{ss} observed for a given dosage depends on the nature and thickness of the metal layer on top of the oxide. A reasonable conclusion to draw here is that the electrons that are responsible for the increases in Q_{ss} are those contained in the low-energy tail of the distribution. This idea is borne out by some recent work in which 5-keV electrons were used to bombard similar devices. Speth and Fang [34] studied devices with oxide thicknesses $\simeq$ 6,000 Å covered by 1,500 Å of Al by exposing them to a total dose of 2×10^{-5} coulomb/cm² and then measuring the transconductance, G_m, of the devices. G_m is defined as dI_d/dV_g. The data are shown in figure 6.9(a) as a function of the gate voltage applied during irradiation. The form of the curve relating G_m to the gate voltage remains unaffected by the magnitude of V_g applied during the exposure, but the threshold voltage, V_{th}, at which the device turns on, moves to more negative values as V_g is increased (in positive sense) during the exposure. If the threshold voltage after exposure is plotted against the gate voltage applied during the irradiation, the plot shown in figure 6.9(b) is obtained. If this curve is compared with the theoretical relationship

$$V_{th} = - V_b \left\{ (2d/x_0) - 1 \right\} + V_{th}°$$

where $V_{th}°$ is the threshold voltage prior to exposure to the electron beam, the value of d obtained is $\sim$ 850 A (however, see section 6.6). The behaviour observed with a negative gate voltage applied during the irradiation is complex; the apparent threshold changes little, but the mobility falls off indicating that trapping effects may become important.

Other studies [35] have shown that the source-drain leakage current increases during irradiation, while the gate leakage current remained essentially unchanged. In addition the drain breakdown voltage is dependent on the dosage. With these devices (enchancement made MOSFET's) the source-drain leakage gradually decayed during storage at room temperature until the pre-irradiation level was restored after several months.

6.5.3 *Irradiation effects in semiconductor devices*: (*ii*) *planar transistors*
Figure 6.10 shows the type of behaviour observed [29, 50] with passivated diodes and transistors. There is a considerable spread in this type of data, but these results are fairly typical and are capable of explanation in terms of the ideas outlined above. It is seen that

there is a gradual increase in I_{CBO} with increase in dose for the transistors. A somewhat variable increase in reverse current for the diodes and a relatively rapid decrease in h_{Fe} particularly at low currents. These effects depend on the bias applied during the irradiation. The gain-degradation rate, for example, is increased if either junction is reverse biassed and decreased if either junction is forward biassed. The effects are virtually stable under no-bias conditions,

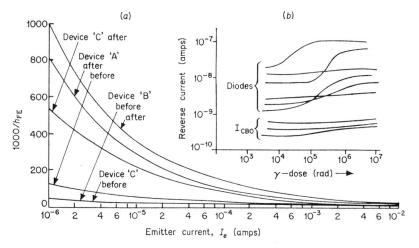

Figure 6.10. Irradiation effects on transistors and diodes [29], [50]; (a) dependence of h_{Fe} on emitter current before and after x-irradiation. (b) irradiation effects on diode reverse leakage and I_{CBO} on diffused, Si, planar devices. $V_B = 20$ volts.

but if a bias is applied recovery is quickened, particularly by high emitter currents. Schmid [37], using Co[60] γ-radiation, has done extensive measurements on both *npn* and *pnp* devices and noted a general difference in behaviour. For *npn* devices there is a rapid drop in d.c. gain, typically to 10% of starting value for a dose of 10^6 rad and a slow increase in I_{CBO}. But for *pnp* devices there is a relatively slow decrease in gain but I_{CBO} can increase by as much as $\times 10^6$ for 10^6 rad. At high doses I_{CBO} sometimes saturates and sometimes even decreases with further irradiation. Schmid explains this difference by assuming that the irradiation produces a positive charge in the oxide above the base region which produces an increase in the surface recombination velocity in *npn* structures and so, by forcing the base

L

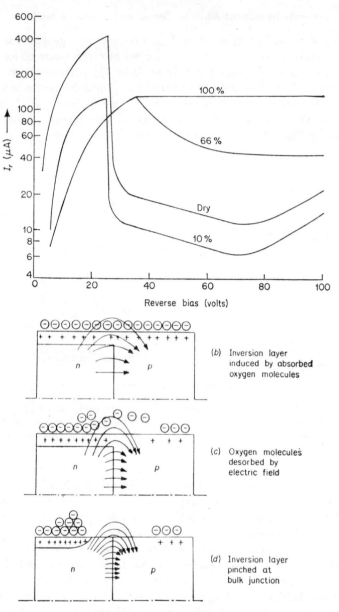

Figure 6.11. (a) Irradiation effects on Ge diode reverse characteristics as a function of bias and relative humidity [40, 41]; (b) to (d) suggested explanation for the decrease in leakage observed at certain levels of humidity with increase in bias.

current up, reduces the gain. In *pnp* structures a collector channel is formed giving an increase in I_{CBO}. Studies [38] of I_{CEO} have revealed corresponding increases with dosage. The degradation rate is bias-dependent and the recovery rate is apparently quicker in the presence of irradiation (no bias). A 'memory effect', i.e. an increased rate of degradation after partial recovery, was observed.

In general, these effects on planar transistors, diodes (and MOST structures) are largely independent of whether the experiments are performed in a vacuum or an ambient gas. In addition, by using low-energy electrons ($\sim$ 2kV) it has been established [39] that only if the electrons penetrate to the vicinity of the Si-SiO$_2$ interface does the degradation occur. Both results support the idea that the effective changes are occurring in the oxide below its surface. This contrasts sharply with the behaviour recorded for unpassivated devices, as we shall now see.

6.5.4 *Irradiation effects in semiconductor devices.* (iii) *non-passivated devices*

Fryer [40] and Verrelli [41] have both studied the effect of Co^{60} γ-radiation on Ge diodes. Figure 6.11 shows how the data are affected by the relative humidity in which the irradiation is carried out. There are two features of these curves which are, at first sight, surprising. These are the sharp decrease in I_r at a given voltage at low humidities and the decrease in I_r with increase in humidity above this critical voltage. To interpret these results it is assumed that the Ge is covered by a thin oxide layer which has acceptor states associated with it. In a dry ambient these states are unoccupied. Irradiation results in a negative charge being delivered to these states so a channel is formed on the *n*-type side of the junction. As the humidity is increased, a positive charge is delivered to the surface which, by opposing the existing negative charge, tends to reduce the surface leakage. Further increase in humidity means that the nett surface charge becomes positive, an inversion layer is formed on the *p*-type side of the junction and the leakage increases again. This model explains the data obtained at high bias values; the low voltage behaviour can be explained in terms of figures 6.11(*b*) to (*d*). The instant a reverse bias is applied to the situation shown in figure 6.11(*b*) the field lines will take the form illustrated in figure 6.11(*c*). If the surface ions have any degree of mobility or can be de-absorbed the equilibrium situation is that depicted in figure 6.11(*d*). If this process becomes possible at a certain field strength the channel will be 'pinched-off' and a rapid decrease in leakage would occur.

The role played by ambient gases during the irradiation of un-passivated devices is also stressed by studies reported by Peck *et al.* [49]. These workers subjected unpassivated devices that were en-capsulated in a gas-filled can to γ-irradiation and observed that the degradation (increase in I_{CBO} and diode leakage current) was

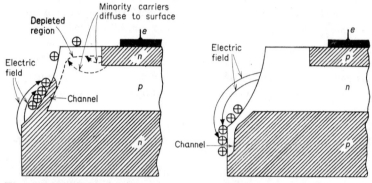

Figure 6.12. Channel formation on *npn* and *pnp* transistors by surface-charge movement according to Peck *et al.* [49].

minimal unless a bias was applied. It was also found that the voltage difference between the device and the can affected the process. If the can is positive relative to the device, the rate of degradation is increased. It is suggested that the γ-rays ionize the ambient gas. The ions drift in the fields due to the applied bias and/or the can-device voltage difference and either become absorbed on the device surface or exchange charge with an existing surface impurity. In either case the situations shown in figure 6.12 can develop and the device is degraded. This general picture is confirmed by the observation that evacuating the can greatly decreases the observed degradation rate. Still further confirmation of the importance of ambient gas is obtained from studies of ion bombardment effects on semiconductor surfaces. (See Chapter 12).

6.6 Discussion

We can now establish an approximate picture of the behaviour to be expected when devices are subjected to bombardment in the SEM. Non-passivated devices will be affected most likely by changes in the occupancy of the slow surface states. The nature of the degradation will depend on the initial surface condition, the sign and magnitude of the bias applied, and possibly on the state of cleanliness of the specimen chamber. This latter possibility arises because, if the electron beam (or reflected primaries) causes the creation of positive ions, these will drift in the collector field towards the specimen and may give rise to the effects outlined by Peck *et al.*, albeit somewhat

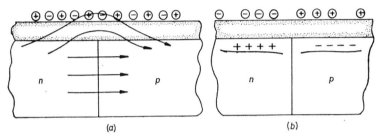

Figure 6.13. The Atalla model [45] of inversion layer formation by surface-charge separation on application of bias voltage.

slowly. In general these changes begin to be significant at doses of 10^3 rad and become saturated at $\sim 10^7$ rad. These figures correspond to exposures of the order of 10 and 10^4 seconds for a 20 kV beam delivering a current of 10^{-8} amps into a $1\mu^2$ area. In general, the most radiation-sensitive parameters are I_{CBO} and h_{Fe} for transistors, the leakage current in diodes (and the threshold voltage in MOS transistors).

By way of contrast good passivated devices will be most affected by changes in the positive charge stored in the oxide near to the Si-SiO$_2$ interface*. Ambients will have little effect, but the behaviour will again be variable depending on the starting condition of the oxide, the biasses applied and possibly the dose-rate. We have stressed the importance of charge storage in the oxide, but this effect may not be the predominate effect if the surface-state density has not been reduced to a low level. In this case surface-state effects and oxide effects are observed simultaneously in parallel. Kooi [42], Whelan [43] and Hofstein [44] have examined the behaviour of devices containing relatively large densities of surface states. In this case the devices are sensitive to ambients. In this context we should consider the early work (1959) of Atalla [45] who discussed irradiation effects

* For recent evidence showing the creation of fast surface states see [51].

observed on passivated diodes in terms of slow states on the oxide surface.

Atalla subjected oxide-covered diodes to γ-radiation and observed the effects of bias and relative humidity. It was found that if a zero or forward bias was applied with humidity during the irradiation no significant degradation resulted, but with a reverse bias and humidity applied during irradiation considerable increase in leakage current was recorded. By optically scanning the surface it was found that the

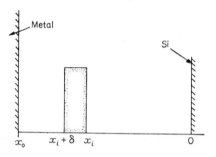

Figure 6.14. Formation of stored charge nearer to metal-oxide interface by low energy irradiations – definition of parameters used in text.

onset of the excess leakage current coincided with the formation of channels above *both* n- and p-type regions. Atalla suggested an explanation in terms of figure 6.13. If mobile ions of both signs exist on the surface, the fringing field may move these ions and then the fascinating situation shown in figure 6.13(b) can develop. This model also accounts for the recovery behaviour. By heating in the absence of bias the ions will move to the neutral condition and so the cause of the leakage is removed. This is what is, in fact, observed and surface-voltage studies [46] have also confirmed that there is a rearrangement of surface charge.

Therefore, on Si devices we have two mechanisms which can occur in parallel in varying degrees depending on the density of surface states. It is not always straightforward to tell which model predominates. Both models predict the existence of saturation effects and that an important role is played by the bias conditions during irradiation. If it is relatively difficult to obtain recovery, the implication is that the charge is stored in the oxide. Similarly, if the device is insensitive to low-energy ion beam bombardment (see Chapter 12), this result is indicative of the minor role played by slow states. As the devices get better the storage in the oxide becomes more important. As this mechanism represents a limiting behaviour, it is of interest to enquire into the way in which this charge storage takes place. The electron drift model, due initially to Von Hippel [32], imagines that in an existing distribution the traps have their occupancy altered by irradiation. The electrons so formed can drift away in the field, but the holes do not and so a nett positive charge results. The difficulty in extending this model arises from the oft-encountered one of not knowing what is the real distribution (both in energy and in space) of the traps, i.e. we are limited by the simple distribution assumed in the quantitative development. One limitation implied so far can, however, be removed: the space charge need not necessarily be formed close to the Si-SiO$_2$ interface. This point is important in another context, i.e. the resolving of the apparent conflict between the observations outlined in section 6.5(b).

Grove and Snow [31] reported that the threshold voltage, V_T, for MOST devices, varied as $\sqrt{V_g}$, where V_g is the gate voltage applied during irradiation. On the other hand, Speth and Fang [34] found that V_T varied as V_g. An important difference existed between the two experimental arrangements used, because, unlike Grove and Snow, Speth and Fang used very low energy electrons; so low an energy in fact that the electrons could barely penetrate through the overlying Al into the oxide. Under these conditions it is reasonable to assume that the space-charge layer is formed nearer the metal contact. Snow [47] has analysed this possibility in terms of the distribution shown in figure 6.14 and obtains an expression $V_T \simeq - V_g [(x_0/x_1) - 1] + V_T°$, which is a linear relation between V_T and V_g and is valid for $x_1 \geqslant 700$ Å. Experimental data, when compared with this model, give $x_1 \sim 400$ Å for $x_0 \sim 6,000$ Å. So the space-charge layer has been formed away from the interface, but is still somewhat deeper than expected from the known penetration depth of the electrons used. This discrepancy could arise from the presence of ion migration. It has been reported [48] that radioactive sodium and hydrogen were found to be in higher concentration near the interface than elsewhere.

We shall meet these ideas again later. They are generally applicable to many other systems, bulk semiconductors and insulators in general, devices passivated by silicon nitride, etc. Of course the application will differ in detail in different systems and the implicit assumption that the surface properties are uniform across the surface will be seen to be inadequate. In fact we shall stress the ability of the SEM to detect these local variations (patch effects). We shall also see that these ideas cannot really be considered in isolation from difficulties imposed by electron-beam contamination; this is discussed in the next chapter.

REFERENCES

[1] H. E. FARNSWORTH, R. E. SCHLIER, T. H. GEORGE and R. M. BURGER, *J. Appl. Phys.*, **26**, 82, (1955)

[2] H. E. FARNSWORTH, R. E. SCHLIER, T. H. GEORGE and R. M. BURGER, *J. Appl. Phys.*, **29**, 1150, (1958)

[3] C. J. DAVISON and L. H. GERMER, *Phys. Rev.*, **30**, 705, (1927)

[4] A. MANY, Y. GOLDSTEIN and N. B. GROVER, *Semiconductor Surfaces*, Wiley, New York, (1965)

[5] K. H. ZAININGER and G. WARFIELD, *I.E.E.E. Trans., Electron Devices*, **ED11**, 179, (1965)

[6] S. R. HOFSTEIN and G. WARFIELD, *Solid-State Electron*, **8**, 321, (1965)

[7] S. R. HOFSTEIN, *I.E.E.E. Trans., Electron Devices*, **ED13**, 222, (1966)

[8] E. YON, W. H. KO and A. B. KUPER, *I.E.E.E. Trans., Electron Devices*, **ED13**, 246, (1966)

[9] R. Y. DECHPANDE, *Solid-State Electron*, **8**, 619, (1965)

[10] B. E. DEAL, M. SKLAR, A. S. GROVE and E. H. SNOW, *J. Electrochem. Soc.*, **114**, 266, (1967)

[11] A. S. GROVE and D. J. FITZGERALD, *Solid-State Electron.*, **9**, 783, (1966)

[12] W. H. BRATTAIN and J. BARDEEN, *Bell. Syst. Tech. J.*, **32**, 1, (1953)

[13] W. SHOCKLEY, *Electrons and Holes in Semiconductors*, Van Nostrand, New York, (1950)

[14] See A. MANY, Y. GOLDSTEIN and N. B. GROVER, *Semiconductor Surfaces*, Chapters 5, 7 and 9, North-Holland Publ. Co., Amsterdam, (1965)

[15] J. R. SCHRIEFFER, *Phys. Rev.*, **97**, 641, (1955)

[16] O. LEISTIKO, A. S. GROVE and C. T. SAH, *I.E.E.E. Trans. Electron Devices*, **ED12**, 248, (1965)

[17] J. P. MITCHELL and D. K. WILSON, *B.S.T. Journ.*, **46**, 1, (1967)

[18] W. SHOCKLEY, *Bell. Syst. Tech. J.*, **28**, 435, (1949)

[19] J. LINDMAYER, C. WRIGLEY and K. SCHOENI, *J. Appl. Phys.*, **34**, 800, (1963)

[20] C. T. SAH, R. N. NOYCE and W. SHOCKLEY, *Proc. I.R.E.*, **45**, 1228, (1957)

[21] A. L. MCWHORTER, *Semiconductor Surface Physics*, (ed. R. H. Kingston), Univ. of Penn. Press, (1957)

[22] See, for example, P. J. COPPEN and W. T. MATZEN, *I.R.E. Trans. Electron Devices*, **50**, 75 ,(1962)

[23] I. E. TAMM, *Z. Phys.*, **76**, 849, (1932)

[24] W. SHOCKLEY, *Phys. Rev.*, **56**, 317, (1939)

[25] See, for example, A. MANY and D. GERLICH, *Phys. Rev.*, **107**, 404, (1957)

[26] W. SHOCKLEY and G. L. PEARSON, *Phys. Rev.*, **74**, 232, (1948)

[27] A. MANY, *Proc. Phys. Soc. Lond.*, **B67**, 9, (1954)

[28] A. STANLEY, Lincoln Lab. Rep. 1965 – 11 Feb. (1965), see also ref. [49]

[29] D. R. KERR, *Proc. I.E.E.E.*, **51**, 1142, (1963)

[30] H. L. STEELE, JNR., *Transistor Reliability Symposium*, New York, Sept., (1956)

[31] A. S. GROVE and E. H. SNOW, *Proc. I.E.E.E., Letters*, **54**, 894, (1966)

[32] See, for example, A. VON HIPPEL *et al.*, *Phys. Rev.*, **91**, 568, (1953)

[33] K. H. ZAININGER, *Appl. Phys. Letters*, **8**, 140, (1966)

[34] A. J. SPETH and F. F. FANG, *Appl. Phys. Letters*, **7**, 145, (1965)

[35] A. G. STANLEY, *Proc. I.E.E.E.*, **53**, 627, (1965)

[36] See *I.E.E.E. Trans. on Nuclear Science*, **NS13**, Dec., (1966)

[37] E. R. SCHMID, Private Communication quoted in ref. [17]

[38] D. R. KERR, *Proc. I.E.E.E.*, **51**, 1142, (1963)

[39] A. G. STANLEY, *Bull. Amer. Phys. Soc.*, **11**, 240, (1966)

[40] G. J. FRYER, Thesis. A.F. Institut. of Tech., Wright-Patterson (ASTIA AD 236496), (1960)

[41] D. M. VERRELLI, Thesis, A.F. Institut. of Tech., Wright-Patterson (ASTIA AD 259720), (1961)

[42] E. KOOI, *Philips. Res. Repts.*, **20**, 306 and 595, (1965)

[43] M. V. WHELAN, *Philips Res. Repts.*, **22**, 289, (1967)

[44] S. R. HOFSTEIN, *Solid-State Electron.*, **10**, 657, (1967)

[45] M. M. ATALLA, A. R. BRAY and R. LINDNER, *Proc. I.E.E.E.*, **106**, Pat. B Suppl., No. 17, 1130, (1959)

[46] W. SHOCKLEY, W. W. HOOPER, H. J. QUEISSER and W. SCHROEN, *Surface Science*, **2**, 277, (1964)

[47] E. H. SNOW. See ref. [17]

[48] S. R. HOFSTEIN, *I.E.E.E. Trans. Electron Devices*, **ED13**, 222, (1966)

[49] D. S. PECK, R. R. BLAIR, W. L. BROWN and F. M. SMITS, *Bell. Syst. Tech. J.*, **42**, 95, (1963)

[50] C. D. TAULBEE, D. L. NELSON and B. G. SOUTHWARD, *ANS-ASTM Conf. on Radiation Effects in Electronics, Syracuse*, (1964)

[51] E. H. SNOW, A. S. GROVE and D. J. FITZGERALD, *Proc. I.E.E.E.*, **55**, 1168, (1967)

CHAPTER 7

The Specimen Environment

7.1 Introduction

In seeking a title to match the contents of this chapter, the author looked for a general term which embraced all the factors that could affect the specimen behaviour in the SEM and that had not been discussed previously. In earlier chapters we have considered the interactions between an electron beam and the specimen. We did not consider the effects of impurities or contamination introduced during observations in the SEM, nor did we consider how various experimental conditions required in some of our studies can be attained in practice. Finally, no mention has been made as yet of specimen preparation. These omissions will now be discussed.

The contents of this chapter can be divided under three main headings: (1) specimen stages, which naturally include some discussion of the specimen chamber itself. (2) specimen contamination, which in this context means the contamination introduced by the SEM during observations. This problem automatically includes a discussion of various vacuum systems and their application to the SEM, and finally (3) specimen preparation.

One general comment must be made. The application of the SEM is a relatively new art and workers in the field are feeling their way in this aspect of the work. Thus the comments made here must be regarded as indicative of the present trends rather than as a discussion of a firmly established or 'crystallized' approach.

7.2 Specimen stages for the SEM

7.2.1 *Introduction*

It is a fair, but oversimplified statement to say that scanning electron microscopy is still a room-temperature art as the bulk of the observations are made at room temperature. There is increasing pressure from would-be users for the production of facilities to heat and cool the specimen. This is but one example of the way in which scanning electron microscopy is currently being generalized and extended. We shall see in Chapters 10 and 12 how the requirements of surface physicists and device engineers concerned with interface studies are leading to the use of high-vacuum systems. Many other requirements will have to be considered in designing the specimen chamber and particularly the specimen stage. Annealing, evaporation, mechanical deformation, melting, recrystallization and alloying are among the many processes which it is desirable to carry out in the SEM, either so that the process itself can be studied, or because it is desired in order to bring about change in the specimen. The use of ion-beam etching has already been reported in the literature [1, 2, 24]. Microcircuitry studies require the ability to make up to, say, twenty-four electrical connections through the chamber wall. Thus the inherent versatility of the SEM places an almost impossible burden on manufacturers, as a whole array of stages is required. Even if the stages are made in modular or kit form the variety is still bewildering. These stages will have one set of specifications in common, that is to say, they must satisfy the needs of electron optics by not introducing vibration and/or astigmatism; they must meet the requirements of the electron collector system and give the necessary specimen movements. Apart from this common feature the specifications rapidly diverge. Often a special stage has to be designed to do a specific job and it is likely that users will have to make their own special-purpose stages. It is of interest to draw up the specification of an ideal specimen stage, not because we can design such a stage, but to set some standard against which we can measure existing or proposed stages.

7.2.2 *SEM stage specification*
The following list contains the major requirements that a SEM specimen stage must meet. In practice the emphasis placed on each consideration will obviously vary from one R and D group to another.

(1) The vibrational stability must be such that the stage leads to no degradation of the resolution of which the electron optics is capable.

(2) The stage must lead to no distortion of the beam between the final lens and the specimen surface, i.e. it must introduce no astigmatism.

(3) The necessary specimen movements should be provided with

fine control, no hysteresis and good repeatability. Ideally, three degrees of transational movement plus a rotation and a tilt relative to the beam direction is needed.

(4) The design should be modular so that: (a) the secondary electron collector can be moved from one position to another or replaced by other types of detectors; (b) heating and/or cooling facilities can be inserted, possibly by sacrificing one or two of the degrees of freedom of specimen movement; (c) multiple detector systems involving possibly solid-state counters, light pipes, infrared detectors (both cooled and uncooled) can be included at will; (d) sizeable translational movements (1") can be obtained possibly with the loss of the tilt and rotational facilities; (e) an ion-focussing lens and shielding system can be included for ion-etching studies; (f) a large number of electrical leads, say twenty, should be available through the wall of the specimen stage itself so that a microcircuit, for example, can be wired up on the stage prior to insertion in the SEM. It is also advantageous if the specimen can be 'floated' at voltages of the order of 10 to 20 kV relative to earth.

(5) Ideally the stage should be designed so that special facilities, such as a tensile-testing machine for paper or fabrics, can be incorporated into the framework. In other words the basic structure (including the chamber) should be capable of taking loads of $\sim 200/\text{kg}$ without hysteris. Other special facilities which may be required include such items as microwave specimen jigs and the use of head amplifiers in the vacuum and very close to the specimen.

(6) Finally, consideration should be given to the possibilities of ultra-high vacuum scanning electron microscopy, i.e. the stage should be capable of sustaining high vacuum without leakage during specimen movement, give minimal outgassing and should be capable of being quickly but thoroughly degreased.

It is a fair comment to say that the commercially available stages were not designed with this generality of application in mind. The reasons for this have been stated. In order to give some idea of the way in which versatility can be built into specimen stages and the problems involved we will now describe two complementary stages in which (i) multi-mode operation without loss of resolution is the major consideration and (ii) a wide range of heating and cooling in a clean environment is the primary concern. These stages have

certain features in common. The specimen movements, both translational and rotational, are introduced via bellows seals which have
been tested to 10^{-8} torr and found to be leak-tight. The stages are
modular in construction so that they can perform many functions
by making only minor changes.

7.2.3 *A multi-purpose stage*
(1) *General.* Figures 7.1 (plate) and 7.2 show a general-purpose stage

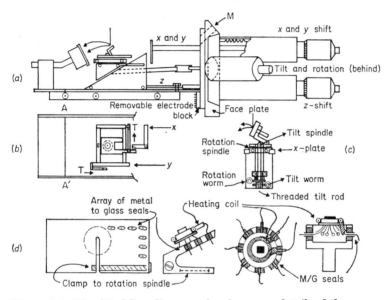

Figure 7.2. Simplified line diagrams showing some details of the movements used in the stage shown in figure 7.1. (*a*) Cross-section of the
wedge movement used; (*b*) corresponding 'top-view' showing x and y
movements; (*c*) showing the rotation and tilt movements; (*d*) modules
for heating of semiconductor devices.

designed by Wayte [3]. The structure is made from stainless steel and
is capable of working in a 10^{-8} torr vacuum in the form shown. The
stage uses existing guide rails (below the stage) to load and position
itself. All the degrees of specimen movement come through the front
plate together with all electrical connections except the EHT for the
scintillator. Rather than set the required metal-to-glass seals in the
face plate itself it was decided to mount these seals into a small plate
which can then be fixed to the main plate with Viton seals. In this

way failures can be replaced with ease and different selections of current rating, EHT leads etc., can be chosen at will. All moving vacuum seals are bellows seals while the demountable static seals use Viton rings. A vacuum lead-through is also provided on the front plate for a high-pressure, gas-flow to supply a miniature Joule-Thomson liquifier used for specimen and/or detector cooling. If more space is required in the specimen neighbourhood, the whole rear end of the stage from the line AA' can be removed and the scintillator EHT brought in through the front face.

(2) *The specimen movements.* The basis of the specimen movement is the underlying wedge which has a total travel of $1\frac{3}{4}$ in. in a horizontal plane and gives a $\frac{7}{8}$ in. movement in the z direction (parallel to the beam). The other movements are obtained by sliding tables on top of the smaller wedge, (see figure 7.2(a) and (b)). These movements are kinematically designed, ball-race movements in which the drive is delivered against the tension of soft 'Tensator' foil springs [4] marked T in figure 7.2(b). The rotation and tilt are obtained by worm-gear drives up through the centre of the wedges in the manner indicated in figure 7.2(c). This system of a wedge-based set of movements was chosen because of its modular construction, the absence of supporting lever arms and because it gives a considerable measure of isotropy in the vibration properties, i.e. no direction is significantly more susceptible to vibration than any other. With the model shown in figure 7.1(a) (plate) the following specimen movements are available:

x direction $\frac{7}{8}$ in., y direction 1 in., z direction $\frac{7}{8}$ in.

tilt – 0 to 90° and rotation – full circle.

Figure 7.1(a) (plate) shows the stage with all these degrees of freedom available. Two specimen stubs can be accommodated, or one specimen and a Faraday cage for making beam current measurements, can be used because the specimen mounts can be electrically isolated. Figure 7.1(b) (plate) shows how a massive heat sink can be used. The example chosen has the full translational movements and a rotation of $\pm$ 45°. The tilt facility has been sacrificed in this case. Figure 7.1(c) (plate) shows how there is sufficient room to use a miniature liquifier for fast cooling (see section 7.2.3(4)).

(3) *Other properties.* When used in SEM that has been sited with

reasonable care regarding vibration levels and a.c. magnetic fields the stage gives an 'edge' resolution in emissive micrographs of 250 Å. The specimen movements are controlled, free from 'stickiness' or hysteresis. (An earlier attempt to use a wedge movement with sliding bearings gave an uncontrolled jerky movement.) One of the pleasing features of this wedge movement is the ability to handle heavy specimens with good control in spite of the fact that very light 'tensator' return springs are used. The large heat sink shown in figure 7.1(*b*) weighs 6 oz (170 g) but does not overload the movements so that a continuous controlled movement free from jerkiness is obtained.

The stage has been operated for hundreds of hours without giving trouble (except for failure of metal-to-glass seals). The small stainless-steel ball-races used are supplied with protection shields against dust-grit and have given trouble-free performance. The bellows seals, the movement transmissions, the 2:1 lever movement in the z-shift (which enables a 2 in. wedge movement to be obtained from a 1 in. micrometer movement) and the specimen table movements have performed well. A quick and satisfactory method of cleaning is described in section 7.6.

(4) *Incorporation of specimen mounting modules.* The basic idea behind the construction of this stage is its modular nature, i.e. the ability to incorporate additional facilities at will. Figures 7.2(*d*) and 7.3 show some of the modules that have been used on this stage. In some applications, where it is necessary to work at low temperatures and to examine many specimens with ease of specimen-change and minimum delay in cooling down to the required temperature, the conventional system based on the use of conduction of heat to a liquid N_2 supply has some disadvantages. In particular its high thermal-capacity leads to long pump-down times and considerable delay if the system has to be exposed to the atmosphere while still cold (due to 'frosting up'). It is apparent that the speed of cooling and 'warm-up' rapidly increases the smaller is made the system which supplies the coolant. Two ways of miniaturizing the system are available; one method uses a flow of cooled gas and the other method uses a miniature liquifier [5]. Miniature Joule-Thomson liquifiers together with ancillary apparatus are available mainly as a result of aero-space needs. Such systems have a high reliability. The application of one such system to specimen cooling in the SEM

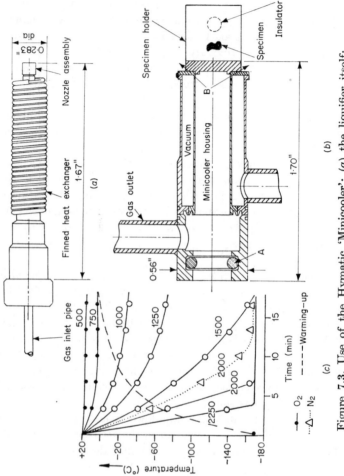

Figure 7.3. Use of the Hymatic 'Minicooler'; (a) the liquifier itself; (b) stainless-steel Dewar vessel used and (c) performance data.

is illustrated in figure 7.3. The construction and dimensions of one liquifier used are shown in figure 7.3(a). This liquifier is inserted into a special stainless-steel vacuum vessel (figure 7.3(b)). In-flowing gas at a pressure of $\sim$ 2,500 lb/in^2 is forced through the heat exchanger and is cooled by adibatic expansion through the nozzle and finally flows back over the heat exchanger to cool the incoming gas. The stainless-steel vacuum container is fitted with a gas exhaust so that the gas, after cooling, can escape to the atmosphere without disturbing the vacuum in the SEM chamber. The liquid refrigerant in the neighbourhood of the nozzle is coupled to the specimen by an OFHC copper disc onto which a suitable OFHC copper specimen stub can be screwed. The liquifier is connected to the system which provides the specimen movements by a clamp which grips the body of the Dewar vessel itself. With a suitable control valve and a molecular sieve system to ensure cleanliness the specimen temperature can be varied by altering the gas-flow rate. The specimen temperature can be measured by means of an Fe-Cu thermocouple placed just below the specimen.

In spite of the use of a high-pressure, gas-input and the presence of boiling liquid close to the specimen no adverse effects due to vibration were found. A resolution of 400 Å has been obtained with the liquifier being operated at a pressure of 2,250 lb/in^2. The specimen movement due to differential contraction during cool-down to 100°K from room temperature is $\sim$ 10μ so that a selected area can be kept in the field of view at high magnification during cooldown. Figure 7.3(c) shows the speed of response using the most efficient gas – oxygen. The lowest temperature obtained was 100°K and was reached in 4 minutes. The warm-up time to room temperature is 15 to 17 minutes. The inclusion of a small 10-watt heatingelement at position B in the figure 7.3(b) reduces this warm-up time to $\sim$ 2 minutes. The stub temperature can be varied by increments of 5°K and the temperature stability is $\pm$ $\frac{1}{2}$°K under constantpressure conditions. The system is economical. Twenty hours running-time at the highest flow rate can be obtained from a standard gas cylinder.

Two technical details are worthy of note. The seal marked A in figure 7.3(b) which separates the high-pressure exhaust gas flow (at 2,000 lb/in^2) from the specimen chamber (at 10^{-7} torr) has to be well made otherwise leakage into the vacuum will occur. Secondly, the data shown in figure 7.3(c) were obtained using oxygen which,

M

although it is the most efficient gas, does entail a slight fire-risk. Unless the system used in free from dirt and metallic dust there is a risk of spontaneous combustion. It is well to stress this point, although no difficulties have been experienced by the author's group in using oxygen. If this risk is not acceptable, nitrogen (or argon) can be used with relatively little loss of speed (see figure 7.3(c)).

Figure 7.2(d) shows rather more conventional modules that have been used with the stage either for heating, examining with many electrical connections made or examining in several modes at once. These diagrams are largely self-explanatory.

7.2.4 *Experimental stage for wide temperature range*

(1) *Introduction.* There are two motives for introducing liquid He cooling into scanning electron microscopy. Many electroluminescent and cathodoluminescent materials become far more efficient at very low temperatures, i.e. below 80°K. Under these conditions the best resolution should be obtainable as the lowest primary beam currents can be used. In addition, some radiation detectors such as Au- or Cu-doped Ge have increased sensitivity in this temperature range. The second use of ultra-low temperatures arises from the inherent pumping properties. A suitably designed container of liquid He about 500 cm^3 in capacity can have a pumping speed for water vapour $\sim$ 10,000 litres/second and for nitrogen the corresponding figure is 1,000 litres/second. Such a pump is clean, vibration-free, compact and of minimal initial cost. (However its running costs are not small.) The use of liquid He as a refrigerant implies the use of extensive thermal shielding. The liquid He container surface has to be protected from room-temperature radiation by the use of liquid nitrogen-cooled shields. Therefore, if a specimen stage is designed for liquid He work, the shielding inherent in it can be used in another application to protect electron lenses, collector systems etc. from the heat generated in rising the specimen temperature to, say, 1,000°C. In brief, specimen stages for ultra-low temperatures and high temperatures have certain features in common. It was these features – the increased luminescence efficiency at very low temperatures, the inherest fast and clean pumping and the common need to use extensive shielding – that led to the specimen stage 'kit' shown in figures 7.4, 5 and 6. It should be stressed that the system described is an experimental model and with hindsight several improvements might be suggested.

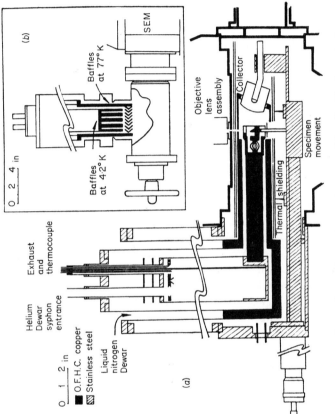

Figure 7.4. Experimental specimen stage capable of wide temperature range operation; (a) general view showing use to cool specimen to liquid He temperatures; (b) use of part of the system with baffles as cryopump.

(2) *Description of stage.* Figure 7.4(*a*) shows the use of the stage to cool specimens to very low temperatures. The cryogenic construction was made by the use of the usual, thin-wall stainless steel which had been argon arc-welded. The only unusual feature arises from the need to cool a specimen which is not vertically below the liquid He container. This requirement is forced upon the user if a vertical electron column extending upwards from the specimen chamber is necessary (for economic reasons, for example). This need to cool the specimen at some distance from the liquid He vessel means that a large-diameter OFHC copper rod is required to minimize the thermal impedence. A similar heavy copper cylinder is used for the liquid N_2 shielding. To protect the final electron lens from the anisotropic cooling of the liquid N_2 shielding, two thin-walled and polished shields are included. The liquid N_2 shielding around the specimen is completed by running the secondary electron collector at liquid N_2 temperatures. Once the He cooling has been brought close to the specimen, the problems resolve themselves into eliminating vibration effects, coupling the specimen to the coolant block and still retaining the essential degrees of specimen movement and ability to change specimens easily without having to strip down the cooling and shielding assembly. To make the structure reasonably rigid the copper rod and the three shields are coupled together and to the underlying platform by pointed stainless-steel screws, specially designed to have a high thermal impedance. This underlying platform not only supports and strengthens the cooling assembly but transmits the specimen movements. These movements are restricted to a $\frac{1}{4}$ in. displacement parallel to the long direction of the copper cylinder and a $\frac{1}{4}$ in. movement at right angles to this axis. No movement parallel to the beam direction is available. The two movements are applied to a plinth into which the specimen stub-holder itself can be inserted and clamped. This specimen stub-holder, illustrated in figure 7.5, has a high, thermal impedance and couples onto the cooling arm by pushing the specimen stub into a sliding block which is thermally connected to the arm by sliding contact, by conduction along a flexible lead and, to some extent, by radiative transfer. This system is shown in figure 7.5(*b*).

Using this system, specimens at temperatures between $\sim 16°$K and $77°$K can be examined with liquid He in the centre container and between $77°$K and $\sim 100°$K with liquid N_2 in the centre container. No difficulties due to vibration, astigmatism, or impedance of specimen movement were experienced. Arrays of detectors (see Chapter 8) can be attached to the liquid N_2 shield or a miniature photo-detector can be coupled to the liquid He housing. The pumping properties of this system and the liquid He consumption rate are similar to those described in the following section.

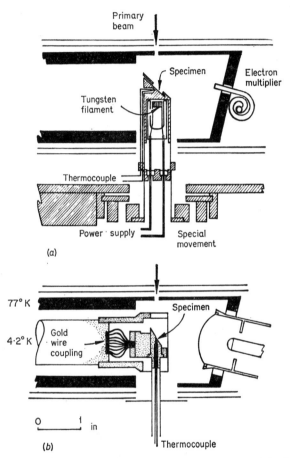

Figure 7.5. (a) Use of heating module in the stage outlined in figure 7.4; (b) the details of the movement in the low-temperature use – coupling by gold-wire bundles.

(3) *Use as cryogenic pump.* Figure 7.4(b) shows how the liquid He container and the liquid N_2 shield can be adapted to form a cryogenic

pump. These units are attached to a bakeable bellows valve and can be quickly valved-off from the specimen chamber. Attached to the bottom of both the He and N_2 containers are suitably designed OFHC copper blocks which provide large surface areas at 4·2° and 77° respectively. In the case of the outer block it also acts as an optically dense shield to protect the surface at 4·2°K from room-temperature radiation. This baffle can be removed at will. The He

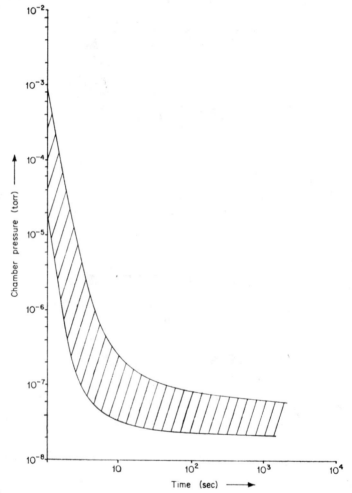

Figure 7.6. Showing the pump-down properties of stage parts as used in figure 7.4(*b*) as a cryopump.

container is pressure-filled from an He storage vessel. This pump can be used with a sorb-pump as a complete pumping unit on its own or it can be used, for example, as a 'back-up' pump for an ion-pump system. When it is required to change specimens the pump is simply valved-off until required again. Briefly the facilities inherent in this cryopump can be summed-up as follows:

(1) The pump when cooled to $4 \cdot 2°K$ can bring the pressure in a leak-tight specimen chamber of volume $12 \times 12 \times 12$ in. from $\sim 10^{-4}$ torr to $< 10^{-7}$ torr in minutes (see figure 7.6).

(2) To cool the He container to $4 \cdot 2°K$ from liquid N_2 temperatures take ~ 2 litres of liquid He. Once cool, the system uses $0 \cdot 5$ litres per hour.

(3) The pump can be used for repeated pumping cycles before the condensed gas has to be released. The present model has been used to evacuate a specimen chamber of the above volume > 10 times without removing the stored gas and this is by no means the limit.

(4) When used as a back-up pump for other pumps it can reduce the pressure in an unbaked system from 10^{-5} torr to 2×10^{-8} torr in ~ 2 minutes.

(5) The system is completely safe. Any inadvertant pressure build-up is automatically released.

(4) *Use of stage in high temperature version.* There are two factors which may, in principle, limit the application of scanning electron microscopy at high temperatures. As the specimen temperature is increased, the photon emission and thermionic emission from the specimen increases. Both of these phenomena can interfere with the observation of the secondary electron emission current; the first, by adding to the effective noise signal in the photo-multiplier, if the specimen temperature is sufficient to bring the emitted spectra within the range of the photocathode and the second by adding to the effective noise in the collector system. Any system design for making scanning electron microscopy observations at high temperatures must take this difficulty into account, although, by screening or eliminating the photomultiplier, and by using a chopped electron beam, these noise signals can be greatly reduced. Figure 7.5(*a*) shows a medium-temperature module used in the construction described in the previous section and which converts it from an ultra-low

temperature stage to one in which specimens can be examined at temperatures up to 900°C. This module has a high thermal impedance to the movement plinth. The heating is obtained by surrounding a 100-watt tungsten iodide bulb in a completely light-tight stainless-steel container. As stressed above, the heat shielding now protects the final electron lens from the heat generated in raising the specimen temperature. The full possibilities of this approach have not been assessed but the indications [6] are that specimen temperatures of about 1,000 to 1,100°C should be obtainable without damage to the electron optics and with a minimal loss of resolution.

Obviously this type of specimen stage is somewhat specialized but it is of interest in showing the technique involved, the complexities and difficulties encountered and the progress made in this field.

7.3 Surface contamination

One problem facing the user of electron-optical instruments is that arising from the beam-induced contamination that builds up on the specimen during its examination. The SEM is no exception. In fact, in the SEM, because of its unique abilities in the surface-physics field, the problem is intensified in spite of the low beam currents used. We must take care in this context to distinguish between two kinds of contamination. Even before the specimen is exposed to the action of the beam and to the contamination arising from water vapour and hydrocarbons boiling off the specimen chamber and stage walls, it is already contaminated, in the sense that the surface layers are different in properties from the bulk material. This contamination of the specimen often takes the form of oxide or nitride layers. Water is often absorbed both physically and chemically and there are often trace impurities present on the surface. The beam can interact with these contaminents even in the absence of any further contamination introduced by the SEM. This interaction takes one or more of the forms outlined in the previous chapter. It is these interactions that we must study in conjunction with surface topography and junction position and we wish to make these studies in an environment which does not change the properties of the contamination unless we make these changes purposely ourselves. Unfortunately this is not always possible unless considerable care is taken. The two main sources of contamination in electron-optical systems at present arise from the use of oil-pumps and from

the contaminents boiling off the chamber and stage walls. The kind
of problem that can arise is discussed in the next section.

7.4 Nature of beam-induced contamination

The first micrograph shown in figure 7.7 (plate) is an emissive micrograph taken of a GaAs injection laser that had been fairly extensively
examined in an oil-pumped SEM and subsequently etched in order

Table 7.1. *Typical Contamination rates in an oil-pumped system without
liquid N_2 baffles*

Specimen	Surface treatment	Contamination properties
Ge photodiode of the type shown in figure 7.7.	Etched in:— 1 H_2O_2: 1 HF: $4H_2O$ and dried	Obscuring film formed at 1 minute or less at × 100, 2 × 10^{-10} amps, 20kV, 300°K
Ge photodiode of the type shown in figure 7.7.	After cesiation and exposure to air	Film formed at similar rates with slightly higher currents ≈ 4 × 10^{-10} amps.
GaAs	Etched in a mixture of $3H_2SO_4$, $1H_2O_2$, $1H_2O$	Etch-resistant film formed in about 10 minutes at × 1,000, 4 × 10^{-10} amps. 20kV at 300°K, . At 100°K, the film is formed more than ten times quicker

that the defects present could be examined in depth throughout the
specimen. Unfortunately a contaminent layer formed on the surface
and the areas of most interest (i.e. those that had been most examined) had been rendered impervious to etchant attack. Not only do
these films impede etching but they also spoil resolution and contrast
because they are electrical semi-insulators. These films are of quite
general occurrence. The author and his co-workers have observed
them as GaAs, InAs, Ge, Si, SiO_2, Si_3N_4, organic materials and on

several metals. The thickness of these films and the rate of build-up depends on many factors, including the pumping oil used, the degree of baffling, the kind of specimen and its temperature and the previous surface treatment of the specimen. Specimens that have been recently etched in very reactive solutions tend to contaminate quickly. Some idea of the speed with which these films can form can be realized from table 7.1.

An operator can often delude himself into thinking that the contamination is minimal because of the apparent absence of a film.

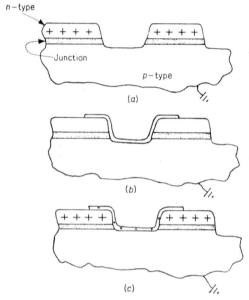

Figure 7.8. Suggested explanation of obscuring effect shown in figure 7.7(*b*): (*a*) uncontaminated diode capable of giving voltage contrast; (*b*) contaminated and unbiassed diode; (*c*) contaminated diode under bias, contamination layer charging up to potential of top side of junction.

This situation can arise when the film is very thin and uniform and so it is not revealed against the surface detail of the specimen. In order to detect such films it is often useful to use its electrical properties. By using very low, primary beam energies these films can often be made to charge-up and so attain a different potential from the rest of the specimen surface. This potential difference can be used to reveal the presence of the beam-induced film by the mechanisms outlined in the next chapter. Some measure of the subtlety with which contamination films can elude detection and some indication of the nuisance they can become can be seen from figure 7.7. The device studied here is a Ge diode of the structure shown in figure 7.8. If the device is examined in the emissive mode in the absence of an applied bias, first at × 300 and then at × 100, there is no evidence of any contaminent film on the emissive micrograph at beam voltages $\approx$ 20 kV. However, when a reverse bias of a few volts is applied the voltage contrast mechanism (see Chapter 8) reveals a contamination square which obscures significant detail, (see figure 7.7). The exact mechanism causing these changes is not understood, but a possible, but unconfirmed, working model can be based on the ideas discussed in Chapter 13, i.e. the cross-linking and polymerization of silicone oil on the surface. This model is illustrated in figure 7.8. Under the action of the beam a nett positive charge is formed in the vicinity of the semiconductor-contamination film interface, or in the film or on its surface. This positive charge causes the voltage difference associated with the biassed pn-junction to be obscured. The contrast mechanisms involved here are discussed in Chapter 8. For the present it is sufficient to establish that oil-induced contamination interferes with SEM studies, particularly those concerned with the detection of surface voltage differences, in a variety of ways, some of which can be rather complex.

Various means of eliminating the beam-induced contamination have been tried. The use of liquid N_2-cooled baffles and shielding can reduce the rate of film formation [7] but does not eliminate it. Nor is it always successful in reducing the rate. The problem of the protection from etchant action can be obviated by heating the contaminated specimen to a moderate temperature ($360 \pm 20°C$ for GaAs, for example). If the temperature of the specimen is raised to $250°C$ during the examination, beam-induced contamination does not form. Other workers [8] have sought to meet the difficulty by blowing oxygen at the specimen during the examination. None of these methods is really satisfactory or of general applicability. With the advent of other types of pump which do not use oil there is a tendency to eliminate this source of contamination by eliminating the pumping oil. Two approaches to this problem are described in the next section.

7.5 Use of oil-free pumping systems

7.5.1 *Introduction*

There are four types of oil-free pumps that can be considered for the pumping of electron-optical systems. These are:

(1) *Sputter-ion pumps* [9]. These pumps work by causing electrons to be accelerated and to spiral in a strong magnetic field and thereby create ionization of the residual gas. The ions so formed are accelerated into a Ti surface where they are either chemically absorbed or physically buried.

(2) *Orbitron pumps* [10], which work in the same general manner as ion pumps, except that the spiraling field is electrostatic in origin rather than magnetic.

(3) *Turbomolecular pumps* [11]. These pumps consist of a set of rotors rotating at 16,000 rev/min in much the same manner as a turbine. The drag caused by the rotating blades causes gas to flow from low to high pressure regions.

(4) *Cryopumps* [12]. These pumps depend simply on the fact that at very low temperatures, particularly liquid He temperatures, each gas is removed from the system by condensation on a surface (or in the 'pores' of some material) which is at a temperature below the solidification temperature of the gas.

We have no complete assessment of the relative merits of these pumps in this application. Such work is under way in several laboratories but the results are not generally available. However, some practical experience has been gained with the use of sputter-ion pumps in this field.

7.5.2 *Use of ion-pumps*

The approach adopted depends on the nature of work programme for the SEM, the environment (scientific or development) and the funds available. It is apparent that, in addition to the 'standard-type' of SEM pumped by an oil-pump system, two other types of SEM are required. One is the ultra-high vacuum version which is completely bakeable and uses metal gaskets for the demountable seals. This is the approach adopted by Miller and Pease [12] and is suitable if a complete SEM column, specimen chamber and stage can be made available for the periods of time required for the pump-down and bake-out. Typically the pump-down time to $< 10^{-9}$ torr will be greater than 48 hours (author's estimate). Thus a very clean environment is obtained at the sacrifice of the number of specimens that can be examined in a given time. Intermediate between these two extremes there is a need for a third type of pumping unit in which the oil-induced contamination is largely eliminated by the use of ion pumps giving a 10^{-7} to 10^{-8} torr

Table 7.2. Alternative approaches to pumping systems for electron-optical instruments

Pumping unit	Properties and limitations
Oil diffusion pump with liquid N_2 baffles	Oil contamination risks accepted in return for speed of specimen change and economy in capital outlay
Oil-free system (but unbaked)	Relatively straightforward adaption of oil-pumped system – Viton seals – moderate pump-down time and moderate vacuum (10^{-7} torr in < 4 hours). Oil contamination greatly reduced, but not eliminated. Wide range of surface physics problems now tractable, but not all
Ultra-high vacuum SEM	Specially designed SEM column forced upon designers by need to bake. Highest degree of hygiene practically realizable. All surface physics become tractable at the expense of long pump-down time (~ 48 hours to $< 10^{-9}$ torr) and some inconvenience due to use of metal gaskets

vacuum in the specimen chamber and which still gives a reasonable rate of specimen examination. This approach is more suitable when one electron column has to meet the needs of several projects which need the virtual elimination of oil-contamination and of other less specialized projects simultaneously. The different approaches are summed up in table 7.2.

The system shown in figure 7.9 has been used for over a year and is typical of the intermediate approach [13]. The electron column is the standard column used on the oil-pumped Cambridge Instrument Company SEM. The scanning coils, brass aperture holders etc., are all included in the vacuum system. The only modification made was to replace the usual elastomer seals by Viton seals and to replace the rotary o-rings seals by bellows seals. The specimen chamber is the one commercially available. The specimen stages used are those described in sections 7.2.3 and 7.2.4. The pumping system is made of argon arc-welded stainless steel and, where possible, is joined by copper gasket seals. The pumps have the same pumping speeds as

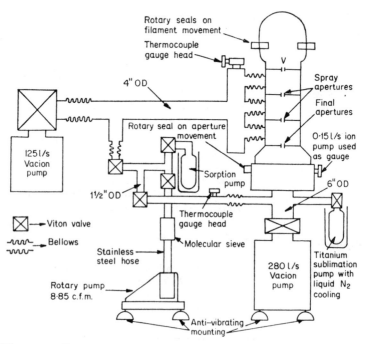

Figure 7.9. Ion-pumped SEM built by Sulway [16] and used for semi-conductor device and materials studies.

the oil-diffusion pumps previously used. An additional auxiliary pump in the form of a liquid N_2 cooled Ti sublimation pump is available when required. No facilities have been incorporated for baking either the pumps or the specimen chamber. The specimen chamber can be brought to atmospheric pressure by a dry N_2 supply.

The system is 'roughed-out' to 20μ pressure by the rotary pump which is then valved off. A further 'roughing-out' pumping of 20 minutes duration is carried out with the sorbtion pump, which is in turn valved-off and the ion-pumps opened up. The SEM is now ready for use as the pressure drops within seconds to 10^{-5} torr. The subsequent performance depends on the state of cleanliness of the specimen chamber and state. (What is meant by a clean stage in this context is defined later in section 7.6). With a clean stage and Ti-sublimation pump in use, the specimen chamber pressure (as measured by a 0·15 litre/sec ion-pump mounted on the specimen chamber) drops to $< 2 \times 10^{-6}$ torr in 20 minutes and reaches a limiting pressure of 10^{-7} torr in 3 to 4 hours. (This limiting pressure is determined by leaks introduced by the rotary seals associated with the aperture changer.) The pumping system proved reliable and rugged in operation. The specimen chamber has been cycled between 10^{-6} torr and atmospheric pressure ten times in one day. The pumping system operated for over 2,000 hours before baking was required. The resolution obtained was no different from that obtainable on the oil-pumped system. An 'edge' resolution of $250°Å$ and an ability to resolve detail of 400 Å in diameter can be obtained. Only two adverse effects arose from the use of ion-pumps, both of a minor nature. One is the inability of the pumps to cope with the gas flow inherent in the use of ion-etching systems (see section 7.7.2 and Chapter 11). The second arises when the ion-pumps are used at a high pressure (4×10^{-6} to 10^{-5} torr) during pump-down. In this pressure range some light appears [14] to be given off by the ion-pump. A fraction of this radiation reaches the photomultiplier used in the emissive amplifier chain and adds to the noise. So the effective contrast is lowered. The effect disappears at pressures less than 2×10^{-6} torr and can be reduced to insignificance at higher pressures by simple optical shielding or by partially closing the valve between the specimen chamber and the large ion-pump.

With regard to contamination, provided the specimen chamber and stage are clean (see section 7.6), it is possible to examine a variety of surfaces which are sensitive to beam-induced contamination for prolonged periods without observing such contamination in spite of a thorough search. Some measure of the mprovement obtained by the use of ion-pumps in a clean environment can be obtained by comparing the data in tables 7.1 and 7.3.

These observations represent the best performance obtained. If the specimen is examined in a specimen chamber and stage that is not clean then beam-induced contamination is observed. But, on Ge and GaAs at least, this contamination forms much more slowly

Table 7.3. *Contamination rates in clean ion-pumped SEM*
(*Compare Table* 7.1, [15, 16])

Specimen	Surface treatment	Dosage	Contamination formed
Ge, p-type $\sim 1\,\Omega$ cm	Optically polished, etched in CP4 and dried	$\frac{3}{4}$ hr. at $\times$ 1,000 with current 1 $\times$ 10^{-8} amps. Specimen at 300°K, 20kV	No evidence visible in SEM or on etching
Ge, p-type $\sim 1\,\Omega$ cm	,,	As above but 2 hours exposure	Film visible on emissive micrographs under conditions of very high contrast and film visible after etching
Ge photo-diode as described in text	Cesiated and then exposed to air	Repeated examination for 7 hours at 300°K at 20kV, 3 $\times$ 10^{-8} amps at $\times$ 100 and $\times$ 300 followed by 3 hours at 100°K; no beam-induced contamination visible	

than in an oil-pumped system. Even in an extremely dirty chamber, (e.g. one used for over a 100 hours without cleaning), the contamination formation rate is ten to fifty times slower than in the oil-pumped system. Nor do these residual contamination films have the contrast-destroying properties observed in the oil-pumped system. These films tend to obscure the contrast rather than eliminate it. To eliminate this residual contamination still further it is necessary to bake the system.

To bake the system completely it is necessary to bake the column as well, this unfortunately creates a major difficulty. Stainless-steel valves and metal gaskets can be baked to 450°C, but metal-ceramic seals tend to fail if heated to much greater than 250°C. But we may wish to bake to a temperature of 250 to 300°C at least. We saw in Chapter 3 that the specification on the electron lens roundness is very rigid. Attempts to heat complete lenses to these temperatures result in distortions which produce an unacceptable degree of

astigmatism. To obviate this difficulty the idea of removing many
of the electron-optical components from the high-vacuum system is
being explored [13, 17, 18]. This can be done, in principle, by passing
a tube down the centre of the column in the manner shown
schematically in figure 7.10(*a*). In this way a considerable surface
area is removed from the uhv system as are several components
which tend to outgas considerably. Heating coils can be included to
provide some degree of outgassing or to keep apertures free of contamination [17]. The main difficulty is that the tube represents a

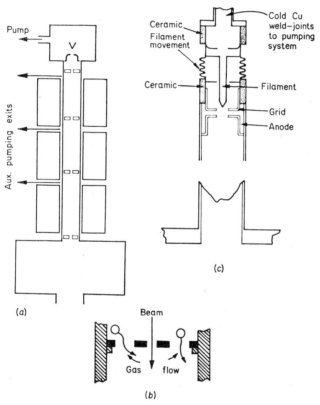

Figure 7.10. Use of bakeable ultra-high vacuum systems: (*a*) exclusion
of outgassing components by use of central tube; (*b*) increasing pumping
speed by cutting away parts of aperture holders; (*c*) unrealized approach
using a long-life filament sealed in a narrow bakeable tube system so
that electron lenses can slide over the tube after bakeout.

N

considerable pumping impedance. Even if the aperture holders are cut away to increase the gas flow, (see figure 7.10(b)) the impedance is still considerable. One way to overcome this impedance is by the use of differential pumping, as indicated in figure 7.10(a).

Obviously these systems still suffer from the limitations forced on the baking temperature by the presence of the electron lenses. An ideal, but currently unrealized system is illustrated in figure 7.10(c). The whole tube including the anode, filament assembly and an auxiliary pump are contained within a ~ 1 in. diameter so that the system can be baked without the lenses which can then be slipped over the tube. Finally, the gun assembly can be lowered onto the top. Obviously the technical problems are formidable. With the advent of a long-life LaB_6 filament [19] the lifetime problem of the filament is greatly reduced. But the difficulties arising from tracking, filament line-up, close mechanical tolerance and volume limitation etc., have still to be solved. Obviously systems of this type are some years off but a start has been made. Miller & Pease [12] have reported the construction of a SEM with a predicted 100 Å resolution in 10^{-9} torr in which all the lens parts, with the exception of the polepiece of the final lens, the scan and stigmator coils, are all outside the uhv system, while Loeffler [18] has illustrated the use of a central tube in an automated electron-beam system for digital recording. This system can be operated unattended for a fortnight, gives a 1 to 2μ spot-size and a 5 in. working distance. With a suitable stage design, a suitable system of air locks, and remote handling arrangements it may be possible to change specimens without the necessity of an extensive bake-out each time. Obviously, some of the approaches sketched out here have a wider application than just to the SEM.

7.6 Specimen preparation

We have included here not only an indication of the way in which specimens can be prepared but also a suggested method for cleaning the specimen stage and the specimen chamber.

We referred in the previous sections to a 'clean' specimen chamber. By 'clean' we mean, in this context, a specimen chamber of which the walls and all accessible surfaces have been thoroughly washed by warm degreasant by an operator using plastic (or rubber) gloves and applying the degreasant (CCl_4, followed by acetone and methonal) with a cleaning material which does not 'tear' or leave 'fluff' behind in the chamber, particular attention being paid to the moving and bearing surfaces. Relatively complex units, such as an aperture changer, can be removed and ultrasonically cleaned without being stripped down in warm degreasant, and then dried by a mild bake in a vacuum furnace. After the surfaces have been degreased and washed in methyl alcohol, the chamber can be roughed-out (preferably by an oil-free pump), to remove the degreasant vapours. A similar treatment can be given to the specimen stage. If possible this is best done by immersing the stage up to the face plate in a container of boiling trichlorotetraeythelene which is ultrasonically vibrated. The stage is subsequently drained free of solution and baked to $\sim 100°C$ in a vacuum furnace, cooled and the air admitted. Such a procedure will clean the stage up to the face plate. If it is required to clean rotary or bellows seals these must be stripped down. In general, such a cleaning treatment (without the strip down) if carried out after above 60 to 70 hour's use, keeps the performance up to the level indicated in section 7.5. If such a procedure does not give good performance, a general dismantling of the complete chamber unit is required and a cleaning in much the same way as is recommended by manufacturers for the electron column. Finally we come to the question of specimen preparation.

Specimen preparation is still something of a matter of personal choice but certain guide lines can be laid down. Consider first a conductive specimen that has to be examined by the emissive mode only but for which high resolution is required. The specimen is fixed by a conducting cement (or spring if suitable) to a stub in such a way that the required area is visible from as wide a range of viewpoints as possible. It is often a wise precaution to put the specimen in a vacuum-tight enclosure (overnight if possible) particularly if its behaviour in a vacuum is not known. This test will give some idea of its outgassing properties and will indicate if the specimen is likely to explode in the vacuum. If the specimen is an insulator it is necessary to avoid charging-up. The standard procedure is to evaporate a thin layer of metal of ~ 200 Å thick onto the specimen. In addition to the obvious precautions of suitably degreasing the specimen beforehand if possible and to ensuring that the specimen does not get 'burnt' by heat from the evaporator filament, there is the possibility that the evaporation will obscure or add detail to the surface. It should be noted that it is often not necessary to coat the whole specimen; windows can be left in the coating. All that is required of the coating is that it reduces the impedance to earth of the examined area to such a level that the excess charge can leak away at least as fast as it is formed. This can often be achieved by bringing the film to within $\sim \frac{1}{4}$mm of the area to be examined. This technique is often of value on biological specimens. Such specimens, containing soft tissue, present something of a difficulty and it is a fair comment to say that we do not really know how to prepare them. Often, after a specimen has been prepared by the usual methods of freeze drying, etc., it is not always possible to tell whether the observed detail is significant or whether an artifact has been introduced by the preparation. It sometimes helps if parts of the specimens can be left uncoated.

When the specimen is a complex microcircuit other minor complications can arise. Soldering of the required leads is a convenient method of making the essential electrical connections, but it is a poor practice from the viewpoint of specimen-chamber hygiene. A better method is to use crimped leads with 'push-on' connections. It is well to consider quite carefully the positioning of the specimen relative to the electron collector, as an electrode post between the area examined and the collector can lead to considerable loss of signal, and to charge-up effects. In the case of flat-pack devices the pack itself often shields the collector, thus leading to loss of signal. One useful rule may be stated: it pays not to be satisfied with the first positioning. A little initial experimentation with the device position is often well worth while. The same rules apply to detector positions, if several detectors are used simultaneously.

7.7 Use of ion-beams

7.7.1 *Introduction*

One of the limitations of scanning electron microscopy arises from the fact that it gives information only about the surface of the specimen. It is obvious that there are many instances in which surface detail represents the cross-section of some bulk feature which extends down into the specimen. In such cases it is often of interest to be able to trace the shape of such features through the specimen. Obviously some form of etching is required, but the use of conventional wet etches presents certain difficulties. First there is the time factor. The need to etch, dry, pump-down, examine and then to repeat the process is time-consuming. Secondly, it is notoriously difficult to keep a selected area of interest free from the contamination which obscures significant detail after several etching cycles. An alternative approach, based on the use of ion-etching, has certain advantages and some limitations. A controlled ion-beam of the type described below has several uses based on the ability of the ion-beam to remove material from the surface of a specimen. The rate at which material is removed depends on a variety of factors. The more important ones are listed in table 7.4.

Table 7.4. Factors affecting rate of material removal by ion-etching

---

(1) Nature of ion used, its energy, the ion current density and angle of incidence onto the specimen surface.

(2) The crystallographic orientation of the specimen, its atomic number and electrical resistivity.

(3) The presence of mechanical stress, surface contamination and inhomogeneities of many kinds including microcracks, second phases etc.

(4) The specimen temperature.

The factors given in (2) and (3) (table 7.4) may lead to selective etching and the presence of these factors in inhomogeneous specimens can be revealed in this way. Selective etching by ion-beams has been used to examine materials [20, 21]. The more immediate application to scanning electron microscopy was pioneered by Stewart [22] who used an r.f. ion source and who, in collaboration with Boyde [23], used this method to study dental tissue. Broers [24] improved the technique by incorporating a mass spectrometer and considered microelectronic applications. Because of their material removal properties ('sputtering' ability), another way in which ion-beams can be used is in the cleaning of the surfaces of specimens. A variant of this technique, in which a glow discharge is used to clean a specimen prior to evaporation, is a well-established procedure. However, the cleaning property of ion-beams has yet to be fully exploited, particularly in the semiconductor field. Recent Russian work [25] has shown how the luminescence behaviour of SiC can be made more efficient by ion-beam bombardment, and Estrup [26] has illustrated how this form of excitation interacts with Si surfaces and how the approach can be used to examine surface

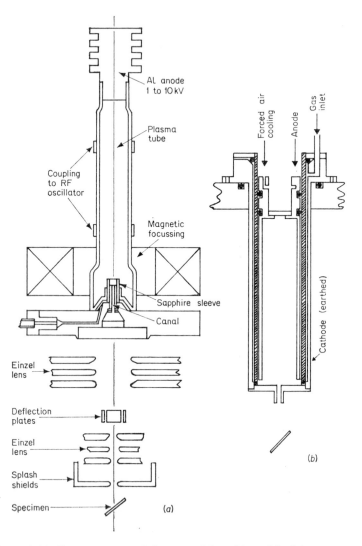

Figure 7.11. Ion sources used for material etching: (*a*) rf ion source, canal and focussing system useful for relatively controlled etching; (*b*) gas discharge ion source suitable for etching insulators.

properties. In a wider sense the use of ion-beams is becoming increasingly important in the semiconductor field. In the last two years the fabrication of a limited range of special devices by ion 'implantation' [27, 28] has already extended the considerable technology available for integrated microcircuit manufacture. At the same time, focussed ion-beams of 1μ spot-size that can be scanned, are becoming available [24] for etching selected areas. It is in this context that ion-beams are being incorporated into scanning electron microscopy.

There is another, more general application that should be considered. We have already seen how insulators charge-up if the resistivity is so high that the surface charge developed by electron-beam bombardment cannot be neutralized by current flow through the specimen. If, instead of providing a conducting path by means of a thin metal layer, we arranged for a simultaneous bombardment of ions of an inert gas, the charge-up effect could be virtually eliminated by varying the ion-beam current until no nett charge adhered to the surface.

To get some idea of the practical side of this work, we shall now describe an ion source suitable for selective etching, surface cleaning, and surface and device physics studies.

7.7.2 *Typical ion-etching systems*

The ion source [30, 31] shown in figure 7.11 can be thought of as consisting of three parts: – a plasma tube in which the ions are formed, a canal system which forms the ion beam and a lens, deflection plate and aperture system for focussing, deflecting and defining the beam.

The plasma tube is often made of quartz and is carefully cleaned. The upper tube is terminated by an aluminium anode which can be maintained at a variable potential, typically 1 to 20 kV, by a power-pack capable of delivering a milliamp. The lower end is closed by the canal assembly which is at earth potential. A controlled gas-flow is introduced through the cathode plate as shown. The tube is pumped through the canal. An r.f. supply is coupled either inductively or capacitatively into the residual gas which is ionized. The resulting plasma is at, or approaching, the anode potential. The density of the plasma is determined by the gas-flow rate, the rate at which energy is coupled into the gas and by the loss processes; which are the escape of ions down the canal and the loss by recombination on the surface of the tube. If this surface is not clean, the surface recombination rate increases considerably and the source is inefficient.

The canal or 'extraction' system requires careful consideration. The aim is to obtain a field configuration between the plasma edge and the canal which helps focus the ions down the canal. This focussing can be aided by the use of an external applied magnetic field. The canal itself is often made of aluminium as this material is usually oxidised and has a low sputtering rate. The insulators which help to determine the field configuration have to be carefully made to avoid tracking and to ensure a parallel and co-axial system. The ends of the movable sleeve must be carefully treated and the system made demountable for cleaning and replacement. The final section can be, for example, a three-component Einzel lens [32] to provide focussing, together with two sets of plates for electrostatic deflections. We also have to include apertures and some 'splash shields'. The need for the former arises because the ions emitted from the canal in this type of system have a considerable velocity spread and so cannot all be focussed by a simple Einzel lens system. Apertures are, therefore, needed to define the beam. They also limit, together with the shielding, the amount of sputtered material which is deposited on the chamber and stage walls and so reduce the amount of chamber and stage cleaning required. An ion system such as this can be used with H_2, He, A, N_2 with varying degrees of efficiency. When used with argon, for example, a beam current of 0·1 mA of 5 kV, argon ions can be delivered into a spot-size of 1 to 2 mm.

Stewart [22] has successfully used a similar system which was oil-pumped, had a liquid N_2 cooled baffle system and gave a 1 to 2×10^{-6} vacuum. This pressure did not increase when the ion source was switched on, nor was any trouble experienced from contamination, at beam currents of 10 to $100\mu A$. Wayte [35] has operated an argon ion source of this kind in an ion-pumped system at pressures of this order. The system was satisfactory at low ion-beam currents but at high beam currents ($\sim 0·1$ mA) the gas-flow tended to turn off the ion-pumps because of the low pumping speed with argon in these pumps. If a greater degree of control over the ion properties is required, a duo-plasmatron ion source [33] is more suitable as the emitted ions have a greatly reduced energy spread and are relatively easy to focus. In the presence of active gases

(O_2 is particularly worrisome in this respect) a mass filter can be incorporated, as shown in figure 7.12 (after Broers [24]). When control can be sacrificed for speed of etching, the type of source [34] shown in figure 7.11(b) is useful. The specimen is simply immersed in a plasma (a glow discharge) and subjected to a bombardment from all directions of ions with a wide range of energies. Because the specimen is located in a region of high-conductivity plasma, it

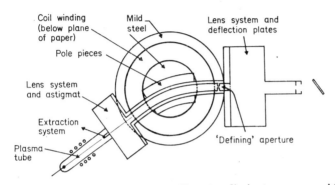

Figure 7.12. Use of magnetic mass filter to eliminate oxygen. After Broers [24].

does not charge-up as it would otherwise do if it is electrically insulating and bombarded by a beam of ions. With this type of source, insulating materials such as glasses and ceramics can be etched at rates of ~ 10 microns per minute.

In order to interpret the results obtained by ion etching it is essential to understand the basic process that occurs when ions strike a specimen surface. A comprehensive and up-to-date survey is already available in Kaminsky's book [36], see also reference [24].

REFERENCES

[1] J. STARK and G. WENDT, *Ann. Phys.*, **38**, 921, (1912), and W. FEITKNECHT, *Helv. Chim. Acta*, 7, 825, (1924)

[2] T. BAUM, *Z. Phys.*, **40**, 686, (1927)

[3] R. C. WAYTE and P. R. THORNTON, *Annual Report on C.V.D.*, Contract No. CP13436, Bangor, U.C.N.W., (1967)

[4] Tensator Ltd., 190, Acton Lane, London, N.W.10

[5] 'Minicooler', Hymatic Ltd., Redditch, Worcs., U.K.
'Emicooler', EMI Ltd., Hayes, Middlesex, U.K.

[6] N. F. B. NEVE, Unpublished work

[7] A. E. ENNOS, *Brit. J. Appl. Phys.*, **5**, 28, (1954). G.V.T. RANZETTA and V. D. SCOTT, *J. Sci. Instr.*, **43**, 816, (1966)

[8] R. CASTAING and J. DESCAMPS, *C.R. Acad. Sci.*, *Paris*, **238**, 1506, (1954)

[9] See, for example, A. E. BARRINGTON, *High Vacuum Engineering*, Prentice-Hall, New Jersey, (1963)

[10] See, for example, J. C. MALIAKAL, *et al.*, *J. of Vac. Sci. and Tech.*, **1**, 54, (1964)

[11] W. BECKER, *Vakuum Technik*, **7**, 149, (1958)

[12] D. E. MILLER and R. F. W. PEASE, *I.E.E.E. 9th Annual Symposium on Electron, Ion and Laser Beam Technology, Berkeley, Calif.*, (1967)

[13] P. R. THORNTON, N. F. B. NEVE, D. V. SULWAY and R. C. WAYTE, *I.E.E.E. 9th Annual Symposium on Electron Ion and Laser Beam Technology, Berkeley, Calif.*, (1967)

[14] K. B. WEAR, *J. Appl. Phys.*, **38**, 1936, (1967), and R. V. STUART and G. K. WEHNER, *J. Appl. Phys.*, **33**, 2345, (1962)

[15] I. G. DAVIES, Ph.D. Thesis, Bangor U.C.N.W., (1967)

[16] D. V. SULWAY, Ph.D. Thesis, Bangor U.C.N.W., (1967)

[17] F. KURZWEIL, JNR., R. R. BARBER and M. H. DOST, *I.E.E.E. 9th Annual Symposium on Electron, Ion and Laser Beam Technology, Berkeley, Calif.*, (1967)

[18] K. H. LOEFFLER, *I.E.E.E. 9th Annual Symposium on Electron Ion and Laser Beam Technology, Berkeley, Calif.*, (1967)

[19] A. N. BROERS, *J. Appl. Phys.*, **38**, 1991, (1967)

[20] See, for example, G. J. OGILVIE and M. J. RIDGE, *J. Phys. Chem. Solids*, **10**, 217, (1957), and ref. [36]

[21] G. K. WEHNER, *Advances in Electronics and Electron Physics*, **7**, 239, (1955)

[22] A. D. G. STEWART, *Proc. 5th Inter. Conf. on Electron Microscopy, Philadelphia*, (ed. S. S. Breese), Academic Press, New York, (1962)

[23] A. BOYDE and A. D. G. STEWART, *Nature*, **198**, 1102, (1963)

[24] A. N. BROERS, Ph.D. Thesis, Cambridge, (1965)

[25] V. V. MAKAROV and N. N. PETROV, *Soviet Phys., Solid-State*, **8**, 1272, (1966)

[26] P. J. ESTRUP, *Solid-State Electron.*, **8**, 535, (1965)

[27] See, for example, T. MAGUIRE, *Electronics*, April 19, 26, (1963)

[28] W. J. KING, National Electronics Conference, (1964)

[29] I. W. DRUMMOND, Private Communication

[30] P. THONEMAN, J. MOFFATT, O. ROAF and J. SANDERS, *Proc. Phys. Soc. Lond.*, **61**, 483, (1948)

[31] C. D. MOAK, H. REESE, JNR. and W. M. GOOD, *Nucleonics*, **9**, 18, (1951)

[32] H. MAHL, (1941). *Z. Tech. Phys.*, **22**, 23, (1941)

[33] See, for example, M. VON ARDENNE, *Tabellen der Elektronenphysik, Ionenphysik* and *Übermikroskopie*, V.E.B. Deutscher-Verlag d. Wissenschafter, Berlin, (1956), or D. KAMBE, *Handbuch der Physik*, **33/1**, Springer-Verlag, Berlin, (1956)

[34] R. A. DUGDALE and S. D. FORD, *Trans. Brit. Ceramic Soc.*, **65**, 165, (1966)

[35] R. C. WAYTE, Unpublished results

[36] M. KAMINSKY, *Atomic and Ionic Impact Phenomena on Metal Surfaces*, Springer-Verlag, Berlin, (1965)

CHAPTER 8

The Emissive Mode of Operation

8.1 Introduction

The scanning electron microscope was developed in the first instance to utilize the electron emission which results when a specimen is bombarded by a finely focussed electron beam to obtain information about surface topography. In Chapter 3 we have described how electron optics provides a small-diameter electron beam which can be focussed, corrected for astigmatism when necessary and which can be scanned across the specimen surface. We have already seen how the secondary electron yield and the back-reflection coefficient depend on the significant parameters, in particular on the beam voltage, the target atomic number and the specimen inclination. We have done no more than mention the type of detector used in this mode of operation nor have we considered the factors which determine the contrast and the resolution. In this chapter we utilize the background established in Chapters 4 and 5 to examine how the electron emission is used to obtain high-resolution micrographs of specimen surfaces. The initial part of the chapter describes electron detectors which are currently used. Subsequent sections deal with the factors determining the contrast and the resolution. A final section describes areas in which more work is required.

8.2 Electron detector systems

8.2.1. *The scintillator-photomultiplier combination*

The most commonly used detector system, due initially to Everhart and Thornley[1], is illustrated in figure 8.1(a). The secondary electrons emitted from a surface element are pulled towards a positively charged Faraday cup. Some of these electrons penetrate through the top gauze and are accelerated towards the scintillator element which has the upper surface coated by a thin (500 Å) layer of Al and which is maintained at a positive voltage in excess of 10 kV. Each electron which reaches the scintillator therefore has a kinetic energy in excess of 10 keV. This energy is used to excite the scintillator material by the creation of electron-hole pairs which subsequently recombine via impurity atoms ('recombination centres', see Chapter 10) to create photons. Some of these photons travel via the light pipe (with some loss) to the photomultiplier where they are converted to a photo-current, which in turn intensity modulates the CRT. Such collector systems can be made with a variety of dimensions, can be put in any free position relative to the specimen and can subtend a range of

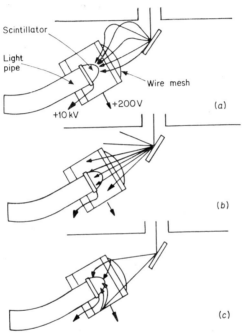

Figure 8.1. Contributions to emission signal: (a) secondary electron signal; (b) 'line-of-sight' reflected electron signal; (c) 'indirect' contribution due to bombardment of Faraday cage.

solid angles at the specimen by the use of apertures of different size, shape and inclination. Such electron detection systems will not only receive a signal from secondary electrons emitted by the specimen but also from those back-scattered electrons which are reflected into the solid-angle subtended by the scintillator. (See figure 8.1(b)). In addition some of the reflected electrons which strike the Faraday cage may create secondary electrons which then contribute to the signal. An example of this is shown in figure 8.1(*c*). The proportion of the signal obtained from secondary electrons as opposed to reflected primary electrons will depend on the collector voltage, the collector aperture and position and on the specimen inclination and atomic number. In normal use the bulk of the signal ($\sim 80\%$) is derived from secondary electrons.

Normally the Faraday cage and scintillator are placed in the

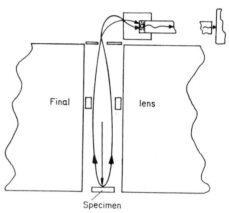

Figure 8.2. Detection system used by Kimura and Tamura [2] (Schematic).

position illustrated in figure 8.1, but recently a new application of the scintillator-photomultiplier combination has been proved by Kimura and Tamura [2].

The specimen is located, as in figure 8.2, near the final lens polepiece and is perpendicular to the beam. The secondary electrons are attracted by an electrostatic field back through the final lens and in the free space above this lens are deflected into a collector-scintillator-light-pipe combination. In the experimental version discussed [2] there were indications that the voltage-contrast mechanism (see below) is made more sensitive by the use of this type of geometry.

8.2.2 *Solid-state detectors*

In figure 8.3 we have illustrated the use of Si surface barrier counters to detect back-scattered electrons. This approach was first realized by Kimoto and Hashimoto [3]. There are several ways in which the method can be made to work; the figure shows a simple but satisfactory method used in the author's laboratory. The detectors are surface barrier counters made in n-type Si ($\sim 1{,}000\,\Omega$ cm). The depletion layer width at zero bias is approximately 10 microns. Such detectors can be used with or without a thin layer of Au on the active, barrier surface. With such a layer a slightly increased stability is obtained at cost of a small decrease in efficiency of electron detection. In addition, any near infrared radiation emitted by the specimen is not

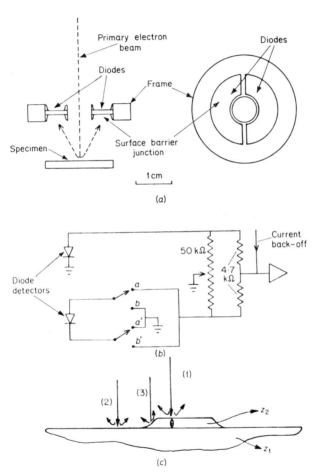

Figure 8.3. System used to detect compositional contrast: (*a*) detectors used (in section and in plan view); (*b*) circuit used; (*c*) diagram used in text to discuss compositional contrast.

detected. A pair of such detectors (made* from the same slice to give near-identical performance) are placed in the position shown. The beam passes through the central hole and strikes the specimen which in this case is held perpendicular to the beam. The reflected electrons that reach the detectors lose their energy by creating electron-hole pairs and so cause a current to flow in an external circuit in the manner described in Chapter 2 (see also Chapter 9). The circuit is

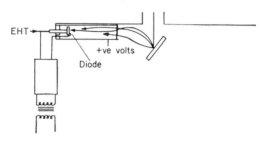

Figure 8.4. Use of semiconductor diode to detect secondary electrons [4].

arranged so that the signals from the detectors can either be added or subtracted. The resistor network enables differing fractions of the two signals to be added (or subtracted) and subsequently fed to the amplifier. In this approach the diodes are used without bias, as this causes a standing current in the devices and does not increase the electron detection efficiency, as the depletion layer width at zero bias is greater than the range of the back-scattered electrons in silicon. The amplifier employed is a low-impedance current amplifier. A system in which the diodes are biassed and with a high impedance voltage amplifier has been used successfully [3], but it is somewhat more complex and is slower in operation. This method essentially rejects the emitted secondary electrons, because a typical secondary electron of energy $\leqslant 10$ eV would create approximately three electron-hole pairs in a detector whereas a back-scattered electron of energy 10 keV would create approximately 3,000 pairs.

Gonzales [4] has shown how it is possible to use Si diodes to detect secondary electrons. The method, which is illustrated in figure 8.4, is basically a combination of the two approaches outlined above. A collector, in this case, a flat rectangular 'box' placed above the

* These counters were specially made by the Electronics Division of A.E.R.E. Harwell but similar devices can be obtained commercially.

specimen and to one side, is positively charged and so attracts the secondary electrons onto a Si diode which is maintained at a positive potential of ~ 10 kV. Thus the secondaries are accelerated and can create roughly the same number of electron-hole pairs as back-scattered, primary electrons. The mode of signal formation is the same as in the method previously described. The signal which is at high potential is coupled out by means of a transformer and fed to an operational amplifier. Gonzales used a Si diode which had been made by diffusion and had not been optimized for this particular

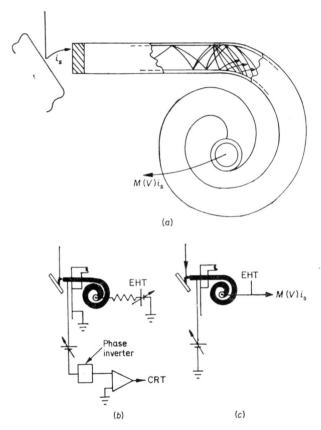

(a)

(b)   (c)

Figure 8.5. Use of channel electron multipliers [5]: (a) structure, position and mode of operation of channel electron multiplier; (b) coupling out of signal via low voltage 'input' end; (c) alternative circuit for coupling by either of the methods shown in figure 8.6.

o

application and he was able to show that approximately 60% of the energy incident on the diode is effective in creating current flow.

8.2.3 *Channel electron multipliers*

Miniature channel electron multipliers [5] having the form illustrated in figure 8.5(a) have recently become available commercially. The tube itself is made of glass and the inside is coated with a material which gives a good secondary electron yield. A bias is applied along the

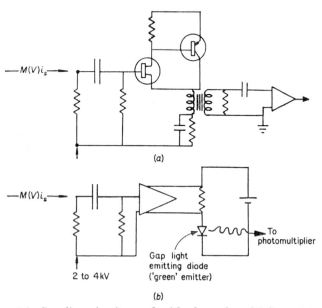

Figure 8.6. Coupling circuits used with channel multipliers: (a) magnetic coupling; (b) optical coupling.

layer by means of suitable contacts. When the tube is electron bombarded the secondary electrons take the paths indicated and statistically a large current burst flows through the layer as a result of bombardment by a single electron. In one sense this system represents a continuous distribution of 'dynodes' of the form used in photomultipliers, as one electron creating secondary electrons at the bombarded end is equivalent to $M(V)$ electrons being delivered to the 'output' contact, where $M(V)$ is the effective multiplication and is a function of the accelerating voltage. The multiplier can be placed very close to the specimen. The earthed metal screen is inserted to avoid distortion of the collecting field at the bombarded end by the EHT applied to the 'output' end of the multiplier.

Two ways of using channel multipliers are illustrated in figures 8.5 (*b*) and (*c*). In the first of these the signal is taken from the 'input' or bombarded end of the detector. This method [6] requires the use of a phase invertor but eliminates the need to 'float' the input of the amplifier at a high voltage. The second method requires the use of an amplifier that can be floated above earth, or some means of decoupling the signal from the EHT supply. Two ways of doing this are shown in figure 8.6. Of these the second is the best in that it gives a wide bandwidth, is bakeable to $\sim 200°C$ and uses available equipment. We can now consider the factors which limit the contrast and resolution available in this mode of operation.

8.3 Factors affecting the contrast

8.3.1 *Introduction*

To calculate the predicted contrast observed on the CRT screen or on a photographic film we have to take the following steps:

(1) Estimate the signal that results from a given excitation in terms of the important parameters of the system.

(2) Determine the resulting signal-to-noise ratio by assessing the noise currents flowing in the system.

(3) Having determined the signal-to-noise ratio from a single element of the surface we then have to adopt some criterion of the performance to be expected from the system. For example, we may wish to distinguish between two adjacent elements which give signals S and $S + \Delta S$, when the fractional difference in signal, $\Delta S/S$, is equal to F. This difference has to be detected against the noise level in the system.

(4) The required performance is obtained by observing a fractional change in brightness, $\Delta B/B$, on a CRT screen or on a photographic film. We have therefore to determine the relationship between $\Delta S/S$ and $\Delta B/B$.

To indicate which parameters are important we can analyse the situation applicable to the scintillator-photomultiplier combination following the original treatment given by Everhart [7]. We have already seen that the signal consists of three components: (*i*) the collected fraction of the secondary emission current, (*ii*) the fraction of reflected electrons reaching the scintillator and (*iii*) electrons reaching the scintillator as a result of secondary and/or reflected electrons from the specimen hitting the collector and leading to further electron emission. The final contribution is usually assumed to be small. In this case the total current reaching the scintillator can be written as

$$i_{\text{scin}} = i_{fs} + i_{fp} = i_p\, \sigma(s) f\,(N_a,\, V_c,\, E_s) + i_p \int_\Omega \eta(s\theta)\, d\Omega \qquad (8.1)$$

where i_p is the primary electron current, i_{fs} is the contribution from the secondary electron current and i_{fp} is the primary electron contribution. Consider i_{fs} first.

(1) *Secondary electron signal i_{fs}.* σ is the secondary emission yield and is written as σ (s) to indicate that it depends on the specimen properties, in particular, on the surface inclination. $f(N_a,\, V_c,\, E_s)$ is the fraction of emitted current which is collected by the Faraday cage and which reaches the scintillator. This fraction depends on the numerical aperture, N_a, of the collector system as this affects the number of the emitted secondary electrons which are ineffective (i.e., which hit the outside of the collector) as opposed to those which reach the scintillator. The collected fraction is also a function of the collector volts, V_c, or, more strictly, the voltage difference between the emitting surface element and the collector. The trajectory followed by a secondary electron is determined by the

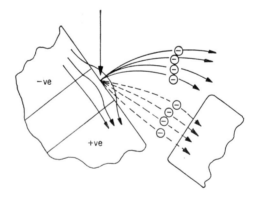

Figure 8.7. Illustration of the way in which surface fields can affect the electron collection. The continuous trajectories represent the paths in the absence of a device bias. The dashed trajectories indicate the paths with such a bias.

integrated effect of the local electrical field, its magnitude and direction, along its path. As the collector voltage contributes significantly to the local field, it affects the electron trajectories and so the fraction collected. Finally the existence of surface fields, E_s, on the specimen can perturb the electron trajectories and so affect the collected fraction (see figure 8.7).

(2) *The back-scattered contribution,* i_{fp}. If $\eta(s\theta)\, d\theta$ is the back-scattering coefficient for electrons reflected through θ to $\theta + d\theta$, then, because the reflected electron trajectories are largely un-affected by the collector field, we can obtain the back-scattered contribution by integrating over all solid angles, Ω, substended by the scintillator itself.

In order to obtain the signal delivered to the photocathode of the photomultiplier we have to take account of the fact that the energy of the secondary and reflected electrons are different. If a current I of electrons of energy E_i hits the scintillator then the number of photons reaching the photocathode per second is given by [8]

$$\frac{(I/q)\, E_i\, f_{\text{scin}}\, \eta_{ip}\, f_{\text{light}}}{E_p} = I/q\; E_i F_{\text{scin}} \tag{8.2}$$

where f_{scin} is the average fraction of the incident electron energy absorbed in the scintillator, η_{ip} is the energy conversion efficiency of the scintillator, f_{light} is the fraction of the photons formed that reach the photocathode and E_p is the photon energy. In the case outlined by eqn. (8.1) $E_i = E_{\text{scin}}\ (= eV_{\text{scin}})$ for secondary electrons and $E_i = \bar{E} + E_{\text{scin}} \approx 2E_{\text{scin}}$ for reflected electrons where $\bar{E}$ is the mean energy of the reflected electrons. Within this rather approxi-mate treatment the photon flow to the photocathode, N_p, is given by

$$N_p = \frac{i_p}{q}\, E_{\text{scin}}\, F_{\text{scin}} \{\sigma(s)\, f\, (N_a, V_c, E_s) + 2\int \eta(s\theta)\, d\Omega\} \tag{8.3}$$

For reasons which we shall clarify below it is often expedient to reduce the component due to reflected electrons to a small fraction of the total signal. In this case the signal current delivered to the amplifier chain is given by

$$I_s \sim qN_p\, \eta_{pm}\, g(V) \simeq i_p\, E_{\text{scin}}\, F_{\text{scin}} \{\sigma(s) f\, (N_a, V_c, E_s)\} \eta_{pm} g(v) \tag{8.4}$$

where η_{pm} is defined by the number of electrons emitted by the photocathode per indicent photon of energy E_p and $g(V)$ is the photo-

multiplier gain. Having established in general terms the magnitude
of the signal, we have to consider the noise properties.

8.3.2. *Noise considerations*

There are two sources of noise that can degrade the contrast in
situations where the signals involved are small. Firstly, there can be
a standing current flowing in the detector circuit. This standing
current in the detector circuit can, for example, be surface leakage
in the case of surface barrier detectors or the dark current leaving
a photomultiplier photocathode even in the absence of an excitation.
Secondly, there is the shot noise inherent in the signal itself. Because
the information arrives in the form of a random stream of discrete
quanta it is subject to the statistical fluctuations inherent in all such
systems. In Chapter 10 we shall meet situations in which the system
is 'detector-noise limited', but here it is the 'short-noise limitation'
with which we are concerned, because the optical coupling effectively
reduces the detector noise to insignificance.

The first question to answer is: 'At what stage in the information
flow is the shot noise greatest?'. We shall answer this question by
noting that if we make a series of statistical trials in which a number
of events n is measured with a mean value $\bar{n}$ and if the events are
random then the mean square deviation is also given by $\bar{n}$ [9]. Therefore the 'signal-to-noise ratio', i.e., the mean value compared to the
uncertainty, varies as $\bar{n}/\sqrt{\bar{n}} = \sqrt{\bar{n}}$. Thus the smaller number of
events counted or the smaller the number of particles carrying the
information the smaller the signal to noise ratio. Therefore the
limiting stage is that where the number of particles is smallest. We
can now calculate the signal-to-noise ratio in the present case.

We assume that the primary beam spot remains on each picture
frame, for a time, τ_f. Then if there are N_f elements per frame the
average number, $\bar{n}$, of primaries hitting an element is

$$\bar{n} = \frac{i_p}{q}\frac{\tau_f}{N_f} = \frac{i_p}{q}\tau \tag{8.5}$$

where τ is the time spent on each surface element. There will, in fact,
be a distribution n about $\bar{n}$ and each primary electron has a probability $p(\sigma)$ of creating σ secondary electrons. The mean number of
secondary electrons formed per picture element is given by

$$\overline{N} = \bar{\sigma}\,\bar{n} \tag{8.6}$$

and Shockley and Pierce [10] have shown

$$\overline{(N - \overline{N})^2} = \bar{\sigma}^2 \overline{(n - \bar{n})^2} + \bar{n} \overline{(\sigma - \bar{\sigma})^2} \tag{8.7}$$

If the primary electrons follow a random distribution $\overline{(n - \bar{n})^2} = \bar{n}$ and, therefore,

$$\overline{(N - \overline{N})^2} = \bar{n}\bar{\sigma}^2 \left[1 + \frac{\overline{(\sigma - \bar{\sigma})^2}}{\bar{\sigma}^2} \right] = \bar{n}\bar{\sigma}^2 (1 + b) \tag{8.8}$$

If σ is distributed randomly about $\bar{\sigma}$ then $b = 1/\bar{\sigma}$, but it is found [11] experimentally that b increases above $1/\bar{\sigma}$ near linearly with primary beam voltage at low beam voltages (see figure 8.8). If this relationship

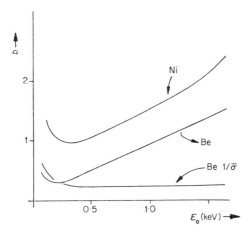

Figure 8.8. Data quoted by Everhart [7] illustrating the dependence of b on E_0 for Ni and Be [11] at low beam energies.

holds up to 10 to 20 kV then b should be ~ 10 to 20 in this energy range. This estimate represents an upper limit to the true value of b. (Everhart has suggested that the departure from a random distribution may be due to the role played by reflected electrons in creating secondary electrons.) If we assume that it is this stage that limits the performance then the signal-to-noise ratio is given by

$$\overline{N}/[\overline{(N - \overline{N})^2}]^{1/2} = \sqrt{(\bar{n})}/(1 + b)^{1/2} \tag{8.9}$$

The minimum detectable contrast that can be observed when the signal-to-noise ratio has a given value is given [12] by

$$(\Delta S/S)_{\text{threshold}} = K/(\text{signal: noise ratio}) \tag{8.10a}$$

In our case

$$(\Delta S/S)_{\text{threshold}} = K(1 + b)^{1/2}/\sqrt{(\bar{n})} = K\{qN_f/\tau_f i_p (1 + b)\}^{1/2} \quad (8.10b)$$

Or, we can write the threshold current, I_{th}, necessary to observe a difference in contrast $\Delta S/S$ as

$$I_{\text{th}} \sim [K/(\Delta S/S)]^2 \, \frac{q\,N_f\,(1 + b)}{\tau_f} \qquad (8.10c)$$

In eqn. (8.10) K is a measure of the sensitivity of the contrast-recording system: the phosphor-eye combination or the phosphor-photographic film system, for example. K can vary from unity to ≈ 6. In this context a value of $K = 5$ is usually assumed [13]. Equation (8.10c) indicates that an ability to detect smaller and smaller differences in contrast requires an increase in beam current. On the other hand the resolution improves as the beam current is decreased (see section 3.4). However, good contrast discrimination can be obtained with low beam currents by integrating for a longer time, or, in terms of eqn. (8.10c), increasing $\tau(\equiv \tau_f/N_f)$ the time spent by the spot on each surface element.

Several points about eqn. (8.10) should be stressed.

(1) The threshold contrast drops as the beam current is increased, i.e. it becomes possible to detect smaller contrast differences. This result is important because, as shown in Chapter 3 and in section 8.4, the beam spot-size, which largely determines the resolution, increases with increase in beam current. Therefore the design compromise is to choose the beam current so that the resolution and contrast performance are optimized.

(2) Equation 8.10 is a simplification. First there is some uncertainty in b. Everhart's [7] estimate of $b \approx 20$ for $V_0 = 20$ kV, obtained by extrapolation from low V_0 values, has to be compared with a newer estimate of $b \sim 4$, quoted by Oatley, Nixon and Pease [13], based on data obtained by Pease [14]. There is an additional uncertainty caused by the third component to the signal mentioned in section 8.3(b). Finally, there is the question of shot-noise effects when the electrons strike the scintillator and when the photons reach the photocathode. Since about 50 or more photons are produced in the scintillator per incident electron, shot-noise effects at this stage can be neglected. Everhart [7] estimates that about two photons reach the photocathode per electron incident on the scintillator. Therefore the neglect of the

photomultiplier noise underestimates the current required to observe a given change in signal by between 20 and 30%.

Equation (8.10) defines the theoretical contrast limit in the shot-noise limited case for the photomultiplier-scintillator combination. Similar analyses can be performed for the other detectors in the manner outlined in Chapter 10. We can now consider the way in which the formal quantities included in eqn. (8.1) can be related to the physical

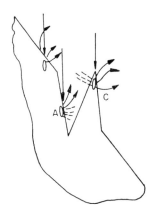

Figure 8.9. The loss of collected signal by specimen modulation. Those electrons emitted along dashed trajectories are lost to the specimen itself.

properties of the specimen, still excluding, for the present, the contribution from reflected electrons.

8.3.3 *Contrast*

(1) *Secondary electrons.* Of the two factors affecting the secondary electron signal one, the local secondary electron yield, has been discussed in Chapter 5. Here we have only to consider how sensitive the system is to the changes outlined in that chapter. Wells [5, 16] and Everhart [7, 16] have shown that over the range of angles of incidence of interest in the SEM the number of emitted secondaries can be written as $d(\theta) = d(0) \sec \theta$ where θ is the angle between the specimen normal and the beam. Therefore, if C_T represents the minimum (or 'threshold') contrast that can be observed, the minimum detectable difference in angle, $\Delta\theta_{\min}$, that can be detected using secondary electrons is given by $\Delta\theta_{\min} = C_T \cot \theta$, which gives for

$C_T \sim 5\%$ and $\theta \sim 60°$, $\Delta\theta_{min} \sim 1\cdot3°$. Therefore, provided the surface is essentially smooth, variations of the order of 1° are detectable. If the specimen surface is rough then two other effects have to be considered. These effects are indicated schematically in figure 8.9 and have been termed [15, 7] specimen modulation and specimen collection. The first of these we have already mentioned in Chapter 5 and is concerned with the fact that when the surface is rough the number of secondary electrons formed within the escape distance of the surface varies from a rather low value for situations such as position A to far higher values for positions such as that indicated by C in figure 8.9. 'Specimen collection' is the name given to the shielding of the collector by adjacent parts of the specimens. For example, electrons having trajectories indicated by the dashed lines in figure 8.9 are unlikely to reach the collector because they will re-enter the specimen before doing so.

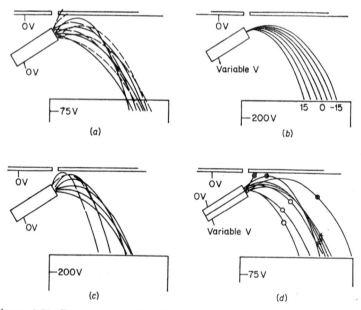

Figure 8.10. Data compiled by Everhart [7] and Wells and Everhart [15, 16], (a) to (d) trajectory plottings. (a) 4eV electron trajectories as function of angle and position; (b) effect of varying specimen potential; (c) corresponding to (a) but with increased collector potential; (d) analogue of *pn* junction; O represents trajectories with + 10 V on

This specimen collection is just one way in which the specimen and system properties can affect the collected fraction. Our understanding of this topic is by no means complete in the sense that we do not know sufficient about the mechanisms involved to ensure that we always work under conditions of maximum sensitivity. The collected fraction depends on the difference in potential between the emitting element and the collector, the collector position and numerical aperture and on the position of the aperture on the collector. It also depends on the position of the specimen relative to the earthed parts of the specimen chamber. The Cambridge group have [15, 7] over the years conducted experiments to establish the trajectories followed by the emitted electrons. This was done in two ways, one was by using an electrolytic tank model of the specimen environment and a trajectory plotter to determine how the trajectories depend on the available variables. Figure 8.10 (taken from Everhart's thesis [7]) shows the

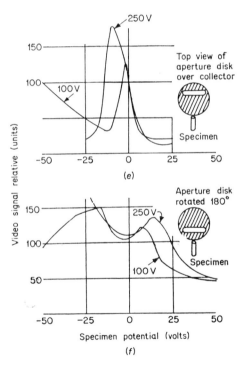

specimen $x = 0$V and ● $= 10$ V; (e) and (f) collected electron signals as a function aperture position, collector voltage and specimen potential.

type of data available for electrons leaving the specimen with an energy of 4 eV which is typical of the mean energy of secondary electrons. If the collector voltage is low, figure 8.10(*a*), those electrons emitted towards the final lens may hit the final lens and be lost. As the collector voltage is increased, this loss by 'lens collection' is reduced. Figure 8.10(*c*) shows how the specimen voltage affects the trajectories, while figure 8.10(*d*) shows a situation analoguous to a *p-n* junction. These studies give only one-dimensional data in that they represent the trajectories followed by electrons emitted in the symmetry plane through the centre of the collector, but they do imply that the position of an aperture moved about the collector surface will greatly affect the observed signal. This prediction is borne out by the experimental data represented in figures 8.10(*e*) and (*f*). If we assume that a 5% change in current is detectable then these data imply that surface voltage differences of ~ 0.5 volts should be detectable. This estimate is near the observed sensitivity in this situation under conditions of good resolution.

These observations really represent the state of our present knowledge, as the bulk of the remaining observations are reports [17, 18, 19, 20] showing that the existence of transverse fields on the specimen surface can affect the observed contrast in a variety of ways that are not understood, (see below). Ideally we need to be able to predict the best place to position the collector aperture, its optimum size (bearing in mind the conflicting requirements of signal level and ability to discriminate between small changes in surface potential) and the best collector voltage to use in a given situation. At the present we cannot do this; we have to rely on an empirical approach which nearly always gives satisfactory results. (See section 12.4, which illustrates the abilities and some of the limitations of the method.)

(2) *Reflected primary electrons.* So far we have neglected the contribution of the reflected electrons. We shall discuss the role played by reflected electrons in limiting the resolution obtainable in section 8.4 below. Here we shall just note that McMullan has made [21] measurements of the reflection coefficient as a function of the inclination and showed that the most probable angle of reflection is that corresponding to specular reflection. In addition, we can expect that the reflection will increase with increasing inclination because the electrons tend to be scattered 'along' the specimen surface rather than into the specimen and so the distance to the surface is reduced (figure 8.11) and the

electrons scattered through a relatively small angle will be able to leave the specimen. From McMullan's data it is reasonable to conclude that, using reflected electrons, it is possible (at $\theta \sim 60°$) to detect variations in surface angle on a smooth specimen surface of $\sim 0.5°$. This estimate is about twice as sensitive as that obtained using secondary electrons.

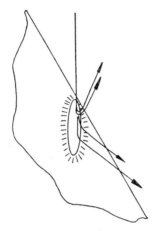

Figure 8.11. Showing how an increased component from forward scattered electrons can be obtained at oblique angles of incidence.

(3) *Compositional.* Finally we should consider the use of the reflected electrons to investigate compositional variations. Consider the situation shown in figure 8.3. A somewhat idealized specimen is depicted which may be realized in practice by evaporating an Au film onto a Si substrate, for example. Such a specimen has a well defined change in composition and some variations in surface inclination. With the beam in position 1, each detector will receive very nearly the same energy per unit time from back-scattered electrons and if the counters are identical in behaviour then the current flowing in each will be equal to

$$I(\mathscr{Z}_2) \simeq (Ci_p/E_i) \int_\Omega \eta'(\mathscr{Z}_2\theta) \, E(\mathscr{Z}_2\theta) \, d\Omega \qquad (8.11)$$

where Ω is the solid angle subtended by the active area of the device, C is a constant of proportionality and the other parameters have their usual meaning. Similarly, with the spot in position 2, the diode current will be given by

$$I(\mathscr{L}_1) \simeq (Ci_p/E_i) \int_\Omega \eta'(\mathscr{L}_1\theta)E(\mathscr{L}_1\theta)\, d\Omega \qquad (8.12)$$

so that by using the output from either diode we will observe the signal contrast between regions 1 and 2 as $2[I(\mathscr{L}_1)-I(\mathscr{L}_2)]/[I(\mathscr{L}_1)+I\mathscr{L}_2)]$. This contrast arises because of the way in which η' and E vary with atomic number and so we can call this a compositional contrast. Compare the case where the beam is in position 3. As a result of the asymmetry introduced into the distribution of back-scattered electrons by the surface inclination the diode on the left-hand side will receive a slightly higher energy rate than when the beam is in position 1 and the right-hand diode a little less. We can write the respective currents induced in the diodes as

$$\left.\begin{array}{l} I_L(\mathscr{L}_2) = I(\mathscr{L}_2) + \Delta_1 \\ I_R(\mathscr{L}_2) = I(\mathscr{L}_2) - \Delta_2 \end{array}\right\} \qquad (8.13)$$

In general Δ_1 and Δ_2 will not be equal (except in simple geometries of high symmetry) but will be of the same order. If the inclination is small then Δ_1 and $\Delta_2 < I(\mathscr{L}_2)$. On the other hand, if the inclination changes are large, Δ_1 and Δ_2 can approach $I(\mathscr{L}_2)$. Kimoto and Hashimoto [3] realized that if the output currents from the two diodes are added the total current is

$$I_c = 2I(\mathscr{L}_2) + (\Delta_1 - \Delta_2) \qquad (8.14)$$

i.e., the effective 'compositional' current is doubled and the effects of surface inclination reduced to a difference signal. If the signals are subtracted the current is given by

$$I_T = |\Delta_1 + \Delta_2| \qquad (8.15)$$

and so contains topological information only.

Obviously the effectiveness of this method of separating contrast due to compositional variations from that due to surface roughness depends on the symmetry of the surface structure and on the degree of surface roughness. In practice the method works remarkably well, as we shall see in Chapter 11. There is one other factor which must be considered in relationship to the contrast in this situation: it must be remembered that back-scattered electrons can penetrate a relatively large distance into the target before being reflected out of the crystal. In general terms we are dealing at 20 kV with electrons which can penetrate into the specimens for distances of 4 to 6 μ before losing all their energy, therefore some electrons can be back-scattered out of the specimen from depths of ~ 2 to 3 μ at this beam voltage. Thus, with surface films which are thinner than half the penetration distance, the compositional contrast will be reduced. The usefulness of this approach under conditions in which surface topography and film thickness play a role has yet to be established, but where the specimens consist of polished metallurgical surfaces the method is already capable of useful qualitative application. This use of dual detectors to eliminate unwanted signal is, of course, not limited to semiconductor detectors. It is, in fact, just one example of the way in which sum and difference information can be utilized. The approach can be extended by modulating the beam and/or the specimen bias in conjunction with the operation of the detectors (see Chapter 11).

8.4 Resolution limitations

8.4.1 *General*

We have already seen how the electron column is designed to produce at the specimen a finely focussed electron beam of uniform properties, i.e., the intensity as a function of the distance from the spot centre has circular symmetry about the column axis. We have also seen how, with increasing refinement, the spot-size measured in terms of the diameter of the equivalent Gaussian distribution has now reached a value of ~ 50 Å. We have to ask how we relate the observed resolution to the spot-size. The question immediately resolves itself into two questions. How does the interaction between the specimen and the electron beam affect the resolution and how do we access the resolution? To answer the first question, consider the situation shown in Figure 8.12 where the Gaussian spot-shape has been replaced for convenience by a step function. This beam is assumed to be incident normally on the specimen and creates a region of ionization of the general form shown in figure 8.12(a). The dispersion of the beam energy arises from the scattering of the electrons in the specimen. In general, the estimates of the escape depth of secondary electrons lie between 100 and 500 Å. So from the viewpoint of the collector system the secondary electrons appear to come from an area which lies between the spot-size and the size (πR_e^2) of the ionization region at

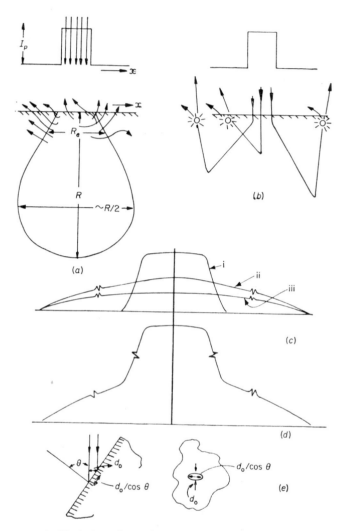

Figure 8.12. Entirely schematic drawings showing the origin of the emitted electron signal: (a) showing the relationship of the main secondary electron signal in relation to the incident beam diameter; (b) showing a wider signal due to reflected electrons and to secondary electrons created by these reflected electrons; (c) the form of these three components, (i) main secondary electrons, (ii) reflected electrons, (iii) secondaries created by reflected electrons; (d) approximate spatial distribution of emitted signal; (e) effect of specimen inclination converting a circular spot into an elliptical one.

the escape depth. In addition the reflected primary electrons, which can be reflected after penetrating $\sim R/2$ into the specimen, will appear to come from a spot-size which lies between the electron spot-size and the size of the ionization region at $z \sim R/2$. The reflected electrons can create secondary electrons near the surface over a wider area and these secondary electrons can also be emitted, see figure 8.12(b). We can therefore say that the signal consists of the three components shown in figure 8.12(c). If we arrange to reject the bulk of the primary electron signal the secondary electron signal will appear to have a spatial origin of the type shown in figure 8.12(d), i.e., the bulk of the signal coming from a central spot somewhat larger than the spot-size and a prolonged tail due to the inherent presence of reflected electrons. A measure of the inherent degradation forced on the resolution by the specimen properties (and possibly by the recording system) can be obtained by noting that Pease and Nixon [22] using a spot-size of 60 Å obtained a resolution of 100 Å. We have two estimates available of the exit area of the reflected electrons and of secondaries created by reflected electrons. Everhart [7] used a straight p-n junction as a test specimen and, with microdensitometer, measured the distance in the plane formed by the beam axis and a line in the specimen surface at right angles to the junction over which the signal decayed to a low value. The estimate obtained was ~ 0.5 ($\pm$ 0.2)μ, which indicated an exit area of radius equal to a quarter of the penetration distance. This figure is to be compared with more refined studies made by Pease [23] using a projection method to obtain a magnified image of a very fine grid. From the sharpness of the projected image of the grid bars, it was possible to estimate that the effective source area was constant to within 20%, for Al and Cu targets bombarded by electron energies of 15 and 30 kV. The average source diameter obtained was 4,500 Å which, in the case of Al bombarded at 30 kV, is approximately $R/16$. Therefore the resolution obtainable on micrographs obtained using reflected electrons should be $\sim 0.5\mu$. We can now be a little more specific by what we mean by resolution.

We have first to consider the effect of specimen inclination. Figure 8.12(e) shows a flat specimen inclined at an angle θ being examined by a spot of diameter d_0. The distance bombarded by the beam in the direction in the specimen plane perpendicular to the tilt axis is $d_0/\cos \theta$, therefore the resolution is degraded in this direction by $1/\cos \theta$. In general the circular spot appears as an elipse of major and

P

minor axis of $d_0/\cos\theta$ and d_0, respectively. If the specimen has a relatively coarse structure of the kind illustrated in figure 8.9 then the instantaneous inclination varies. In view of these variations it is often best to test instrument performance by measurements made along the direction of the tilt axis. The most usual method of assessing resolution is in terms of 'edge' resolution i.e., a suitable 'edge' of the specimen which gives a high contrast ratio is photographed and the

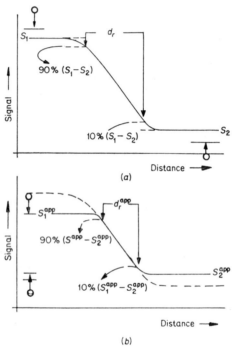

Figure 8.13. Over-optimistic claims of resolution resulting from the use of the system outside its working range. The symbols ♀ and ♂ represent the limits of the working range; (a) correct use of system; (b) incorrect use resulting from too high a signal level.

resultant film and negative brightness measured with a micro-densitometer. Then some suitable criterion is adopted for estimating the resolution at this point. For example, the resolution can be defined as the distance between which the signal difference goes from 10 to 90% of the full value as in figure 8.13. Two points should be borne in mind about such estimates of the resolution; the first is that care should be taken to ensure that *all* the signals recorded are within the working range of the film. Consider the rather extreme case shown in figure 8.13(b) in which both S_1 and S_2 lie outside the working range of the film. In this case the resolution would appear to be R_{app}. Thus an over-optimistic claim will result unless care is taken. The second point is that an 'edge' resolution of, say, 200 Å does not necessarily imply that features of ~ 200 Å will be resolved on a flat specimen surface. The point is that the resolution obtained is a function of the contrast that exists at the place where the measurements are made. If the contrast is low, the resolution will not usually be so good as the 'edge' resolution. It is not possible to quote reliable figures of the relationship between the resolution and the contrast, but indications of this relationship can be obtained by comparing the equations given in Chapter 3 with eqn. (8.10).

8.4.2 *Future possibilities*

We have seen how the conflicting requirements of a small spot (for good resolution) and a threshold information rate (to give sufficient contrast in reasonable times) effectively determine the available resolution. The only way in which the information rate can be kept at the required level with smaller spot-sizes is to increase the brightness of the source. This is one motive behind current efforts to improve on the performance available with the hairpin W filament. The need for unattended electron sources of long life and good stability suitable for use in an industrial environment is another driving force. There are two approaches: either to find another and better thermionic emitter or to use a field emitter.

In the first category, Broers [25] has developed an excellent source based on the use of LaB_6, which has a higher ratio of electron emission density to evaporation rate than tungsten. The LaB_6 cathode is made by spark machining a 1·6 cm × 1 mm × 1 mm rod from the bulk material and grinding a fine point on one end. The other end is brazed into a copper heat sink which is maintained near ambient by oil-cooling while the pointed end is heated by direct radiation from a nearby tungsten loop. In this way only cold pieces of LaB_6 are in contact with other elements. This method avoids difficulties due to the chemical reactivity of hot LaB_6. This source has the following properties.

(1) Source lifetime. Assuming that the lifetime is determined by the evaporation of the hottest part of the rod (the region opposite

the heating coil not the tip), Broers estimates that the source should last for 8,000 hours with a tip temperature of 1,600°C corresponding to an emission current density of 5 amps/cm². (N.B. corresponding life of a tungsten filament is < 30 hours.) This estimate was made on the assumption that 75% of the hottest region (at $\sim$ 1,750°C) evaporates before the useful life is ended. No systematic estimates of lifetime have been made, but two filaments have been run, one for 1,100 hours and the other for 900 hours, without change in geometry.

(2) Conservative measurements indicate a maximum brightness of $5 \cdot 6 \times 10^5$ amp/cm²/steradian. This value is about twice that obtained with a tungsten filament with the same gun geometry. This increase is probably due to the increased curvature of the omitting area on the LaB_6 source compared to the tungsten source and to the decreased thermal energy spread due to the lower eperating temperature.

(3) The mechanical stability is excellent. The movement caused by 'turn-off' followed by 'turn-on' is minimal if $\sim$ 10 to 20 minutes is allowed for warm up. Repeated exposure of the cold filament to air leaves its emission properties unaffected.

(4) The source has been successfully operated in a scanning electron microscope. At present 50 watts of radiant heat are required to heat the filament. This requirement can probably be reduced by refinement in design.

Attempts are being made in several laboratories to develop a reliable field-emitting filament, although very little data are available [26] in widely distributed journals. The problems are formidable but so is the 'pay-off' if the approach can be realized. The vacuum requirements (10^{-9} torr or better) are somewhat severe and the questions of mechanical stability and filament lifetime have to be resolved. Some measure of the capabilities of a field emitter can be obtained from calculations made by Everhart [27] who estimates that a field emitter should be capable of passing 10^{-10} amps with an effective emitting diameter of 100 Å (c.f. $\sim 40\mu$ with W filament).

8.5 Comparison between the different collection systems

The salient feature of the optical coupling system is its low noise properties. The power of the approach can be judged when it is realized that the system can give micrographs with acceptable noise levels for primary beam currents of 10^{-13} to 10^{-12} A within reasonable frame times. Not only has the system a low noise level but it has a large bandwidth. The use of light to transmit the information to the inherently fast photomultiplier means that, in practice, the bandwidth is limited by the response of the photomultiplier head amplifier. These two properties indicate that in one form or another, it will remain an important detector system for some time, particularly in high-resolution studies where the primary beam current is kept as small as possible ($\sim 10^{-12}$ A). It is, of course, capable of modification and adaptation; the limitations are only in somewhat specialized applications. When a high beam current is required (as in some semiconductor studies, for example) the Al film over the scintillator can be sputtered away leading to a degradation of performance. In other applications (see Chapter 12) the system in the form shown in figure 8.1 suffers from the fact that the signal utilized consists of both secondary and back-scattered electrons, as the back-scattered electrons can 'swamp' significant information contained in the secondary electron signal. This difficulty can be overcome, as in the Kimura-Tamura system, by using a small field to deflect the secondaries into the collector without collecting the back-scattered electrons. Two more general limitations arise from the fact that the system is difficult to miniaturize to any large extent and because it cannot conveniently be used in an ultra-high vacuum system. The first of these limitations arises from the need to have an EHT of ~ 10 kV applied to the scintillator. If the collector-scintillator system is miniaturized, surface breakdown becomes a problem. The second limitation arises because scintillator materials outgas considerably and are difficult to bake. It is in over-coming these limitations that channel multipliers may find extensive application. The inherently small cross-section means that arrays can be built and can be used with other detectors. The voltage require-ment is greatly reduced compared with the scintillator approach. The channel multipliers can be placed close (3 mm) to the specimen and can be used with good results at low (10^{-13} to 10^{-12} A) beam currents. If the epoxy resin used to protect the outer tube is removed these units can be baked to 250°C and hence can be employed in uhv systems. The bandwidth of the system depends on the method of coupling the signal to the photomultiplier. A simple system using the 'earthy' end of the multiplier gives [6] a bandwidth of $\geqslant 5$ kHz, magnetic decoupling gives [24] ≈ 100 kHz and a bakeable optical coupling gives, at present, ≈ 24 kHz [24].

The use of semiconductor diodes to detect secondary electrons has not yet been fully assessed, but they are unlikely to have as good a noise behaviour as the optically coupled system or the channel multipliers. Leaving aside the question of the ubiquitous surface noise, the bulk generation-recombination noise in a diode of the size required for this work is likely to give a current of 10^{-11} to 10^{-10} A if the diode is operated at room temperature. In practice this value is exceeded because of the presence of surface leakage. Experimentally,

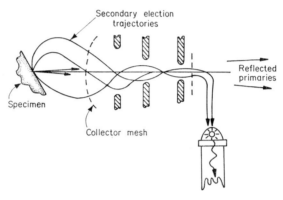

Figure 8.14. A selective collector system for rejecting primary electrons (entirely schematic) [28].

Gonzales found that satisfactory results can be obtained with beam currents of $\sim 10^{-10}$ to 10^{-9} A. This method also requires a scintillator voltage of ~ 10 kV. One possibility of interest lies in its application in uhv systems. The tendency to use pumping systems not based on the oil-diffusion pump and to employ ultra-high vacuum versions of the SEM has already been noted in the previous chapter. Semiconductor diodes present no problems of outgassing in an ultra-high vacuum system as they can, in a suitably constructed form, be baked at temperatures of 250 to 300°C without detriment to the device. In addition, semiconductor detectors can be made in miniature form very cheaply and may find fairly extensive application in diagnostic experiments in which arrays of such detectors are used to determine the actual distribution of the trajectories of the secondary and primary electrons in the specimen chamber under conditions of practical interest.

The use of semiconductor diodes to detect primary electrons does not really compete with the optically coupled system as it represents an attempt to do a different job. With an optically coupled detector using a predominantly secondary electron signal the main aim is to observe surface topography at high resolution. With semiconductor devices detecting reflected primary electrons the main practical aim is to detect compositional variations in the specimen. A pair of channel multipliers will also detect such variations. The relative merits of these two methods has yet to be assessed. Finally, we are left with the merits of the Kimura-Tamura approach. We have already mentioned two of its virtues – a separation of the secondary electron signal from the reflected primary signal and an increased sensitivity to voltage contrast. It retains the good noise performance inherent in the use of optical coupling and it can have a relatively large, effective collection angle. Much interest centres around this approach because of the possibility that it suggests for incorporating some elements of scanning electron microscopy in a transmission electron microscope. From some points of view its main drawbacks are the limitations of specimen movement implied by its position, the restriction on the specimen stage size and the inability to use other detector systems simultaneously with it. The ability to discriminate between secondary and reflected primary electrons can be incorporated into other collector systems. For example, figure 8.14 shows how an additional lens system can be used to reject primary electrons and which does not suffer from the limitations imposed by the geometry of the Kimura-Tamura method.

It is very apparent that, although no one system is ideal, there is sufficient versatility to meet the vast majority of foreseeable needs. The difficulties that may arise in exploiting these techniques are discussed in Chapter 12.

REFERENCES

[1] T. E. EVERHART and R. F. M. THORNLEY, *J. Sci. Inst.*, **37**, 246, (1960)

[2] H. KIMURA and H. TAMURA, *I.E.E.E. 9th Annual Symposium on Electron, Ion and Laser Beam Technology*, Berkeley, Calif., (1967)

[3] S. KIMOTO and H. HASHIMOTO, *The Electron Microprobe*, (editors: McKinley, Heinrich and Wittry), Wiley, New York, (1960)

[4] A. J. GONZALES, *I.E.E.E. 9th Annual Symposium on Electron, Ion and Laser Beam Technology*, Berkeley, Calif., (1967)

[5] J. ADAMS and B. W. MANLEY, *Phillips Tech. Rev.*, **28**, 156, (1967)

[6] K. A. HUGHES, D. V. SULWAY, R. C. WAYTE and P. R. THORNTON, *J. Appl. Phys.*, **38**, 4922, (1967)

[7] T. E. EVERHART, Ph.D. Thesis, Cambridge, (1958)

[8] J. B. BIRKS, *Scintillation Counters*, Pergamon Press, (1953)

[9] See, for example, *Noise* van der Ziel, Chapman and Hall, (1955) or C. E. WEATHERBURN, *Mathematical Statistics*, Cambridge Univ. Press, (1952)

[10] W. SHOCKLEY and J. R. PIERCE, *Proc. I.R.E.*, **26**, 321, (1938)

[11] B. KURRELMEYER and L. J. HAYNER, *Phys. Rev.*, **52**, 952, (1937)

[12] A. ROSE, *Advances in Electronics*, **1**, 131, (1948)

[13] C. W. OATLEY, W. C. NIXON and R. F. W. PEASE, *Advances in Electronics and Electron Physics*, **21**, 181, (1965)

[14] R. W. F. PEASE, Ph.D. Thesis, Cambridge, (1964)

[15] O. C. WELLS, Ph.D. Thesis, Cambridge, (1957)

[16] T. E. EVERHART, O. C. WELLS and C. W. OATLEY, *J. Electronics and Control*, **7**, 97, (1959)

[17] G. V. SPIVAK, G. V. SAPARIN and N. A. PEREVERZEV, *Bull. Acad. Science, U.S.S.R.* (*Physical Series*), U.S. translation, **26**, 1362. [Original: *Izv. Acad. Nauk. U.S.S.R. Ser. Fiz*, **26**, 1339, (1962)]

[18] P. R. THORNTON, M. J. CULPIN and I. W. DRUMMOND, *Solid-State Electronics*, **6**, 523, (1963)

[19] P. R. THORNTON, K. A. HUGHES, HTIN KYAW, C. MILLWARD and D. V. SULWAY, *Microelectron and Reliability*, **6**, 9, (1967)

[20] G. V. SPIVAK, G. V. SAPARIN, B. MASSARINI and K. V. BIKOV, *Proc. 3rd Europ. Reg. Conf. on Elect. Microscopy*, *Prague*, (ed. M. Titlebach), State Publishing House, Prague, (1964)

[21] D. MCMULLAN, Ph.D. Thesis, Cambridge, (1952)

[22] R. F. W. PEASE and W. C. NIXON, *J. Sci. Instr.*, **42**, 81, (1965)

[23] R. F. W. PEASE, *J. Sci. Instr.*, **42**, 158, (1965)

[24] D. V. SULWAY, Ph.D. Thesis, Bangor, U.C.N.W., (1967)

[25] A. N. BROERS, *J. Appl. Phys.*, **38**, 1991, (1967)

[26] A. V. CREWE, *J. Microscopie*, (Soc. Franc. de Microscopie Electronique), **2**, 369, (1963)

[27] T. E. EVERHART, *9th Annual Symposium on Electron, Ion and Laser Beam Technology*, Berkeley, Calif., (1967)

[28] D. KINESTON and HTIN KYAW. Unpublished work

CHAPTER 9

The Conductive Mode

9.1 Introduction

In this chapter we will consider the mode of operation of the SEM that depends on the observation of beam-induced currents in the specimen. We have already seen (Chapter 2) that several effects are exploited in this conductive mode, as we have chosen to call it. Two effects are of particular importance. The first, which is of extreme value in the semiconductor field, is the phenomenon of charge collection [1] which occurs in the built-in field of a *pn* junction or a surface barrier or in any high-field region existing in a bulk semiconductor under an applied bias. The second mechanism which is relevant to metallurgical studies is the 'specimen absorbed' current which flows in the specimen circuit in order to maintain electrical neutrality in the specimen. A third mechanism [2] which is analogous to a displacement current is introduced in this chapter and discussed briefly in relation to the other mechanisms.

Emphasis is placed on the physical processes which occur and on the way in which these determine the contrast observed on conductive micrographs. No discussion of the necessary electronics and ancillary equipment is given as these aspects present no difficulty; the available space is given instead to a detailed discussion of charge-collection contrast. This discussion is essentially qualitative although the formalism for a quantitive development is given. Subsequent sections are devoted to the other mechanism, while a final section introduces an additional way in which the information can be displayed in order to clarify or augment the usual intensity modulation display. Current applications, limitations and possible extensions are described in Chapters 11 and 12. We begin our discussion here by examining charge collection by built-in fields, taking as an instructive example the collection of electron-beam-induced, free carriers by a *pn* junction.

9.2 Charge collection by *pn* junctions

The basic effects can be studied in terms of figure 9.1(a) which represents two situations which are commonly met with both in experimental and production-line devices. The first of these corresponds to a planar transistor typical of a modern microcircuit. The second figure illustrates the older, but still very important 'mesa' configuration. Figure 9.1(*b*) illustrates the factors which affect the charge collection by the junction. In the case depicted the primary electron loses its energy by creating electron-hole pairs in four regions. First there is the top layer of SiO_2 of thickness z_0, secondly there is

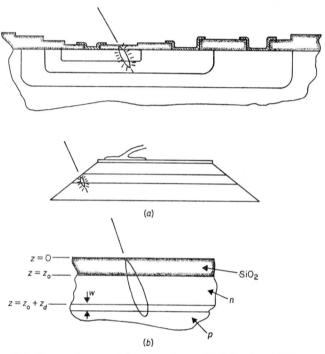

(*a*)

(*b*)

Figure 9.1. Type of geometries usually studied in the SEM: (*a*) the 'planar' and 'mesa' structures; (*b*) definitions of the relevant distances discussed in the text.

the region of n-type Si of thickness, z_d, above the junction, thirdly there is the depletion layer itself which is of a width $W(V_b)$ which is determined by the doping levels in the n- and p-type regions and by the applied voltage. Finally the remainder of the primary electron energy is used to create electron-hole pairs in the p-type region below the junction. The free carriers created in the depletion layer itself will be collected by the field inherent in the depletion layer. The holes will drift towards the p-type layer and the electrons will be pulled by the field towards the n-type layer. This charge movement leads to current flow in an external circuit. Some of the holes created in the n-type layer will diffuse towards the depletion layer. Those that reach the junction will also be collected by the field and contribute to the external current. A similar contribution will arise from electrons created in the p-type layer and which subsequently diffuse to the junction. Thus the magnitude of the collected signal depends on the depth of the junction, its width, the atomic number(s) of the material above and below the junction and the minority carrier lifetimes in these materials.

The importance of these factors is shown schematically in figure 9.2. If we take the curve in figure 9.2(a) to represent the number of electron-hole pairs created in a layer of thickness dz at z, then the number of pairs created in a junction depleted layer as a function of junction depth and applied bias is as shown in figure 9.2(b). Figures

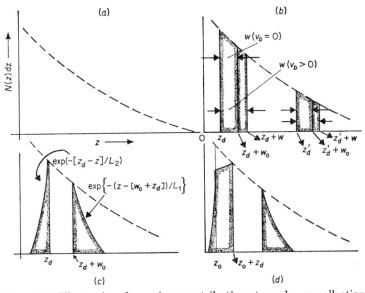

Figure 9.2. Illustrating the various contributions to a charge collection signal: (a) idealized representation of the carrier generation as a function of depth; (b) contribution from carriers created in depletion layer as function of depth and bias; (c) contributions from carriers diffusing from bulk regions in diffused diode; (d) as (c) but in passivated diode formed by epitaxy.

9.2(c) and (d) show how the carrier lifetimes affect the fraction of the carriers which diffuse to the junction. The first of the diagrams illustrates the situation that exists at a typical diffused junction. The second figure could represent the situation in a junction formed by epitaxy and then 'passivated' by covering with a layer of SiO_2. The epitaxial layer could have a long carrier lifetime while the carrier lifetime in SiO_2 is taken to be very short. A formal expression for the number of carriers, N_c, collected by the junction can be written down:

$$N_c = \int_0^{z_0} N(z) \exp\left[-(z_0 - z)/L_d\right] \exp\left[-(z_d)/L_p\right] dz$$

$$+ \int_{z_0}^{z_d + z_0} N(z) \exp\left[-[(z_d + z_0) - z]/L_p\right] dz + \int_{z_d + z_0}^{z_d + z_0 + W} N(z) dz$$

$$+ \int_{z_d + z_0 + W}^{\infty} N(z) \exp\left\{-[z - (z_d + z_0 + W)]/L_n\right\} dz \qquad (9.1)$$

In eqn. (9.1) $N(z) dz$ is the number of electron-hole pairs created at a depth z to $z + dz$; L_p and L_n are the minority carrier diffusion lengths in the n- and p-type layers respectively and L_d is the hole lifetime in the SiO_2 layer (or any other surface dead space, see Chapter 10). Implicit in this equation is the assumption that, once created, the relevant carriers diffuse *directly* towards the junction layer (see Chapter 11). This equation also assumes that the carrier lifetimes are long, so that the diffusion lengths are at least as great as the depletion layer width. This assumption is often valid in 'well behaved' materials such as good quality Si and Ge, but there are cases where it is not valid. In the initial stages of the development of new materials, the carrier lifetimes are often very short so that $L < W$. Even in technologically advanced materials such as near-intrinsic Si in which the depletion width at high reverse bias can exceed a millimetre the assumption may not be valid. We therefore must consider the situation in which $L < W$. In this case it should be remembered that the carrier lifetime in the bulk regions may well differ from that in the depletion layer itself. If the bulk lifetime is relatively large then a significant fraction of the signal can arise from carriers diffusing to the junction.

We will now consider how effective the carriers are once they have reached the junction. Consider the situation shown in figure 9.3, in which is depicted an abrupt junction with a local field $E(z)$. In the following discussion we have, for simplicity, changed the origin to correspond to the upper side of the depletion layer (see figure 9.3). Consider an electron-hole pair created at a point z. In a time interval dt the electron will drop down a voltage $dV = E(z)dz$ so that the energy made available by the electron to cause current flow in the

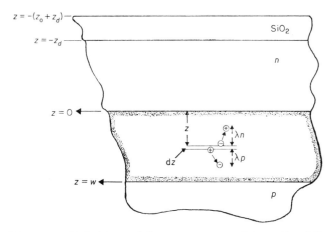

Figure 9.3. Definitions of the parameters used in section 9.2.

external circuit is $qE(z)dz$. Taking account of the movement of the hole as well, the energy available to cause external current is given by

$$\Delta E = \left| q \int_z^{z - \Delta z_n} E(z)dz \right| + q \int_z^{z + \Delta z_p} E(z)\, dz \qquad (9.2)$$

where Δz_n and Δz_p are distances travelled by the electron and hole before recombination. The average energy will be given by

$$\overline{\Delta E} = \frac{q \int_0^\infty p(\Delta z_n) \left| \int_z^{z - \Delta z_n} E(z)dz \right|}{\int_0^\infty p(\Delta z_n)} + \frac{q \int_0^\infty p(\Delta z_p) \left| \int_0^{z + \Delta z_p} E(z)dz \right|}{\int_0^\infty p(\Delta z_p)} \qquad (9.3)$$

where $p\,(\Delta z_n)$ and $p\,(\Delta z_p)$ are the relative probabilities that an electron and hole will drift distances Δz_n and Δz_p respectively. Further development in terms of these general expressions gets cumbersome and tends to obscure the issue so we follow Northrup and Simpson [3] and make the simplifying assumption that all the electrons travel a distance λ_n and the holes a distance λ_p before recombination. In the case

$$\overline{\Delta E} = -q \int_z^{z-\lambda_n} E(z)dz + q \int_z^{z+\lambda_p} E(z)\,dz \qquad (9.4)$$

In the case of the well-behaved abrupt junction, $E(z)$ can be taken as a constant E_m to give

$$\overline{\Delta E} = qE_m(\lambda_n + \lambda_p) = \frac{qV_b(\lambda_n + \lambda_p)}{W} \qquad (9.5)$$

where V_b is the total voltage drop across the depletion layer. This energy will be neutralized by external charge movement and we can define an effective charge q_{eff} as $\Delta\bar{E} = q_{eff}V_b$ i.e. q_{eff} is the effective charge transferred externally from one electrode to the other due to the partial charge collection of a pair created at z. Therefore

$$q_{eff}/q = (\lambda_p + \lambda_n)/W. \qquad (9.6)$$

Tacit in the above discussion is the assumption that z is situated so that $W - \lambda_n \geqslant z \geqslant \lambda_p$, i.e. that both the hole and electron recombine before reaching the electrode. If we wish to consider how q_{eff} varies as function of z we have to divide the depletion layer into three regions [3]:

(1) $0 \leqslant z \leqslant \lambda_p$, in which holes alone are completely collected.
(2) $\lambda_p \leqslant z \leqslant W - \lambda_n$, neither electrons nor holes completely collected and
(3) $W - \lambda_n \leqslant z \leqslant W$ where only electrons are completely collected.

In these three regions q_{eff} is given by

$$q_{eff\,1}/q = (z + \lambda_p)/W; q_{eff\,2}/q = (\lambda_p + \lambda_n)/W; q_{eff\,3}/q = [\lambda_p + (W-z)]/W \qquad (9.7)$$

respectively. So, if the primary beam creates $N(z)\,dz$ at z, the total charge collected will be proportional to

$$\frac{q}{W}\left[\int_0^{\lambda_p} [N(z)(z+\lambda_p)dz] + \int_{\lambda_p}^{W-\lambda_n} [N(z)(\lambda_p+\lambda_n)dz] \right.$$
$$\left. + \int_{W-\lambda_n}^{W} [N(z)(\lambda_p + W - z)dz] \right] \qquad (9.8)$$

This integral can be evaluated when $N(z)$ is known. In the case where $N(z)$ is constant ($\equiv N$) the charge collection signal, S, is given by [3].

$$S \propto qN \left\{ \frac{\lambda_p + \lambda_n}{W} - \left[\frac{\lambda_n{}^2 + \lambda_p{}^2}{2W^2} \right] \right\} \tag{9.9}$$

A similar calculation can be made for the case when $\lambda_n + \lambda_p > W$. Again the depletion layer can be divided into three regions. But, in this case, in the second region both electrons and holes are completely collected. The charge-collection signal is again proportional to the expression given in eqn. (9.9) provided λ_n/W and λ_p/W are replaced by $(1 - \lambda_n/W)$ and $(1 - \lambda_p/W)$ respectively.

The first point to notice about eqn. (9.9) and about similar equations that can be derived by assuming more realistic forms for $N(z)dz$ is that they express the signal in terms of a collected charge. In order to measure or use this signal we have to use a circuit such as that shown in figure 9.4. Here a simplified equivalent circuit of the junction

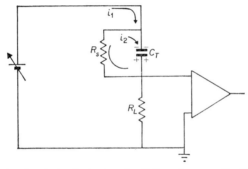

Figure 9.4. Simple equivalent circuit of the charge-collection process.

is given in terms of the junction capacitance and a parallel leakage resistance. Any capacitance due to contacts and any series resistance have been neglected. In terms of this circuit the beam excitation and the field inherent in the junction lead to the 'condenser' tending to become charged up as shown. This tendency is counterbalanced by external current flow in two paths – one through the load resistance and the second through the leakage resistance. An ideal amplifier could measure the instantaneous value i_1, of the current through the load resistance by measuring, for example, the associated voltage drop across R_L. It is straightforward to show that if a charge $\pm \Delta Q(o)$

is delivered internally to the 'plates' by charge collection that the instantaneous current through R_L at time t due to this excitation is

$$i_1 = \frac{\Delta Q(\mathrm{o})}{C_T R_L} \exp - (t/R_{\mathrm{eff}} C_T) \qquad (9.10)$$

for $t >$ the charge-collection time where $R_{\mathrm{eff}} = R_s R_L / R_L + R_s$. The total beam-induced current is obtained by summing the effects of all such charge increments. Therefore if i_1 is to remain finite for a measurable time then $i_2 \ll i_1$, i.e. $R_s \gg R_L$. We shall return to this point again in section 9.5. The final point to stress about eqn. (9.9) is that it only represents the signal from carriers generated in the depletion layer itself. To obtain the full signal in the case where the lifetime in the depletion layer is small we have to add terms representing signals from carriers diffusing to the junction.

9.3 Physical origins of conductive contrast

So far we have analysed charge collection rather formally in terms of the carrier-drift lengths and an equivalent circuit. We have over-simplified the picture and not enquired into the physical processes which determine these drift lengths; nor have we considered any local variations in charge collection that may occur.

We will now consider the physical origins of contrast on conductive micrographs by enquiring into the processes limiting charge collection and the ways in which these can vary throughout the specimen. In general, the charge collection processes consist of three mechanisms which occur sequentially: the creation of electron-hole pairs, the diffusion of the carriers to the junction and, finally, the behaviour during the charge collection process itself. Any factor which affects any of these mechanisms can lead to contrast on charge collection 'maps'. The creation of electron-hole pairs can be affected by those mechanisms which affect the back-reflection loss and to a lesser extent the secondary electron yield. From the viewpoint of charge collection, a high back-scattering represents a loss of energy. Such 'topological' contributions can be recognized by comparision with emissive micrographs. Insulator effects can also contribute here because they may lead to variations in yield in the manner indicated in Chapter 5. With regard to the second and third mechanisms involved, any localized process which leads to a change in movement of the relevant carriers towards the junction or which affects the speed of charge collection or carrier lifetime in the depletion layer can lead to contrast. These processes are obviously dependent on the biases applied and on the specimen temperature.

Figure 9.5 illustrates schematically the more important physical mechanisms that may lead to local variations in the observed signal. Figure 9.5(a) shows a situation in which a non-uniform distribution of surface traps and/or recombination centres can lead to contrast.

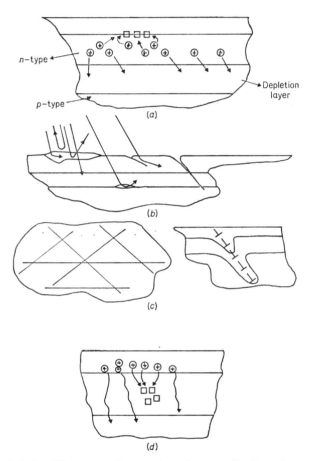

Figure 9.5. Possible causes of contrast on charge-collection micrographs: (a) localized surface recombination; (b) surface contamination, internal faults and microcracks; (c) dislocation arrays either planar and parallel to junction, as in the first figure, or in sub-boundaries, as in the first figure, or in sub-boundaries inclined to the junction as in the second figure; (d) trapping in the depletion layer.

Q

For example, if a local increase in surface recombination results in the recombination of carriers which would otherwise diffuse to the junction then a local reduction in charge collection signal may occur. A beam-induced change in the occupancy of surface traps can lead to surface charge-up and local variations in the back-reflection coefficient. Figure 9.5(*b*) illustrates the way in which microcracks, thin ($\lesssim 200$ Å) contaminant films and small precipitates can lead to variations in charge-collection signal because of (*i*) variations in the back-scattering coefficient, (*ii*) changes in the effective absorption, and (*iii*) reflection and scattering at interfaces. In addition, the presence of microcracks which extend into the depletion layer may lead to localized recombination which effectively decreases λ_p or λ_n and so leads to a local reduction in signal.

It is of interest to note that inclusions *below* the junction can lead to variations in signal either because of reflection or because of changes in carrier lifetime. We shall return to figure 9.5(*b*) when we consider high-field effects.

Figure 9.5(*c*) shows dislocation effects. The left-hand diagram shows a planar array of diffusion-induced dislocations [4, 5] lying in or very near the junction plane, while the right-hand diagram shows how enhanced diffusion at a dislocation sub-grain boundary can lead to distortions of an otherwise planar depletion layer. Both types of array can produce contrast on charge-collection maps, the first by introducing local variations in trapping and/or recombination, the second by simply altering the extent and depth of the junction. Finally, in figure 9.5(*d*), we may remind ourselves that traps can exist in the depletion layer itself. The manner in which trapping affects the observed signal becomes apparent when we remember that many devices have a significant leakage across the junction. Therefore if trapping delays the charge collection by impeding the process of one or more carriers (see reference [1]) then the charge collection current may be of the order of the leakage current and so i_1 will be small and difficult to detect. In addition, we use a scanning electron beam in the SEM which remains on a particular surface element for a time τ. If, because of trapping, the collection time τ_c, is greater than τ, the charge-collection signal from a given element will be delayed and appear to come from another element further along the scan. As a result the resolution suffers.

Figure 9.5 summarizes the main causes of contrast that are 'built-in' to materials and devices. Although the examples given are all related to a *pn* junction, the points discussed have a wider application in that they are applicable to any situation in which there is a high-field region to give the necessary charge collection. It is apparent that the charge-collection signal will depend on the bias applied to the device; in particular, reasons why the contrast due to defects should be voltage-dependent can be advanced. The ability to relate the voltage dependence of defect contrast to the macroscopic device properties, in particular to device failure, represents a major use of the SEM at the present time. In view of this we must discuss the details of the processes leading to variations in contrast with applied voltage.

9.4 High-field effects
There are two effects which can lead to the passage of high currents under high-field conditions. These are avalanche breakdown [7] and internal field emission [8] which are both well known from the viewpoint of device operation and because they can contribute to device failure. Avalanche breakdown depends on the occurrence of current multiplication in high electric fields. Let us now return to figure 9.3 and follow one of the beam-induced electrons as it drifts in the depletion-layer field towards the positive contrast. The kinetic energy of the electron in the direction of the field will increase because of the energy gained from the electric field. At the same time thermal vibrations, departures from periodicity in the lattice etc., will tend to randomize this energy. Both the gain in kinetic energy and the subsequent scattering are field dependent, but in general the nett effect will be a gain in energy in the field direction until, at high enough fields, the electrons attain energies sufficient to impact-ionize one or more of the atoms in their path. The threshold energy required to strip electrons off the host atoms is of the order of $3Eg/2$ according to a rather simplified calculation [9]. Experimental estimations of the total energy are shown in table 9.1.

For electrons to acquire kinetic energies of this order, fields of $\gtrsim 10^5$ volts/cm are needed. In fields of this strength the energy balance can be pictured as follows [21]. Every l_r centimetres an electron will emit an optical phonon of average energy E_r (usually taken as the Raman energy), but if the field is high enough, the electron will gradually gain energy until its kinetic energy exceeds the threshold energy for ionization, E_i. It will then cause an ionization and will drop back to an energy $\sim kT$. Subsequently it will again

228   *Scanning Electron Microscopy*

Table 9.1. *Experimental estimates of the average energy required to cause impact ionization*

Material	Value	Reference
Si	3·6	[10]
Si	3·6 ±[0·3	[11]
Ge	2·84 ± 0·12	[12]
Ge	2·85 ± 0·1	[13]
GaAs	4·6	[14]
GaAs	4·5	[15]
GaP	7·8] ± 0·8	[11]
CdS	7·3	[16]
PbO	8·8	[16]
InSb	0·42	[17]
CdTe	5·0	[18]
PbS	1·6	[19]
SiO_2	∼ 2·40	[20]

be accelerated and the ionization process will be repeated every l_i centimetres on average. A similar process occurs with holes which can be accelerated and subsequently lose energy by pair formation. In addition the pairs created by these collisions can be accelerated and cause ionizations themselves. In this way a 'cascade' or 'avalanche' of carriers can be created which can increase rapidly in extent with increase in field. The current carried increases to such an extent that breakdown of the material can result. Two convenient parameters used to describe this behaviour are (*i*) $\alpha(E)$, which is defined as the probability that a free carrier will cause an ionization in a unit length of path and (*ii*) $M(E)$ the current multiplication, which is the number of carrier pairs collected by the depletion layer per carrier-pair injected into the depletion layer. M and α are both functions of the electric field and are therefore interconnected. The exact relationship depends on the field distribution and the relationship between the ionization probabilities for electrons and for holes. For the case in which the field is constant and the ionization probabilities for electrons and holes are equal, M and α are related by

$$[1 - (1/M)] = \int_0^W \alpha(E)dz$$

where W is the depletion layer width. Several workers have estimated

α as a function of the electric field. Shockley [21] estimates that α is proportional to exp $(E_i/l_r qE)$ when $qE \leqslant E_r/l_r$, while Wolff [22] shows that α is proportional to exp (c/E^2) for $qE \geqslant E_r/l_r$. More recently Baraff [23] has computed α for a wide range of fields and obtained curves which approach the Shockley and Wolff expressions at low and high fields. In the intermediate range the general result

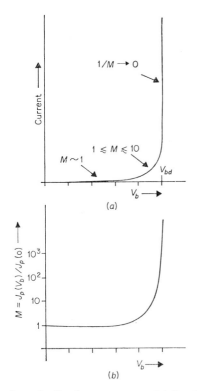

Figure 9.6. Variation of effective current multiplication with applied voltage: (a) order of the value of M as function of position on VI curve; (b) typical experimental determination of M. $J_p(V_b)$ is the photo-current induced by a given flux at a voltage V_b.

can be regarded as an admixture of these expressions. An important point to stress is the rapid increase in α with increase in field.

   From the viewpoint of the reverse characteristic of junction diodes we can divide the VI curve into three regions: (i) a low-voltage region in which $M = 1$, and (ii) a high-voltage region near the breakdown voltage in which $1/M \rightarrow 0$. These are separated by (*iii*) an intermediate region ($V_b \leqslant V_{bd}$) in which M goes from unity to ~ 10 (see figure 9.6). Traditionally M has been determined by measuring the photocurrent at a fixed flux as a function of the applied voltage, [24, 25, 28]. See figure 9.6(*b*). An analogous situation exists when a diode is subjected to electron-beam bombardment. At low bias voltages each primary electron leads to a certain number, $n(o)$, of pairs being collected by the highfield region. This number remains constant until the voltage creates a sufficiently high-field for $\alpha(E)$ to become significant. So the charge-collection signal increases with bias in the ratio $n(V_b)/n(o)$ i.e. the charge-collection signal increases with the effective multiplication. In the case of a junction in which the properties do not vary from place to place, the charge-collection signal from the bulk would increase in a manner which gives direct information about the effective current multiplication. In the case where the junction properties do vary across the device, these variations can be studied. Consider the situation in which the field is, for some reason, enhanced in a small local area compared to the field elsewhere. As the bias is gradually increased, the current multiplication in this region will be greater than elsewhere because of the sensitivity of α to slight increases in field. As a result the charge-collection signal from this high-field region will grow rapidly relative to the bulk signal until it 'swamps' all of the bulk signal. As such regions are sites of localized breakdown they also represent faults in the device. This ability to locate regions of high-field means we can detect the regions of localized avalanche leakage that may lead to the rejection of devices. We shall see in Chapter 12 that the SEM can detect regions of avalanche-induced leakage with a resolution and sensitivity far greater than any previous method over a wide range of experimental situations.

We have previously mentioned internal field emission as being a cause of leakage in junction devices. In highly doped materials the depletion layer width can be very small and the application for an external voltage can lead to a very localized barrier-to-current flow which can be overcome by tunnelling. There are various barriers which can be overcome by tunnelling (see reference [8]). The situation relevant to our topic is illustrated in figure 9.7. Here the current flow in a heterojunction, for example, is limited at low voltages by the activation energy needed to overcome the barrier presented by the ¡nsulator layer. At higher voltages the electrons can tunnel through

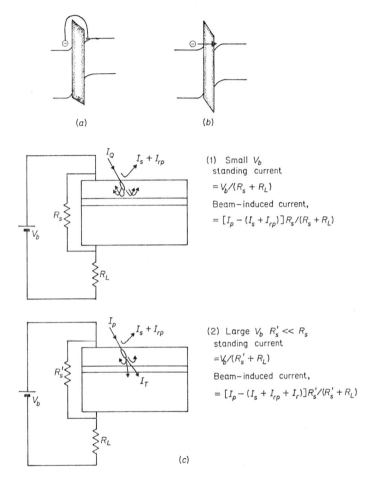

(a)   (b)

(1) Small V_b
standing current

$$= V_b/(R_s + R_L)$$

Beam−induced current,

$$= [I_p - (I_s + I_{rp})]R_s/(R_s + R_L)$$

(2) Large V_b $R_s' \ll R_s$
standing current

$$= V_b/(R_s' + R_L)$$

Beam−induced current,

$$= [I_p - (I_s + I_{rp} + I_r)]R_s'/(R_s' + R_L)$$

(c)

Figure 9.7. Tunnelling in a heterojunction structure: (a) thermal activation at low bias; (b) tunnelling process at high bias; (c) possible method of detecting tunnelling in the SEM.

the barrier leading to an increased current flow. No SEM studies of tunnelling have been described in the published literature, but it may be possible to examine both bulk and localized tunnelling by using the arrangement shown in figure 9.7(*c*). The electron-beam energy is varied until beam-induced electrons can just diffuse to the junction. If, as the bias is increased, the tunnelling probability becomes significant in local regions then the increased beam-induced current flow in these regions will increase. In effect, the tunnelling mechanism leads to a reduction in the leakage resistance R_S. The change in the beam-induced current may be detectable against the standing current flowing in the circuit (see figure 9.7).

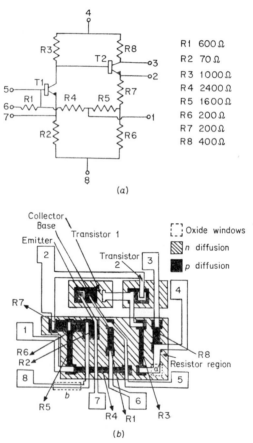

R1	600 Ω
R2	70 Ω
R3	1000 Ω
R4	2400 Ω
R5	1600 Ω
R6	200 Ω
R7	200 Ω
R8	400 Ω

(*a*)

(*b*)

Figure 9.8. (*a*) Circuit and (*b*) layout of the device studied in figure 9.9.

9.5 Complications arising in complex microcircuits

9.5.1 *Introduction*

So far we have considered the charge collection at a single isolated junction under ideal experimental conditions, i.e. the loss of signal due to leakage across the condensor is minimal. In microcircuitry applications the junctions we have to observe form part of complex arrays in which parallel leakage paths exists and junctions interact one with another. In this section we illustrate these co-operative effects. We will do so by considering an actual example, but not all the effects mentioned here are necessarily seen in one device. The device circuit is shown in figure 9.8(*a*), while figure 9.8(*b*) illustrates the device layout and surface structure. A series of charge-collection maps was taken of the device with an operational amplifier (which controlled the CRT brightness) connected to pin 3 and a variable d.c. bias applied to pin 4 (fig. 9.8(*b*)). A selection from this series is shown in figure 9.9 (Plate). Further data were obtained at the same time to aid in the interpretation, namely (*i*) the overall gain of the specimen amplifier (figure 9.10) and (*ii*) the behaviour of the transistor T_2 over the voltage range in which T_1 was not conducting. This was studied by setting up an analogue of the specimen amplifier (see figure 9.10(*b*)), applying a small positive current pulse to the base and observing the corresponding voltage excursions of the collector and emitter (see figure 9.10(*c*)). Two points should be made about the micrographs shown in figure 9.9 (Plate). Both the amplifier gain and the 'backing-off' level were altered during this sequence in order to accommodate the wide range of signals observed. In this sequence a signal which is 'white' compared to the 'no signal' level represents electrons being delivered to the amplifier input and a 'black' signal corresponds to electrons being extracted from the input.

Without going into detail, the changes in contrast observed in figure 9.9 (Plate) can be explained in terms of known physical mechanisms:

(1) The presence of parallel paths to earth which can lead to a restoration of equilibrium after beam excitation without current flow through the output amplifier.

(2) The parallel paths can have a voltage-dependent impedance, particularly if they include an active element such as a transistor.

(3) The presence of voltage-dependent impedances in series with the examined junctions.

(4) The interaction between two near-by junctions (e.g. the emitter-base and base-collector junctions of a transistor).

(5) The signal from a given area may not result from one junction but may come from two junctions one above the other. The signals from the two junctions may oppose each other, i.e. one may result in electrons being delivered to the amplifier, the other in the removal of electrons.

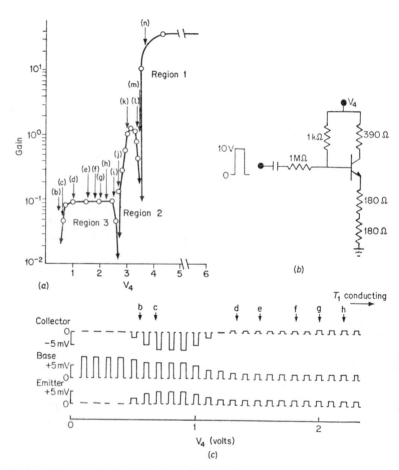

Figure 9.10. (a) Gain measurements as $f(V_4)$; (b) analogue of output stage used to obtain the relationships between base, collector and emitter voltage changes indicated in (c).

We can quickly illustrate all these points by taking an example of each from figure 9.9 (Plate).

9.5.2 *The existence of parallel paths and opposing signals*
In figure 9.9(a) (Plate) the resistors R_1, R_2, R_4, R_5 and R_6 together with the isolation junction assciated with the resistor block give a 'white' signal by the mechanism outlined in figure 9.11(a) for R_4 and

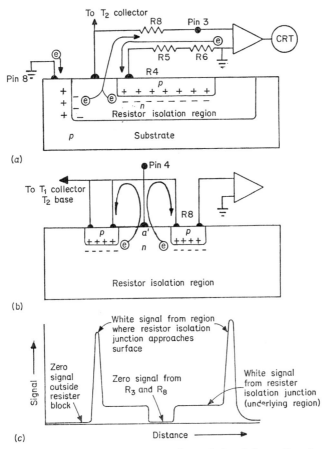

(a)

(b)

(c)

Figure 9.11. (a) Showing the mechanism of signal formation from R_4 and resistor block isolation junction; (b) showing the short-circuit path obscuring signal from R_3 and R_8; (c) explaining the apparent 'black' signal from R_3 and R_8.

the isolation junction. On the other hand R_3 and R_8 give *no* signal. The reason for this is shown in figure 9.11(b). The existence of a short circuit to the n-type side of the junction via the window at a' (see figure 9.8) means that the beam-induced voltage change can leak away to earth without flowing through the output amplifier. The word 'no' has been italicized in the sentence above to stress that the resistors R_3 and R_8 give no significant signal, yet a clear demarcation can be seen around the edge of each of these resistors. This arises by the mechanism shown in figure 9.11(c). The underlying isolation junction gives a small 'white' signal which outlines R_3 and R_8. If the signal from R_3 and R_8 is compared with the background signal *outside* the isolation junction no difference can be detected. This was confirmed by the use of more sensitive line scans.

9.5.3 *Parallel and series paths with voltage-dependent impedances*

Consider the behaviour of R_3 over the voltage range implicit in figures 9.9(c) to (i) (Plate). In the first three micrographs R_3 gives a white signal. In figure 9.9(f) this element gives a weak white signal and in subsequent micrographs an increasing 'black' signal. We can explain this change in terms of figure 9.10. Under the beam excitation the p-type resistor R_3 collects holes which cause a positive voltage excursion to the base of T_2. At low bias voltages this positive voltage excursion produces a negative change at the collector (i.e. amplifier input), see figure 9.11(c), so that a white signal is observed. As the bias voltage is increased a positive base voltage change is passed to the collector unchanged in sign so that a 'black' signal results. The reason why the zero signal occurs at a different voltage in figure 9.10 compared with figure 9.9 (Plate) is because an imperfect analogue of the device was used to obtain the data in figure 9.10. It should be stressed that a voltage applied to the base T_2 causes an excursion of both collector and emitter voltages. The *nett* excursion of the operational amplifier input relative to earth depends on the relative magnitudes of the changes in collector and emitter voltages and on their sign. These in turn depend on the conducting state of T_2. The apparent absence of a signal from R_3 (and from the collector-isolation junction of T_1), at the bias voltage corresponding to figure 9.9(f) implies that the conducting state is changing at this voltage ($V_4 = 1 \cdot 8$ volts).

Something of the complexity that may arise will be seen by considering the behaviour of the signal from the base-collector of T_1 over this voltage range. We have stated that at $V_4 = 1.8$ volts (micrograph 9.9(f)) T_2 starts transmitting voltage differences from base to collector without change of sign, hence in figure 9.9(f) the signals from R_3 and the collector isolation junction of T_1 change sign. On this argument so should that from the base-collector junction, whereas, in fact, the transition to whiteness is only complete at $V_4 = 2.7$ volts (micrograph 9.9(j)). This delay in transition is occurring because the black signal from the base-collector junction in figures 9.9(g) and (h) is derived by a different mechanism from that in micrographs 9.9(c), (d) and (e). In particular, the holes collected by the base of T_1 are fed to the emitter of T_2 via the feedback loop and so give a black signal which competes with (and overwhelms initially) the white signal through the collector of T_1. If this argument is valid then the incorporation of a capacitor between pin 1 and earth should short out the feedback loop to a.c. and hence remove the 'black' component of the signal. This behaviour was observed [27] in practice, the base-collector junction signal from T_1 (and the signal from R_1 and R_4) disappear when a condensor is added.

9.5.4 *Interactions between neighbouring junctions*
In addition to the factors outlined above, the type of situation shown in a simple schematic form in figure 9.12(a) can occur. The output amplifier is connected to the emitter of a transistor. The base is connected to earth via a relatively high impedance (~ 1 kΩ) to earth and the emitter is connected to earth via a low impedance. Let us imagine that this circuit is being scanned with a beam which penetrates both the emitter-base and base-colletor junctions. Consider the signal from the base-collector junction. If the emitter junction is self-biassed the carriers collected by the base have to be neutralized by the relatively high impedance circuits shown in figure 9.12(a). On the other hand when the emitter is taken into forward bias, the impedance to earth is greatly reduced and the current signal from the collector-base junction is increased. Particularly if the emitter junction is forward biassed can these interactions become pronounced. If the charge-collection signal from an isolated diode junction is measured as a function of forward bias, it takes [27] the form shown in figure 9.12(b) because at high biases the increased conduction by minority carrier injection tends to neutralize the charge-collection signal, see figure 9.12(c), and so the current flowing in the amplifier is greatly reduced. If the same experiment is repeated with an emitter-base

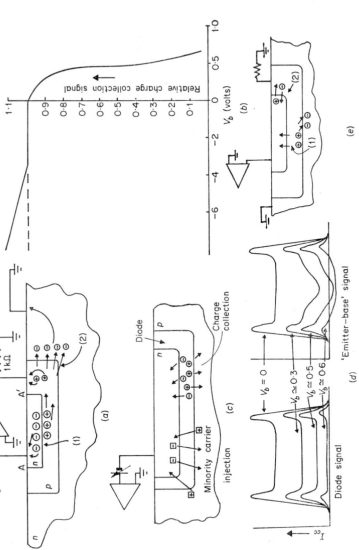

Figure 9.12. (a) Charge collection at neighbouring junctions (i) at base-collector junction (ii) at emitter-base junction; (b) charge collection signal from isolation junction as function of bias; (c) short-circuiting' of charge collection signal at forward biases by minority carrier injection; (d) comparison between the charge-collection signal from an isolated junction and that from a transistor with emitter base forward-biassed; (e) showing how the charge collection (process (i)) from the base-collector junction can oppose (and overwhelm) the signal from the emitter-base junction (process (ii)) when the latter is forward biassed.

junction using the circuit shown in figure 9.12(a), the data take the form shown in figure 9.12(d), i.e. at high forward biases the centre part of the signal apparently changes sign and gives a 'black' signal corresponding to the apparent collection of holes by the emitter region.

The mechanisms occurring are illustrated in figure 9.12(e). The charge-collection signal from the base-collector junction is relatively large because the junction is not forward biassed, but is not observed in the amplifier because, as, in figure 9.12(a), it is neutralized by current flow in a circuit not containing the amplifier. However, holes collected by the base immediately below the centre of the emitter are separated from the base contact by the resistance of the base (typically $\sim$ 1 to 10 Ω). This means that a small fraction of holes can effectively be injected into the emitter region and flow to earth via the operational amplifier circuit (typically 1 to 10 Ω if no protector resistor is used or $\sim$ 100Ω if protected by a series resistor). If this fraction is sufficiently large it can override the white charge collection signal from the emitter-base junction, which gives a small signal because it is forward biassed. Obviously this type of interaction depends not only on the relative impedances to earth and on the device bias but on the device temperature.

This section has given some indication of the interactions and complexities that can exist with circuits containing many elements. So far we have not considered the examination of circuits in which the elements are not conductively joined, but which are capacitively linked to the operational amplifier. This type of application is best discussed after we have considered the use of the 'specimen current' method of analysis.

9.6 Specimen current mechanism

So far we have considered only the phenomena which take place in a specimen containing a pn junction or a similar barrier. Now we will examine the behaviour of a specimen in which charge collection does not occur, such as a metal specimen connected to earth via an operational amplifier. If the specimen is subjected to a primary beam current of I_p amperes and if the instantaneous secondary electron and reflected electron currents are I_s and I_{rp} respectively, then an instantaneous current of $[I_p - (I_s + I_{rp})]$ will have to be neutralized by current flow through the amplifier. This 'neutrality' or 'specimen absorbed' current as it is usually called can be used to obtain a micrograph, the contrast on which is determined mainly by variations in both secondary electron emission and in the back scattered electron coefficient across the specimen surface. The factors which affect this contrast have already been discussed in Chapters 4 and 5. The difficulty with this technique is that the specimen current is low, being approximately equal to I_p, whereas the maximum charge collection current created by a primary current I_p is

$$\left(\frac{I_p}{q}\right)\left(\frac{E_0}{E_i}\right) \gtrsim 10^3 \, I_p.$$

Therefore the specimen current is only detectable in specimens either not containing a *pn* junction or containing a very inefficient junction.

In metallic specimens the smallness of the specimen current means that a high beam current or a long integration time has to be used to

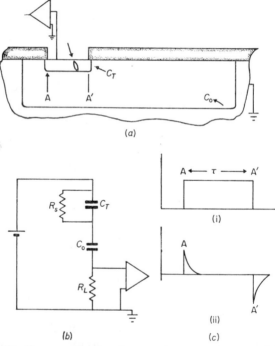

Figure 9.13. Charge collection in capacitatively coupled circuits; (*a*) typical situation; (*b*) corresponding circuit; (*c*) (*i*) charge collection signal when $CR \gg \tau$, ($C = C_0 C_T/(C_0 + C_T)$) (*ii*) charge collection signal when $CR \ll \tau$.

obtain noise-free micrographs. Usually the resolution obtainable is 1μ or slightly greater, being limited by the specimen properties and by the beam currents required. In the author's opinion a better approach is to use an optically coupled secondary electron collector to obtain high-resolution micrographs of surface structure and a pair of *pn* junction particle detectors to detect the back-scattered electrons in the manner indicated in Chapter 8. In this way essentially the same information can be obtained by using somewhat lower beam currents and the components of the signal due to emitted secondary electron and back-scattered electrons can be identified. The ability to use a lower beam current (10^{-9} to 10^{-8}A as opposed to 10^{-8} to 10^{-7}A) in this latter approach arises because of the effective current gain introduced by the charge collection in the junction detectors (see Chapter 8). However, both methods have been used, as we shall see in Chapter 11.

9.7 Signals obtained by capacitative coupling

We often have to study a situation such as that depicted in figure 9.13(*a*). In terms of the simplified circuit shown in figure 9.4 this case can be considered by including a capacitor as shown in figure 9.13(*b*). Under certain conditions in which CR is small compared with the time taken to sweep across the junction the signal observed is the time differential of the charge-collection signal. This signal is much larger than the specimen current and can be of the order of the charge-collection signal. As a result it can be used to locate junctions not connected directly to the amplifier. This approach has already been exploited, notably by the Westinghouse and Berkeley groups. (See Chapter 12.)

Before discussing the luminescent mode we shall take the opportunity to introduce another way of displaying the information obtained in the SEM. This method, known as deflection modulation, is of general applicability, but it is particularly useful in conductive-mode studies.

9.8 Deflection modulation

We have assumed that the information obtained has been displayed either as an intensity modulation, or as a line scan. Figure 9.14 illustrates another technique, borrowed from microanalysis and scanning electron diffraction studies [28], in which the signal is fed to the Y-plates at the same time as the frame time-base. In this

R

way a series of line scans are superimposed one behind the other across the micrograph, and therefore useful quantitative data can be quickly, and often elegantly, presented. Such displays are also very useful for recording time-dependent data. This application is useful in all three modes of operation.

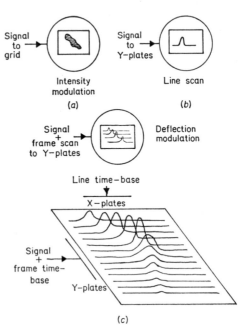

Figure 9.14. Comparing the information displays used in the SEM: (*a*) intensity modulation; (*b*) 'line scans'; (*c*) deflection modulation.

REFERENCES

[1] See, for example, G. DEARNALEY and D. C. NORTHROP, *Semiconductor Counters for Nuclear Radiations*, Spon, (1966)

[2] T. E. EVERHART and C. J. VARKER, *2nd International Conf. on Electron and Ion beam Technology and Science, New York*, (1966)

[3] D. C. NORTHROP and O. SIMPSON, *Proc. Phys. Soc.*, **80**, 262, (1962)

[4] H. J. QUEISSER, *J. Appl. Phys.*, **32**, 1776, (1961) and S. PRUSSIN, *J. Appl. Phys.*, **32**, 1876, (1961)

[5] J. WASHBURN, G. THOMAS and H. J. QUEISSER, *J. Appl. Phys.*, **35**, 1909, (1964)

[6] J. J. LANDER, T. M. BUCK, H. SCHREIBER, JNR. and J. R. MATHEWS, *Appl. Phys. Letters*, **3**, 203, (1963)

   W. CZAJA and G. H. WHEATLEY, *J. Appl. Phys.*, **35**, 2782, (1964)

   W. CZAJA and J. R. PATEL, *J. Appl. Phys.*, **36**, 1476, (1965)

[7] See, for example, H. KRESSEL, *RCA Review*, **28**, 175, (1967)

[8] A. G. CHYNOWETH, *Progress in Semiconductors*, **4**, 95, Heywood, (1960)

[9] P. A. WOLFF, *Phys. Rev.*, **95**, 1415, (1954)

[10] G. FABRI, E. GATTI and V. S. VELTO, *Phys. Rev.*, **131**, 134, (1963)

[11] B. GOLDSTEIN, *J. Appl. Phys.*, **36**, 3853, (1965)

[12] J. M. MCKENZIE and D. A. BROMLEY, *Phys. Rev. Letters*, **2**, 303, (1959)

[13] A. J. TAVENDALE and G. T. EWAN, *Camb. J. Phys.*, **42**, 2286, (1964)

[14] D. B. WITTRY and D. F. KYSER, *J. Appl. Phys.*, **36**, 1387, (1965)

[15] R. BAUERLEIN, *et al.* Spring Meeting, German Physical Soc., Freudenstadt, Fed. Rep. Germany, (1965)

[16] F. LAPPE, *Z. Phys.*, **154**, 267, (1959)

[17] V. N. IVAKHNO and D. N. NASLEDOV, *Sov. Phys., Solid-State*, **6**, 1651, (1965)

[18] V. S. VAVILOV, E. L. NOLLE, V. D. EGOROV and S. I. VINTOVKIN, *Sov. Phys., Solid-State*, **6**, 1099, (1964)

[19] A. SMITH and D. DUTTON, *J. Opt. Soc. Am.* **48**, 1007, (1958)

[20] Estimated as $\sim 3Eg$

[21] W. SHOCKLEY, *Solid-State Electron;* **2**, 35, (1961)

[22] P. A. WOLFF, *Phys. Rev.*, **95**, 1415, (1954)

[23] G. A. BARAFF, *Phys. Rev.*, **128**, 2507, (1962)

[24] M. KIKUCHI and K. TACHNIKAWA, *J. Phys. Soc. Japan*, **15**, 835, (1960)

[25] M. KIKUCHI, *J. Phys. Soc. Japan*, **15**, 1822, (1960)

[26] R. H. HAITZ, A. GOETZBURGER, R. M. SCARLETT and W. SHOCKLEY, *J. App. Phys.*, **34**, 1581, (1963)

[27] D. V. SULWAY, Ph.D. Thesis, Bangor U.C.N.W., (1967)

[28] P. N. DENBIGH and C. W. B. GRIGSON, *J. Sci. Inst.*, **42**, 305, (1965)

CHAPTER 10

The Luminescent Mode

10.1 Introduction

Excitation of phosphors by scanning electron beams has of course been of practical application since the invention of the cathode-ray tube. A uniform layer of phosphor grains is used to convert electrical signals into light for detection by the eye. But it is only recently that such techniques have been used to investigate the microscopic properties of the light-emitting materials themselves. The pioneering work was carried out mainly in Europe [1, 2, 3, 4] on phosphors emitting in the visible wavelength region. More recently Wittry and others [5, 6, 7, 8] have extended the method to the near infrared by using modified microanalysers to show that localized defects can be revealed in GaAs by the variations in infrared emission associated with them. The resolution obtainable was of the order of a micron. Shaw et al. [9] showed how, with the improved resolution inherent in the SEM, it is possible with certain specimens to obtain resolutions of slightly better than 1,000 Å. Other workers [10] have shown that the technique has a wider application than just to the semiconductor and insulator field. It has been a standard technique [11] in the biological field to obtain contrast in organic specimens by injecting them with dyes which are selectively absorbed in parts of the specimen and which are revealed by examination in the optical microscope, by photoluminescence and by transmission electron microscopy. Pease and Hayes [10] showed that another variation of this technique is possible in which a cathodoluminescent dye is selectively absorbed and which therefore gives contrast under electron-beam excitation. One can speculate a little about further applications. Some species, such as glowworms and various varieties of deep-sea life, use chemiluminescence in their body processes. Chemiluminescence differs from cathodoluminescence only in that the excitation energy is obtained from a chemical reaction rather than from an electron beam. The recombination processes (see below) which lead to the light emission may be very similar in a given specimen. There is, therefore, the possibility that the location of the chemiluminescence may be determined with high resolution by examining the cathodoluminescence (CL) in the SEM.

So we have an immediate application to a wide variety of phosphors, electroluminescence materials, scintillators and organic specimens and some exciting, but unproved, possibilities in the biological field. In this chapter we examine how the contrast arises and the factors limiting the resolution. The chapter is divided into the following main sections:

(1) A brief introduction to the mechanisms whereby contrast can be obtained on cathodoluminescent micrographs. This introduction includes a discussion of the mechanisms of radiative and non-radiative recombination and of the role played by surface recombination.

(2) A description of the factors affecting the resolution.

(3) The detector systems, the associated circuitry and cooling facilities are discussed in a section which also gives some calculations of the beam currents required in certain cases of importance and which illustrate the difficulties facing possible extensions of the technique. Applications of the method are discussed in Chapter 11.

10.2 Factors affecting contrast on cathodoluminescent micrographs

10.2.1 *Processes leading to cathodoluminescence*

We must first understand the physical processes which lead to cathodoluminescence. We can divide the cathodoluminescent mechanism into four parts:

(1) *Energy must be stored in the specimen.* That is to say the electron beam is used to excite the lattice, usually by creating electron-hole pairs by impact ionization either of the atoms of the host lattice or of impurity atoms.

(2) and (3). *Movement and recombination of the beam-induced carriers.* In the general case the electron and hole pairs need not be created at the same point at which they recombine (see below). They can move, either by drift in an electric field or by diffusion, from the point of formation to some other place in the crystal where the excitation inherent in either a free electron and/or a hole can be converted to a photon.

(4) *Emission of radiation from the specimen.* The recombination of,

say, an electron-hole pair in the crystal can be equivalent to the creation of a photon of visible or near-infrared radiation at that point. In order to be detected this photon must be emitted from the specimen. Two factors can prevent this emission of the internally created light; one is total internal reflection and the other is absorption between the point of creation and the point of emission.

Of these four processes the first has been fully discussed in previous chapters, and the movement of free carriers needs no discussion here [12, 13]. The two remaining factors, the recombination and the emission, are unique to this particular mode and do need further elaboration.

10.2.2 *The recombination of free carriers*

We know that the equilibrium (or steady-state) concentration of electrons and holes in a semiconductor results from a dynamic balance between the creation of such carriers by thermal activation (or external excitation) and the recombination or loss of such carriers. We also know that one, particular, free carrier will only exist for a finite time before recombination, i.e. a carrier has a finite 'lifetime'. Because of the statistical nature of the system there will be a spread or spectrum of lifetimes, but we will simplify the discussion by replacing this spectrum by a suitable average lifetime which will be defined more specifically below. We have to enquire into the processes causing this annihilation or recombination of carriers.

The first point to stress is that these recombination processes consist of two main groups: radiative and non-radiative processes. Radiative processes are those in which at least part of the energy liberated by recombination is used to form a photon of ultraviolet, visible or near-infrared radiation. Non-radiative processes are those in which no photon is formed but in which the energy is dissipated as heat. This distinction is valid provided we are not concerned with processes giving radiation of wavelengths > 3 to 4μ.

In most materials radiative and non-radiative processes occur in parallel. From our point of view the radiative processes are those which lead to cathodoluminescence while the non-radiative processes represent a source of inefficiency as they compete for the available energy. This can be seen from the definition of carrier lifetime.

10.2.3 *The carrier lifetime*

Let us centre our attention on an elementary volume of a semi-conductor specimen. In the steady state under some external excitation the nett number of electrons, for example, created in this volume must flow out of the volume either by diffusion or by drift in an electric field. So we can write the continuity equation: generation rate = recombination rate + loss by diffusion + loss by drift. The recombination rate is assumed to be proportional to the excess density, $\Delta n (= n - n_0)$, of carriers created by the excitation, where n_0 is the equilibrium electron density in the absence of an external excitation. The constant of proportionality is taken as $1/\tau$ where τ is called the electron lifetime. To discuss the validity of writing the nett recombination rate as $\Delta n/\tau$ would take us too far afield, but the main points to remember are: (*i*) τ is a measure of average time that a free electron can expect to exist in the material under the prevailing conditions. (*ii*) Writing the nett recombination rate as $\Delta n/\tau$ is in general a shorthand form of a more complex equation in which the hole density and/or the density of unoccupied traps can occur. As the excitation is increased $(\Delta n \gg p_0)$ these factors can change and so τ will vary. In other words τ is not a true constant for a given material at a fixed temperature but is a function of the excitation level used. In general as the excitation level is increased the carrier lifetime decreases. A similar hole lifetime can be defined and used in the hole continuity equation. The electron and hole lifetimes may or may not be equal, depending on the material, its impurity content, the temperature and the excitation level. There is one important limiting value to the carrier lifetime. This is the low-level lifetime, i.e. the value obtained when the excitation produces an increase in density which is small compared to the existing density of majority carriers.

As mentioned above, in most specimens the radiative and non-radiative processes occur simultaneously in parallel. To determine the relative rates of the radiative and non-radiative processes we define radiative and non-radiative lifetimes, τ_r and τ_{nr} respectively, which are related to τ by

$$1/\tau = 1/\tau_r + 1/\tau_{nr} \qquad (10.1)$$

τ_r can be regarded as the carrier lifetime which would exist in the specimen, under the same conditions of excitation, temperature etc. if the non-radiative process occurred so slowly as to be insignificant. Similarly τ_{nr} can be regarded as the limiting value of τ in the absence of radiative recombination. So we arrive at τ_r/τ_{nr} as a measure of the radiative efficiency. If this parameter is $\ll 1$ the recombination is radiative and the specimen is an efficient light emitter, if it is $\gg 1$ the recombination is non-radiative and no

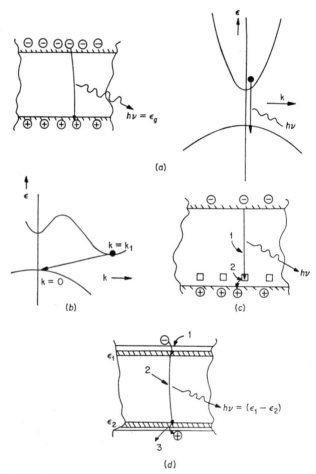

Figure 10.1. Recombination processes in semiconductors: (a) direct recombination of an electron and a hole without phonon participation; (b) corresponding process in 'indirect materials'; (c) radiative recombination via an impurity level; (d) radiative recombination via impurity bands in highly doped materials.

significant emission occurs. The general level of the signal observed from a cathodoluminescent specimen will depend in part on the ratio of τ_r/τ_{nr} and the contrast will be determined by how this ratio (and other factors) vary from place to place on the specimen. We can now review briefly the major physical mechanisms which lead to radiative and non-radiative recombination.

10.2.4 Recombination processes

Figure 10.1 shows the physical processes which lead to radiative recombination. The first of these is the direct 'collision' of an electron and a hole with the emission of a photon. Depending on the details of the band structure of the specimen this process can occur in two ways. This recombination process in which, in effect, a free electron falls into an allowed bound state only occurs if the quantum mechanical equivalent of the laws of conservation of energy and momentum are obeyed. Since the momentum of a photon is insignificant when compared to that of an electron, this means that the electron can only make transitions between states of equal crystal momentum. If this 'direct' process is impossible then momentum can only be conserved if a phonon is emitted or absorbed. This 'indirect' process (see figure 10.1(b)) is in fact a 'three-body collision' as compared to the 'two-body collision' involved in the direct process and is, in general, an order of magnitude less efficient. As a result, materials like GaAs, InAs, etc., in which the band structure is as indicated in figure 10.1 are, in general, more efficient CL materials than materials such as Si and Ge which have band structures favouring indirect processes.

This, then, is the first factor to consider. In relatively pure materials the band structure has a large effect on the radiative efficiency. In impure materials the processes shown in figure 10.1(c) become important. This recombination via impurity centres is a two-stage process. In the example shown, an electron is captured by an impurity atom with the emission of a photon. Subsequently this atom captures a hole with the emission of a phonon. So the atom is now ready to take part in the process again. Figure 10.1(d) shows a variant of this which occurs in materials which contain relatively high densities of both donors and acceptors. Under these conditions we can talk of associated donor-acceptor pairs, i.e. the donors and acceptors are sufficiently close so that the electron clouds overlap. In this case an electron can fall non-radiatively into a state associated with the donor, subsequently it can be transferred radiatively to an acceptor state. From here it finally decays by phonon emission into the valence band. These processes, together with exciton processes [14, 15], constitute the major photon-producing mechanisms.

Figure 10.2 shows the non-radiative processes which occur in the bulk of semiconductors. The simplest to picture mentally is that shown in the first diagram in which an electron falls across the forbidden gap and the liberated energy is emitted as lattice vibrations (i.e. heat or 'phonons'). In fact this is, comparatively, a very

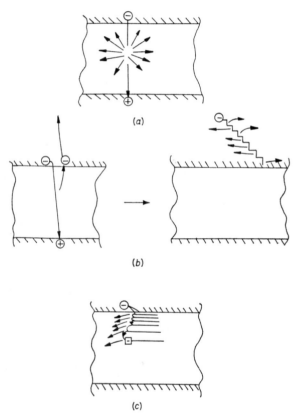

Figure 10.2. Non-radiative processes in semiconductors: (a) the multiphonon process; (b) an Auger process in which the recombination energy is transferred to an electron (first figure) which subsequently 'thermalizes' (second figure); (c) The 'Cascade' process via exciton states.

rare process in all materials except those with very small bandgaps. The reason for this is the fact that a phonon energy is $\sim 1/40\text{eV}$ which is only a small fraction of the bandgap in most semiconductors (e.g. ~ 0.67, 1.05 and 1.41 eV in Ge, Si and GaAs respectively). As a result the process shown in figure 10.2(a) corresponds to the simultaneous emission of ~ 40 phonons, which is a multibody 'collision' of extreme rarity. A more common process is illustrated in figure 10.2(b). This is an example of a general type of process called Auger processes [16, 17], each of which is the converse of an impact ionization process. These Auger processes do away with the need to have the simultaneous emission of many phonons; instead they can be emitted consecutively. Consider the example illustrated in which an electron combines with a hole and the energy released is transferred to a second free electron which is forced into an unstable position high in the conduction band whence it can decay by the successive emission of phonons by 'jumping down' the near continium of allowed states between the upper level and the con-duction band-edge. This is a three-body 'collision'; it is relatively common and is the converse of the impact ionization of a lattice atom by a fast electron. In other Auger processes, the energy is taken up by a near-by hole which is forced deep into the valence band. There are also similar processes in which, for example, an electron falls from an impurity state into the valence band and the energy is transferred to a near-by free carrier. Figure 10.2(c) shows another process whereby the energy introduced by external excita-tion is dissipated non-radiatively. A free electron 'cascades' [18] down the exciton states associated with an impurity atom, losing energy by successive phonon emission until it reaches the ground state. It can decay from this state either by an Auger process or radiatively or by a process associated with the specimen surface.

10.2.5 *Surface effects*

In Chapter 6 we outlined the physical picture we use to interpret surface phenomena. Of particular interest here is the idea of surface recombination. The type of situation that can occur is illustrated in figure 10.3; A free electron in the surface layer falls into the valence band by falling through a series of allowed electron states which might, for example, be associated with the presence of surface impurities. The electron energy loss is dissipated by the successive formation of a series of phonons. Such a process competes with radiative recombination mechanisms so that the surface layer is, unless great care is taken, a layer of poor radiative efficiency. This inefficiency arises from the localized changes in impurity density, field distribution and impurity state occupancy, brought about by the presence of the surface and the associated defects. (See Chapter 6 and reference [19]). In general these changes produce two effects: first and more important, they provide non-radiative recombination

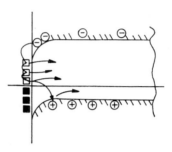

Figure 10.3. One possible non-radiative recombination process associated with the specimen surface.

processes (such as the example given in figure 10.3) which compete with the radiative processes in which we are interested. Secondly, the surface effects may lead [20] to radiative transitions which are of low efficiency and of different wavelengths to those involved in the bulk processes. To take account of this surface inefficiency we can define a surface lifetime, τ_s and, as a first approximation, assume that carriers within the surface layer, i.e. within a distance of the order of the Debye length from the surface, have an effective lifetime equal to τ_s, whereas those created deeper in the bulk have a lifetime, τ, which is characteristic of the bulk and constant throughout the specimen. This surface lifetime can be related to the other parameter, S, the surface recombination velocity used to describe surface recombination.

This section introduces the main recombination processes that occur in luminescent materials; but it should be emphasized that it is very much an introduction only. For a fuller discussion the reader is referred to references [21], [22], [23] and [24]. We must, however, outline how the radiative efficiency depends on the device and experimental parameters. Because of the dependence of the radiative properties on the detailed properties of the specimen any general discussion of this point will, of necessity, be very schematic or over-simplified. In order to investigate the radiative properties we have to know how radiative and non-radiative lifetimes depend on (*i*) the impurity content of the specimen. (This factor determines the number of centres available for recombination.) (*ii*) The excitation level which largely determines the number of free carriers available for recombination. (*iii*) The temperature, as this affects the degree of occupancy of the recombination centres. To make such calculations we have to establish a detailed model of the material and

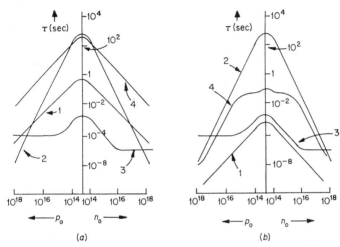

Figure 10.4. Hall's calculations [21] of the effective lifetimes in (*a*) Ge and (*b*) the corresponding 'direct' material; (1) radiative recombination; (2) direct Auger recombination; (3) multiphonon process via impurities; (4) Auger recombination via a particular impurity level.

estimate the minority carrier lifetime that would occur if each process occurred alone. As an example, we have shown in figure 10.4 an instructive set of calculations taken from Hall [21] which compares the room temperature behaviour of Ge with that of an imaginary 'direct' semiconductor of the same bandgap and impurity content. It is apparent that for the real n-type Ge with $n_o \approx 10^{17}/\text{cm}^3$, for example, the recombination rate is determined by multiphonon emission via impurities (for the impurity chosen) while for the corresponding direct material the direct radiative process predominates.

In the SEM it is localized variations in these processes that lead to contrast in the luminescent mode. In the next section we will consider how variations in local recombination rate and other processes lead to contrast.

10.2.6 *Contrast on CL micrographs*

Figure 10.5 illustrates some of the mechanisms whereby variations

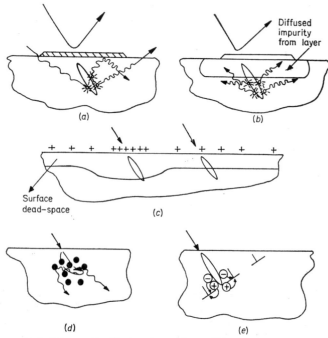

Figure 10.5. Schematic illustrations of possible causes of luminescent contrast: (a) physically absorbed film; (b) chemically interacting film; (c) effect of surface charge; (d) effect of bulk traps, voids or precipitates and (e) possible effect of dislocations.

in local radiative efficiency can lead to CL contrast. It should be noted at the outset that there is a simplification implicit in this figure since we have assumed that the specimen surface is smooth. In practice this is seldom the case. Luminescent materials are not often so well controlled as Si and Ge, for example, and are sometimes only available in small irregular shaped crystals. So, over and above the mechanisms illustrated in figure 10.5, there are variations due to surface topography. As these arise from the same factors which contribute to the contrast on the emissive mode they can (usually) be recognized by comparison with emissive micrographs. Figure 10.5(a) illustrates how the presence of a thin surface film can affect the CL yield in two ways: (i) by leading to a change in reflection coefficient of the primary electrons, and (ii) by leading to variations in internal reflection of the created light. In principle these effects can occur in the region of a film which has not interacted in any way with the specimen. If the presence of the film has resulted in some diffusion of impurity into the specimen, as in figure 10.5(b), the local rates of non-radiative and radiative recombination can be different from elsewhere because of the local difference in impurity content, etc. A variation of this mechanism is shown in figure 10.5(c) in which a specimen with a fixed charge in surface states is depicted as having variations in this charge density. From Chapter 6 we have seen that the degree of band-bending depends on the density of surface charge and we have seen how the degree of band-bending affects the surface recombination velocity, in effect by altering the occupancy of the localized states. Thus a very thin (mono- or bi-molecular) layer can effectively change the width of the surface 'dead space' relative to the penetration distance of the beam and so effect the emitted signal. Not only can changes in surface-charge density lead to variations in internal radiative efficiency, they can also lead to different absorption properties, again because of variations in occupancy of the available states. In this way the external efficiency is further affected.

Figures 10.5(d) and (e) show how features below the surface can lead to contrast. The presence of small (~ 200 Å) voids or precipitates represents additional regions of surface or interface recombination as well as effectively changing the density of electron-hole pairs created by the beam and scattering the created light. Similarly, dislocations, both as individuals and in arrays, may have [25] different recombination, trapping and scattering properties from the bulk and so give rise to contrast.

So far the mechanisms listed all depend on the presence of some imperfection. Figure 10.6 illustrates mechanisms which are not dependent on the presence of imperfections, but are inherent in a device structure. Consider the diode shown in figure 10.6(a). This might represent, for example, a GaAs or a GaP electroluminescent diode [26, 27]. The doping types and the doping density are different on the two sides of the junction. As a result the CL efficiencies will probably be different since the ratio τ_r/τ_{nr} is a function of dopant type and density. This dependence has been used [28] to locate pn junctions and can be readily extended to more complex situations. Consider the p-i-n structure shown in figure 10.6(b). This structure is of importance in electroluminescent materials such as GaAs [29] and SiC [30]. The central near-intrinsic region is often obtained by

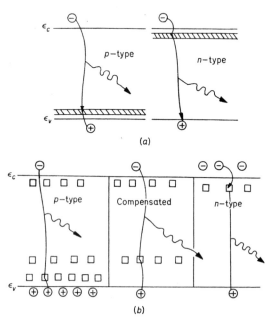

Figure 10.6. Schematic illustrations of how different bulk regions of a device may be revealed by differences in radiative efficiency, etc: (a) pn junction; (b) p-i-n structure.

compensation, using an impurity which occupies a deep level. If a reverse bias is applied and gradually increased the occupancy of this level, and therefore the radiative efficiency, varies as a function of position in the device. This process can, in principle, be followed in the SEM by examining the CL as a function of position and as a function of bias, and over the relevant temperature range. We can see the predicted magnitude of the effects in certain cases from figures 10.7 to 10.10. Figure 10.7, taken from Kyser and Wittry [6],

shows estimates of the calculated hole lifetime as a function of
electron concentration in GaAs at room-temperature. Figure 10.8
illustrates actual measurements of the CL efficiency as a function of
doping level in n- and p-type material at 77 and 300°K. The temperature dependence of the CL efficiency is shown [31] in figure 10.9.
Finally, figure 10.10, shows how the emitted intensity varies as a
function of electron-beam current and specimen dopant type and

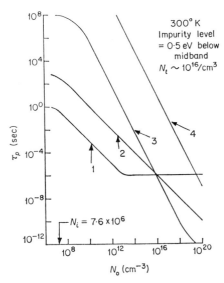

Figure 10.7. Calculations [6] of the effective hole lifeline in n-type
GaAs at room temperature: (1) multiphonon emission via an impurity;
(2) direct recombination; (3) Auger recombination via an impurity;
(4) intrinsic Auger recombination.

level. The application of these phenomena to the study of localized
variations in CL due either to defects or device structure is considered in Chapter 11. We can now consider the way in which the
specimen properties affect the resolution.

10.3 Factors limiting the resolution
We saw in Chapter 8 how the resolution in the emissive mode is
determined largely by the electron optics and to a small extent by
the specimen properties. This situation arises because the escape
distance of secondary electrons is only ~ 100 to 500 Å. As a con-

s

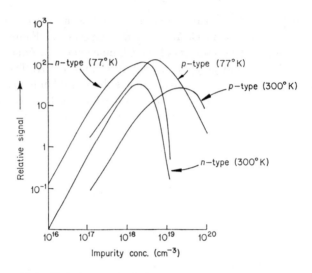

Figure 10.8. Relative cathodoluminescent signal in GaAs [36] as function of dopant level in n- and p-type material at 77°K and 300°K.

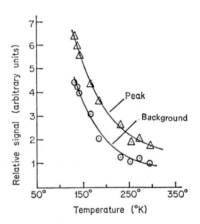

Figure 10.9. Relative cathodoluminescent signal in n-type GaAs as a function of temperature. 'Peak' signal corresponds to that observed in striations (See text) and 'background' signal corresponds to the weaker signal off the striations [31].

258

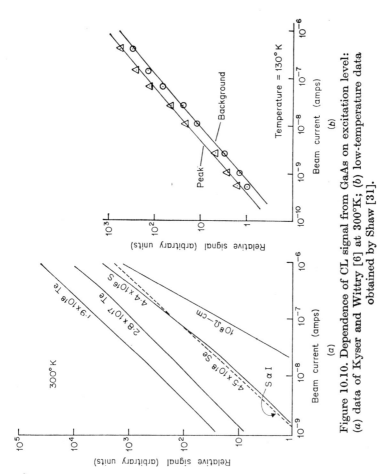

Figure 10.10. Dependence of CL signal from GaAs on excitation level:
(a) data of Kyser and Wittry [6] at 300°K; (b) low-temperature data
obtained by Shaw [31].

sequence there is little spatial integration forced on the signal beyond that inherent in the finite size of the electron beam. This point is illustrated in figure 10.11. Figure 10.11(a) shows schematically the density of electron-hole pairs created by the primary beam as a function of depth. The number of pairs created per unit thickness is greatest near the surface and the area over which these carriers are created increases with increasing depth. If, as in the case of secondary electrons, the escape distance is much less than the penetration distance or if the escape depth is of the order of the

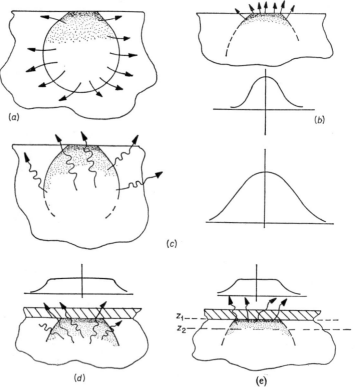

Figure 10.11. Schematic diagrams showing main factors affecting resolution on CL micrographs: (a) schematic drawing of assumed beam induced 'plasma'; (b) resolution obtained with no dead space and a high absorption coefficient; (c) the case of no dead space and a low absorption coefficient; (d) and (c) but with dead space; (e) as (b) but with dead space.

spot size, then the information comes from an area of the specimen which is of the order of the spot size, together with a wider tail. (See figure 10.11(b)). On the other hand, if the escape depth is of the order of the penetration distance then the effective area from which the information comes is of the order of scattering width which can be of the order of 1/3 of the penetration depth. In this case the resolution is limited by the specimen properties. This case corresponds to the situation often met with in CL studies. The CL situation can be more complicated than that depicted in figure 10.11(c) because of the existence of a 'dead layer', or a region of reduced radiative efficiency, at the surface. Thus, as in figure 10.11(d), the carriers created in this 'dead layer' do not lead to a CL signal and so the effective width from which the signal comes, when measured in terms of the half width, is further increased. Finally we have to consider the effect of absorbtion of the photons between the point at which they are created and the point at which they are emitted from the specimen. If the absorption distance is less than the penetration distance the photons formed deepest in the specimen do not contribute to the emitted signal. So, if the absorption distance is less than the penetration distance and if there is a 'dead layer' at the surface only those photons created in layer between z_1 and z_2 (see figure 10.11(e)) will contribute to the external signal. We see that the parameters which can determine the resolution are the spot-size, the penetration distance, the existence and extent of the non-radiative surface layer and the absorption distance. Some important possibilities are summarized in table 10.1.

It is probably best to consider further the claim that the resolution can be of the order of the spot size as, at first sight, this seems remarkable when it is realized that the spot size is $< 1,000$Å and the wavelength of the emitted radiation may be $\gtrsim 1\mu$. In optical microscopy we have to contend with the diffraction limit which imposes a resolution limit of $\sim \lambda/2$ when the specimen is illuminated by light of wavelength λ. In the SEM, even though light is used in the CL mode, we are not limited by diffraction effects. The basic difference between optical microscopy and the SEM is the absence of optical focussing in the latter. In the SEM the known position of the electron beam tells us where the examined surface element is. The magnitude of the signals arriving from such elements at the detector determines the contrast, but the actual paths followed by the emitted photons are not important. In the light microscope they

Table 10.1. *The order of resolution obtainable in the CL mode as a function of various parameters relative to the spot size, d_0*

Penetration Distance, R	Absorbtion length l	Surface layer width L_s	Resolution limit, L_R
$\gg d_0$	$\gg d_0$	$L_s \sim R$	very small signal $L_R \lesssim R/3$
$\gg d_0$	$\gg d_0$	$L_s \to 0$	$\lesssim R/3$
$\gg d_0$	$\lesssim R$	$L_s \to 0$	$d_0 < L_R \leqslant R/3$
$\sim d_0$	$\gtrsim R$	$L_s \sim R$	very small signal $d_0 < L_R \leqslant R/3$
$\sim d_0$	$\lesssim R$	$L_s \to 0$	$\lesssim d_0$
—	—	$L_s > R$	no significant signal

are important because they not only play a role in the contrast properties but give information about the relative position of the surface elements.

10.4 Radiation detection systems

10.4.1 *Introduction*
There are two types of problem encountered. One problem involves the use of *all* wavelengths of the emitted radiation to form a micrograph of the specimen. The second problem is to analyse the emitted radiation from one particular point or line on the surface into its distribution as a function of wavelength. The detection system used can take the form shown in figure 10.12. The first need is to collect a sufficient fraction of the emitted radiation. The simplest way of doing this, which is applicable when the monochromator is not needed, is simply to point the detector at the specimen. To collect a sufficient fraction of the radiation a large diameter detector such as a 2 in. or 4 in. photomultiplier can be placed about 6 inches away from the specimen to give a collection angle ~ 0.1 steradians or a small-diameter detector such as a photodiode or photosensitive field-effect transistor can be placed very close to the specimen. A better or more general method is to use a simple lens or mirror light-collector system of the type shown in figure 10.12. For example, a 1 in. diameter lens of focal length equal to 1 in. can give a collection angle in excess of 0.75 steradians. Such a collection system has to

have a large collection angle and to transmit the collected radiation in a cone angle which matches the numerical aperture of the mono-chromator. A high collection angle can also be obtained by the use of a light pipe. This method has the advantage that line-of-sight optics are not required. There is, however, some absorption loss along the light pipe and, unless specially made, this component would give outgassing problems in an ultra-high vacuum.

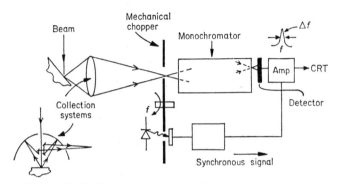

Figure 10.12. Block diagram of coherent detector system.

10.4.2 *Radiation detectors*

These components are most important as it is their sensitivity, speed of response, wavelength response and cooling requirements that determine the properties of the system. In most of the results reported to date in which scanning electron beams have been used to study localized variations in recombination radiation, photo-multipliers have been used as the detectors and, with a few excep-tions [6], no attempts have been made to analyse the emitted spectrum as a function of wavelength. The use of photomultipliers limits the range of wavelengths that can be studied to part of the ultraviolet and the visible and limited part of the near-infrared (up to $1 \cdot 2\mu$). Obviously it is of interest to see how wide a range of wavelength can be examined with good spatial resolution and how studies of localized variations can be combined with spectral studies. Shaw [31] has analysed the difficulties facing the extension of the technique to longer wavelengths. We shall see that the problem can be usefully separated into two wavelength regions: one in which photomultipliers can be used ($\sim$ 3,600 to 12,000 Å) and the other in which semiconductor photovoltaic or photoconductive devices can be usefully employed ($\sim$1 to 4μ). We shall consider both regions in detail below but first we must establish some measure of the relative sensitivities of the available detectors.

In order to predict the signal-to-noise ratio to expect under a given excitation we have to estimate the noise properties of the detector used. To do this we follow the general procedure adopted by Kruse, McGlauchlin and McQuistan [32]. The arguments can be stated briefly by considering the example of a photovoltaic detector subjected to a uniform, monochromatic energy flux $F(\lambda)$. The detector area is A_d and the energy flux generates a signal voltage V_s. The signal V_s is proportional to both $F(\lambda)$ and A_d and can be written $V_s = C_1 F(\lambda) A_d$. The noise limitations of the detector can be expressed in terms of an equivalent voltage, V_n, the magnitude of which depends both on the noise mechanisms present and on the manner in which the measurements are made. The effective noise voltage is decreased by chopping the incident radiation at a frequency f using a selective amplifier of bandwidth Δf about this frequency.

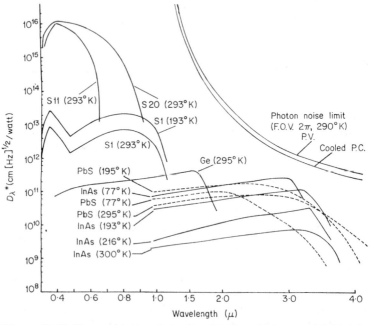

Figure 10.13. Representative data showing the relative sensitivities for the available photon detectors as a function of wavelength.

Table 10.2. Radiation detectors suitable for use with scanning electron beam instruments

Detector	Noise limitation	Typical active area (cm²)	Operating temperature (°K)	Response time (μS)	Reference
S.20 (PM) S.11 (PM) S.1 (PM) S.1 (PM)	Shot noise	15	293 195	0·01	EMI, Mullard Data Sheets
PbS (PC) " "	Current Noise	10^{-6} to 16	295 193 77	100→500 5,000 3,000	Philco, T.I. and Santa Barbara Res. Centre Data sheets
InAs (PV) " "	Thermal Noise	7×10^{-3} to 3×10^{-2}	295 196 77	1·0 1·0 2·0	Putley [35] Data sheets above
InSb (PC) " " (PV)	Thermal noise Current " Current and recombination noise	10^{-4} to ·25 10^{-2} to ·06	295 77	·05 ≤ 10	Putley [35] Data sheets above
PbSe (PC) " "	Current Noise	10^{-4} to 1	295 193 77	≤ 2 ∼ 30 ∼ 40	Santa Barbara Res. Centre data sheets
PbTe (PC)	Current noise		77	25	Putley [35]
Si (PV)		10^{-3} to 10	300	20	T.I. Data Sheet
Ge (PV)			295		Putley [35]

PM = Photomultiplier; PC = photoconductor; PV = photovoltiac.

If the noise distribution as a function of frequency is flat we can write the noise voltage as $V_n = C_2 (\Delta f)^{1/2}$. On this basis we can write the signal-to-noise ratio, $(S{:}N)_\lambda$, as

$$(S{:}N)_\lambda = \frac{V_s(\lambda)}{V_n} = D_\lambda [F(\lambda) A_D]/(\Delta f)^{1/2} \qquad (10.2)$$

where the constants have been collected together into D_λ which gives a measure of the sensitivity of the device at the wavelength λ.

In practice it is more usual to define a detectivity D_λ^* which is related to D_λ by $D_\lambda^* = D_\lambda A_D^{1/2}$ and which gives a measure of the sensitivity per unit area (see below). In terms of the detectivity we obtain the signal-to-noise ratio as

$$(S:N)_\lambda = D_\lambda^*[F(\lambda)A_D^{1/2}]/(\Delta f)^{1/2} \qquad (10.3)$$

Good estimates of D_λ^* are available for the more significant detectors based on experimental determinations.

The data shown in figure 10.13 are based on the sources and assumptions compiled in table 10.2. These data are not exhaustive but represent what are probably the best detectors to use. The information given shows that the problem can be divided into two regions, depending on the sensitivity of the available detectors. In the ultraviolet and visible spectrum the more sensitive photo-multipliers can be used. In the near-infrared devices based on photo-effects in InAs, InSb and the Pb salts have to be used and these devices have to be cooled if good sensitivity is to be obtained. This increase in sensitivity at low temperatures is usually gained at the expense of an increase in detector response time.

So far we have only estimated the predicted signal-to-noise ratio for a stationary electron beam on a specimen giving a constant response and, by using the estimates of D_λ^*, have assumed that the noise properties of the system are those imposed by the detector and by its associated circuitry, i.e. we have neglected any complications introduced by scanning or by response-time effects. In fact the introduction of scanning means that eqn. (10.3) has to be modified. In deriving this equation it was assumed that the detector is subjected to a uniform flux of greater cross-sectional area than the detector itself. Therefore the incident energy flow is proportional to the flux and the detector area. In the SEM all the energy (except for transmission losses) is delivered to the detector. In this case the signal-to-noise ratio is given, in terms of D_λ^*, by

$$(S:N)_\lambda = D_\lambda^*E(\lambda)/A_D^{1/2}(\Delta f)^{1/2} \qquad (10.4)$$

where $E(\lambda)$ is the total energy arriving at the detector per second.

The next point to stress is that eqn. (10.4) gives a valid estimate of the predicted signal-to-noise ratio if the noise conditions are the same as those pertaining when the measurements of D_λ^* were made. Table 10.2 shows the limiting noise mechanism in the case of the relevant detectors. We have to ensure that, as far as possible, these conditions prevail in the SEM. The problem centres on the shot noise inherent in the signal itself. We saw in Chapter 8 how the shot noise in the secondary electron current sets a limit on the minimum beam current and/or scan time that could be used. Here the problem is very similar and is outlined in figure 10.14. Figure 10.14(*a*) shows an idealized specimen from which alternate elements give signals of S and $S + \Delta S$. The scanning electron beam remains

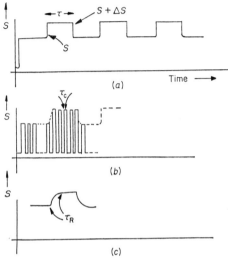

Figure 10.14. (*a*) Idealized specimen signal variation assumed in text; (*b*) signal after 'chopping'; (*c*) signal after integration and showing effect of system response time.

on each element for a time τ. This signal is chopped at a frequency $f \, (= 1/2\tau_c)$ and so the signal presented to the detector will have the form shown in Figure 10.14(*b*). After detection, amplification and integration the signal used to control the CRT brightness will have the form shown in figure 10.14(*c*). In order that the system may give a true representation of the signal the system response time τ_R must be less than the integration time, τ. A further restriction on the minimum value of τ arises from the need to reduce the shot noise to an insignificant value, i.e. to ensure that the system is detector-noise limited and not shot-noise limited. One way of calculating whether the system is shot-noise limited or not can be stated as follows. First, we adopt some criterion for the minimum signal-to-noise ratio required, i.e. we assume that we wish to distinguish between two surface elements which give signals S and $S + \Delta S$ when the fractional difference, $\Delta S/S$, is equal to F. Let the corresponding values in brightness on the CRT be B and $B + \Delta B$. Assuming for the present that a linear relationship exists between S and the brightness B, we wish to know the minimum signal-to-noise ratio required to detect a fractional change in brightness $\Delta B/B = F$. The relationship between the threshold signal-to-noise ratio, $(S{:}N)_{\text{th}}$ required to observe a change in brightness, $\Delta B/B$, can be written

$$(S{:}N) \geqslant (S{:}N)_{\text{th}} = (B/\Delta B) \times K = K/F \qquad (10.5)$$

The value of the constant, K, in eqn. (10.5) depends on the system being used to measure the brightness, i.e. on whether the eye, photographic recording or TV pickup tube is being used. Experimental estimates [33] of K for visual detection put the value between 3 and 6 whereas Rose [33] takes the value $K = 5$. Having adopted a criterion such as that given in eqn. (10.5) we can calculate the threshold primary beam, I_{th}, in both cases, i.e. when the performance is shot-noise limited and where it is detector-noise limited. By the threshold primary beam current we mean the beam current required to give a signal/noise ratio equal to $(S{:}N)_{\text{th}}$. To do this we have to know how efficient the radiative processes in the specimen are and what is the spectral distribution.

10.4.3 *Specimen factors*
If a beam current of I_p amps of electrons of energy E_o is incident on a specimen in which the impact ionization energy is E_i, the number of electron-hole pairs created per second is

$$(I_p/q) \cdot (E_o/E_i).$$

The number of photons with wavelength $\lambda \to \lambda + d\lambda$ emitted per second into a solid angle $d\Omega$ is given by

$$N_e(\lambda) \, d\lambda(d\Omega/4\pi) = (I_p/q) \cdot (E_o/E_i) \, p(\lambda)f(\lambda) \, d\lambda(d\Omega/4\pi) \qquad (10.6)$$

where $p(\lambda) \, d\lambda$ is the probability that a beam-induced electron-hole pair will form a photon of wavelength λ to $\lambda + d\lambda$ and $f(\lambda)$ is the fraction of such photons that is emitted from the specimen. In deriving eqn. (10.6) we have assumed that these photons are emitted isotropically. An efficient way of using this radiation is shown in figure 10.12. Using this system with the effective point source that we have in this application, all the collected radiation passes through the input slit and a fraction, $T(\lambda)$, of the radiation of wavelength λ is transmitted through the monochromator. In an experimental set-up, the wavelength interval $d\lambda$ becomes $\Delta\lambda$ which can be related to the linear dispersion of the spectrometer, $(d\lambda/ds)$, and to the output slit width, Δs, by $\Delta\lambda = (d\lambda/ds)_\lambda \Delta s$. We therefore obtain the number, n_λ, of photons of wavelength λ incident per second on the mechanical 'chopper', which is assumed to be included in the system just before the detector, as

$$n_\lambda = T(\lambda)(I_p/q)(E_o/E_i)p(\lambda)f(\lambda)(d\lambda/ds)_\lambda \Delta s \Delta\Omega/4\pi \quad (10.7)$$

The corresponding energy flow, $E(\lambda)$, is obtained by multiplying the right-hand side of eqn. (10.7) by (Rc/λ). The corresponding quantities n and E which are applicable when all the spectral distribution is used are obtained by integrating n and E over all λ and writing $T(\lambda) = 1$. From these equations we can calculate the signal-to-noise ratio resulting from excitation by a given beam current I_p.

In the detector-noise limited case we obtain from eqns. (10.4) and (10.7).

$$(S{:}N)_\lambda = \tfrac{1}{2}\left(\frac{I_p}{q}\frac{E_o}{E_i}\frac{hc}{A_D^{1/2}(\Delta f)^{1/2}}\right)\frac{D_\lambda^*}{\lambda}T(\lambda)p(\lambda)f(\lambda)\left(\frac{d\lambda}{ds}\right)_\lambda\frac{4\pi\Delta s\Delta\Omega}{4\pi} \quad (10.8)$$

This equation is applicable when a spectrometer is used to analyse the emitted spectrum. The factor of $\tfrac{1}{2}$ is introduced on the assumption that the chopper has a duty cycle of $\tfrac{1}{2}$ and so the integrated current is reduced by this factor. When the whole of the emitted spectrum is used to form a CL micrograph of the specimen the signal-to-noise ratio is given by

$$(S{:}N) = \tfrac{1}{2}\left(\frac{I_p}{q}\frac{E_o}{E_i}\frac{hc}{A_D^{1/2}(\Delta f)^{1/2}}\right)\frac{\Delta\Omega}{4\pi}\int_\lambda\frac{D_\lambda^*p(\lambda)f(\lambda)}{\lambda}d\lambda \quad (10.9)$$

To determine the signal-to-noise ratio in the shot noise limited case we can argue as follows. The electron beam is on each element for a time τ. Therefore the number of photons received from each element is given by

$$\left.\begin{array}{ll} n_\lambda\tau/2 & \dots\dots \text{ when a monochromator is used} \\ \tau/2\displaystyle\int_\lambda n_\lambda d\lambda & \dots\dots \text{ when all photons used} \end{array}\right\} \quad (10.10)$$

These quantities are subject to the usual shot-noise fluctuations of $\sqrt{(n_\lambda \tau/2)}$ and $\sqrt{(\tau/2\int_\lambda n_\lambda d\lambda)}$ respectively. Therefore from eqn. (10.10) we obtain the signal-to-noise ratios

$$(S{:}N)_\lambda{}^1 = \sqrt{(n_\lambda \tau/2)} = \sqrt{(n_\lambda 5/2\Delta f)}$$
$$(S{:}N)^1 = \sqrt{(\tau/2\int_\lambda n_\lambda \, d\lambda)} = \sqrt{(5/2\Delta f \int_\lambda n_\lambda \, d\lambda)} \qquad\qquad (10.11)$$

To make comparisons between the two cases we have to relate the integration time τ to the bandwidth of the system. The best method of amplifying the signal is to use the phase-sensitive system illustrated in figure 10.12. In this method the signal is effectively mixed with a signal of equal frequency to give a d.c. output. In effect the system as a whole acts [34] as a low pass filter with a cut-off frequency $f_{co}(= \Delta f/2)$ where Δf is the bandwidth of the amplifier. The rise time, τ_r, (see figure 10.14) of such a system is related [34] to the cut-off frequency, f_{co}, by $\tau_r \times f_{co} \approx 0{\cdot}5$. In this case, therefore $\tau_r \approx 1/\Delta f$. If the system is to attain the full signal over most of the time τ, then τ should be $\approx 5\tau$. We may therefore obtain an approximate relationship $\tau \approx 5/\Delta f$. From eqns. (10.9) and (10.11) we can now estimate the threshold currents necessary to distinguish between adjacent elements with the required sensitivity as determined by eqn. (10.5). Some sample estimates are described below.

10.4.4 *Estimates of* I_{th}

Table 10.3 gives the values of the estimates assumed in these calculations. With regard to the specimen properties it is apparent that a wide range of specimen characteristics have to be considered. In particular, the extent to which the spectral distribution and the overall efficiency can vary is considerable. It is therefore necessary to choose some idealized spectrum and to consider a range of external efficiencies. We may define the total external efficiency η_{ext} as the total energy emitted as radiation per incident primary electron, i.e.

$$\eta_{ext} = \int_\lambda \eta(\lambda) d\lambda = \frac{1}{E_i}\int_\lambda p(\lambda) f(\lambda) \left(\frac{hc}{\lambda}\right) d\lambda \qquad (10.12)$$

The corresponding efficiency when we only consider photons of wavelength λ to $\lambda + d\lambda$ is given by

$$\eta_{ext}(\lambda) = (1/E_i)p(\lambda)f(\lambda) \, (hc/\lambda) \, d\lambda \qquad (10.13)$$

Table 10.3. *Values of the Parameters chosen in Estimating the values of* I_{th} *given in figure* 10.16 [31]

Parameter and value	Comment or reference
$\Delta\Omega \sim 2$ steradians	Represents feasible maximum
Bandwidth, Δf, taken as 500 Hz	Related to τ by $\tau\Delta f \approx 5$ $\therefore$ Δf cannot be too small without increasing τ to a prohibitive value
Beam energy, E_0, taken as 20 kV	See text
Discrimination. We have assumed that we wish to distinguish between two elements with signals differing by 10%	Linear adjustment for other degrees of discrimination
K, relationship between threshold signal-to-noise ratio and the observable change in screen brightness taken as 5	Rose [33]
T (λ), the transmissivity of the monochromator, $= T = 0.8$	T (λ) is, in fact, a slowly varying function of λ. We have assumed a constant value typical of a good spectrometer
η_{ext} range taken as 3×10^{-1}, 10^{-2} and 3×10^{-4}	Covers the range of plausible values—linear interpretation possible.
$\delta\lambda$ effective wavelength spread taken as constant and $= 1,000$ Å	—
Effective slit width taken as 10 Å unless stated otherwise	—

To obtain some estimate of the spectral distribution we would normally assume some Gaussian or Lorentzian shape to the emitted spectrum. Here we lose little by using the simpler square distribution shown in figure 10.15. Within this limitation we obtain the threshold currents as

$$I_{th} = 2(K/F)q \, \frac{A_D^{1/2}\Delta f^{1/2}}{E_0\eta_{ext}}\left(\frac{4\pi}{\Delta\Omega}\right) \bigg/ \int_{\lambda_0 - \delta\lambda/2}^{\lambda_0 + \delta\lambda/2} D_\lambda^*/d\lambda \, . \, d\lambda \qquad (10.14a)$$

$$I_{th}(\lambda) = 2(K/F) \, \frac{qA_D^{1/2}\Delta f^{1/2}}{E_0 T(\lambda)\eta_{ext}}\left(\frac{4\pi}{\Delta\Omega}\right) \bigg/ D_\lambda^*(d\lambda/ds)\lambda_0\Delta s/d\lambda \qquad (10.14b)$$

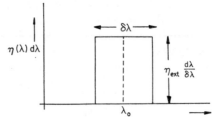

Figure 10.15. Idealized spectral distribution assumed unless otherwise stated.

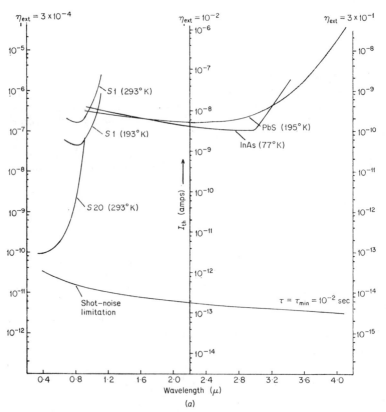

Figure 10.16. Estimates of threshold beam current as function of λ and external efficiency: (a) dispersive case; (b) non-dispersive case.

For the detector-limited case and as

$$I'_{\text{th}} = (K/F)^2 q \frac{2\Delta f}{5E_o} \frac{hc}{\lambda_o \eta_{\text{ext}}} \quad \left(\frac{4\pi}{\Delta\Omega}\right) \tag{10.15a}$$

$$I'_{\text{th}}(\lambda) = (K/F)^2 q \frac{2\Delta f}{5E_o} \frac{hc}{\tau_{(\lambda)} \lambda_o \eta_{\text{ext}}} \times \frac{4\pi}{\Delta\Omega} \bigg/ \left(\frac{d\lambda}{ds}\right)_{\lambda_o} \frac{\Delta s}{d\lambda} \tag{10.15b}$$

for the shot-noise limited case.

From these equations the data given in figures 10.16 were

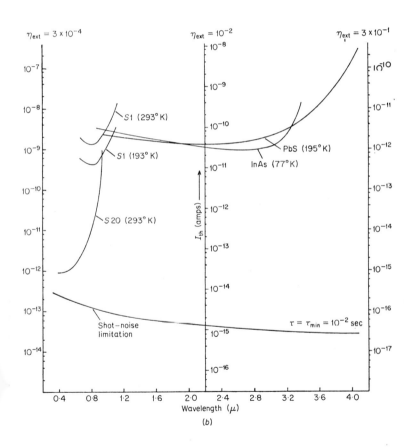

(b)

T

obtained. The main conclusion is that the system is detector noise limited except possibly at visible wavelengths with fast line scans. Except in this region the estimates of the detector-noise limited case can be used to predict the required beam current if allowance is made for the reflection of the primary electrons. If the back-scattering coefficient is η and the mean energy of the reflected electrons is $e\overline{V}$ then the estimates given above are too small by a factor of $(1-\eta\,\overline{V}/V_o)^{-1}$. The estimates of the threshold current in the case where the spectrum is examined indicate the difficulty of obtaining both spectral and spatial resolution at the same time at long wavelengths unless the specimen is very efficient. Under the conditions quoted in figure 10.16(a) a beam current of $\sim 10^{-7}$ amp is required at low efficiencies. This value is too large to obtain a reasonable resolution. On the other hand if we reduce the bandwidth to $\Delta f \sim 5$ Hz at the expense of a hundredfold increase in recording time and decrease the spectral sensitivity to 25 Å, which still gives a useful performance, then the beam current required is reduced to $\sim 5 \times 10^{-9}$. Often it is unnecessary to form complete micrographs as sufficient information can be obtained by the use of line scans displayed on recorders. In this case the factor K in eqn. (10.7) is effectively reduced to unity thus reducing the primary beam current required by a further factor of 5 to 10^{-9} amps. With this current level, spatial resolutions of $\sim 1\mu$ can be obtained.

Finally we have to consider the type of problem sketched in figure 10.17(a). Some defect (A) has to be examined to find the spectral response of the emitted radiation. This spectrum has to be compared with that obtained from the bulk (region (B).) In each case the spot is held stationary and the operative wavelength region scanned and we wish, typically, to detect a minor peak against the main peak. Using the Lorentzian distributions defined in figure 10.17(b) and the assumptions listed in the figure the data shown in figure 10.17(c) were obtained. In making these estimates it was assumed that we wish to discriminate between the minor peak and the adjacent minimum, or, in terms of figure 10.17 and eqn. (10.7), we wish to estimate the $S{:}N$ ratio and hence the value of I_{th} required to distinguish a fractional change in signal $\Delta S/S_2$. The calculation in formally similar to the previous estimates. In this case the integration time τ ($\approx 5\tau_r \approx 5/\Delta f$) is defined as the time needed to scan a wavelength region equal to the spectral resolution of the spectrometer which, for the purpose of this calcu-

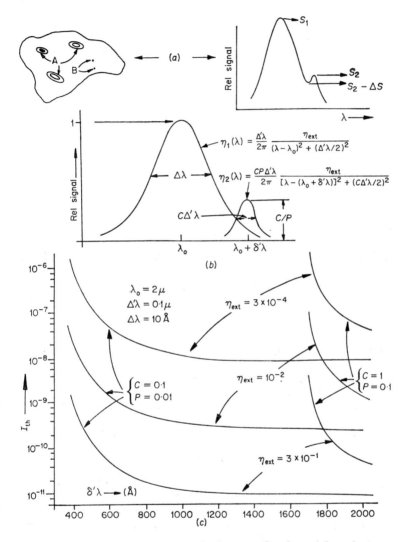

Figure 10.17. Problem of obtaining both spectral and spatial resolution: (a) statement of problem (see text); (b) line-shapes assumed; (c) estimates of threshold beam current as function of external efficiency, line shape and relative line positions [31].

lation, was assumed to be constant, independent of λ. Therefore, from equation

$$I_{th}(\lambda) = \left(\frac{2}{\Delta S/S_2}\right)\left(\frac{qA_D^{1/2}\Delta f^{1/2}}{E_0}\right) \times \frac{4\pi}{\Delta\Omega}\left[\frac{1}{\tau(\lambda)}\right]\left[D_\lambda^*\eta_\lambda\right]_{\lambda_0+\delta'\lambda}^{-1} \times \frac{1}{\Delta\lambda}$$

(10.16)

$(\Delta S/S_2)$ was determined from a computer calculation of $\eta(\lambda)$ as a function of C and P, (see figure 10.17). Using the results of this calculation with an InAs detector of area 10^{-2}cm^2 cooled to $77°\text{K}$ and a wavelength scanning rate of 10Å/second the estimates shown in figure 10.17(c) were obtained. The implication is that spatial resolutions of the order of 3000Å should be obtainable with relatively efficient materials unless $\delta'\lambda$ is very small. If the efficiency is low it should still be possible to examine regions of the order of 1 to 2μ with good spectral resolution.

We shall see in Chapter 11 just how far the ideas discussed in this chapter have been exploited to date. We shall also see that, as is the case with the other modes of operation, the capabilities of the method have yet to be used fully.

REFERENCES

[1] F. DAVOINE, P. PINARD and M. MARTINEAU, *J. Phys. Rad.*, **21**, 121, (1960)

[2] P. PINARD, Ph.D. Thesis, Lyon, (1964)

[3] J. P. DAVEY, Ph.D. Thesis, Cambridge, (1965)

[4] R. BERNARD, F. DAVOINE and P. PINARD, *Compt. Rend. Acad. Sci.*, **248**, 2564, (1956)

[5] D. B. WITTRY and D. F. KYSER, *J. Appl. Phys.*, **35**, 2439, (1964), ibid, **36**, 1387; (1965)

[6] D. F. KYSER and D. B. WITTRY, *The Electron Microprobe*, (ed. McKinley, Heinrich and Wittry), Wiley, New York, (1966)

[7] H. C. CASEY, JNR., and R. H. KAISER, *J. Electrochem. Soc.*, **114**, 149, (1967)

[8] H. C. CASEY, JNR., *J. Electrochem. Soc.*, **114**, 153, (1967)

[9] D. A. SHAW, R. C. WAYTE and P. R. THORNTON, *Appl. Phys. Letters*, **8**, 289, (1966)

[10] R. F. W. PEASE and T. L. HAYES, *Nature*, **210**, 1049, (1966)

[11] *The Encyclopedia of Microscopy*, (ed. G. L. Clark), Reinhold, New York, (1961)

[12] W. SHOCKLEY, *Electrons and Holes in Semiconductors*, Van Nostrand, New York, (1950)

[13] R. A. SMITH, *Semiconductors*, Cambridge Univ. Press, (1959)

[14] R. S. KNOX, 'Theory of Excitons', *Solid State Phys. Suppl.*, **5**, Academic Press, New York, (1963)

[15] S. NIKITINE, *Progress in Semiconductors*, **6**, 235, Heywood, (1962)

[16] A. R. BEATTIE and P. T. LANDSBERG, *Proc. Phys. Soc.*, **249** 61, (1959)

[17] SCLAR and BURSTEIN, *Phys. Rev.*, **98**, 1757, (1955)

[18] M. LAX, *Phys. Rev.*, **119**, 1502, (1960)

[19] A. MANY, Y. GOLDSTEIN and N. B. GROVER, *Semiconductor Surfaces*, North-Holland Publishing Co., Amsterdam, (1965)

[20] E. E. LOEBNER, *R.C.A. Rev.*, **20**, 175, (1959)

[21] R. N. HALL, *Proc. I.E.E.*, **923**, (1960)

[22] D. CURIE, *Luminescence in Crystals*, Methuen, (1963)

[23] H. K. HENISCH, *Electroluminescence*, Pergamon Press, (1962)

[24] P. R. THORNTON, *The Physics of Electroluminescent Devices*, Spon, (1967)

[25] See, for example, W. T. READ, JNR., *Phil. Mag.*, **45**, 775, (1954)

[26] See, for example, W. N. CARR and J. R. BIARD, *J. Appl. Phys.*, **35**, 2776, (1964)

[27] J. W. ALLEN, N. E. MONCASTER and J. STARKIEWICZ, *Solid-State Electron.*, **6**, 95, (1963)

[28] D. V. SULWAY, HTIN KYAW and P. R. THORNTON, *Solid-State Electron*, **10**, 545, (1967)

[29] K. WEISER and R. S. LEVITT, *J. Appl. Phys.*, **35**, 2431, (1964) and T. YAMAMOTO, *Proc. I.E.E.E.*, **52**, 409, (1964)

[30] E. E. VIOLIN and G. F. KHOLUYANOV, *Soviet Physics, Solid-State*, **6**, 465 and 1,331, (1964)

[31] D. A. SHAW, M.Sc. Thesis, Bangor, U.C.N.W., (1967)

[32] P. W. KRUSE, L. D. MCGLAUCHLIN and R. B. MCQUISTAN, *Elements of Infrared Technology*, Wiley, New York, (1962)

[33] A. ROSE, *Advances in Electronics*, **1**, 131, (1948)

[34] R. A. SMITH, F. E. JONES and R. P. CHASMAR, *The Detection and Measurement of Infrared Radiation*, Oxford Univ. Press, (1957)

[35] E. H. PUTLEY, *J. Sci. Inst.*, **43**, 857, (1966)

[36] D. A. CUSANO, *Solid-State Comm.*, **2**, 353, (1964)

CHAPTER 11

Applications of the SEM: (I) To Materials Problems

11.1 Introduction

This and the remaining two chapters will, it is hoped, clearly illustrate the current uses of the SEM. In this part of the book the author has sought to do three things. (*i*) By using illustrative examples to make apparent to the reader the power of the method and its limitations. (*ii*) To give a general picture of how far the method has been exploited within the field covered by this book by examining a representative, but not exhaustive, cross-section of reported studies. As far as possible some reference has been made to the studies that are not examined in more detail. (*iii*) To endeavour to illustrate the ways in which the exploitation of scanning electron microscopy can be extended in the foreseeable future. This last section will be somewhat subjective, in that it reflects the author's interests. It also depends on the author's limited knowledge of what is being attempted in other laboratories.

Another point should be borne in mind about this part of the book. Any description of current applications in an active and expanding field is out-of-date by the time it is published, and these chapters are no exception. At the present rate of progress some fifty to a hundred papers will be published in this field before this book is published! Having stressed this inertia we still have to decide how to present the information. For convenience of representation the data have been classified into three groups: Materials Problems, Surface and Device Physics applications and Device Fabrication. This grouping is somewhat arbitrary in that some problems discussed under one heading could equally well be considered under another. But, in general, the titles reflect the contents. We begin with the use of the SEM to study not only those materials of importance in the electronics industry but materials in general.

11.2 The SEM in materials analysis: Introductory

The relevant results are presented in a series of self-contained sections under the following headings:

(1) Semiconductor materials.
(2) Cathodoluminescent materials.
(3) Metal-physics studies.
(4) Magnetic materials.
(5) General materials.

A final section discusses some additional techniques of general

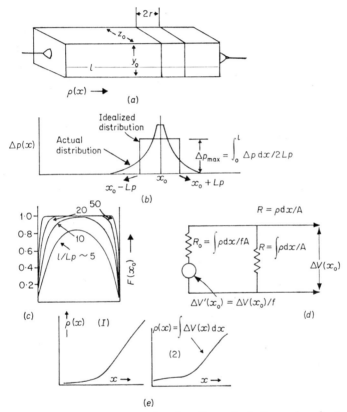

(a)

(b)

(c)

(d)

(e)

Figure 11.1. Electron beam induced voltages in bulk semiconductors:
(a) definition of parameters used by Munakata [2]; (b) actual and
idealized injected carrier concentration as function of position; (c)
$F(x_0)$ as a function of position for various values of l/L_p; (d) equivalent
circuit of beam-induced voltage source when beam irradiates a fraction,
f, of the cross-sectional area; (e) comparison between the resistivity as
measured by probing (1) and that measured by beam induced voltage
studies (2).

applicability. Discussion of the problems involved in insulator studies is included in Chapter 12.

11.3 Semiconductor materials

11.3.1 *Detection of resistivity variations*

We have been preoccupied with measurements of the charge-collection signal from pn junctions, but it is known from the work of Tauc [1] that inhomogeneous bulk semiconductors generate a photovoltage when scanned by a scanning light spot. As a scanning electron beam analogous to a high-resolution light spot it is possible that a similar 'photovoltage' can be developed by the electron beam and can be used to diagnose the properties of inhomogeneous semiconductors in the same manner as light beams but with higher spatial resolution. Munakata [2] has considered this problem in the one-dimensional form shown in figure 11.1. A small n-type specimen is exposed to a beam which is imagined to produce a uniform distribution of electron-hole pairs over a width z_0 and a depth y_0. This idealized situation is compared with a realistic case below. In the approximation that any field term associated with the resistivity variation can be neglected, the hole continuity equation can be written

$$\frac{d^2\Delta p}{dx^2} - \frac{\Delta p}{L_p{}^2} = \frac{g\tau_p}{L_p{}^2} \qquad (11.1)$$

where g is the local generation rate, τ_p and L_p have the usual meaning. For the uniform distribution shown in the figure we can write

$$g = \left(\frac{I_p}{q}\right)\left(\frac{E_0}{E_i}\right)/(2ry_0z_0)$$

for $x_0 - r \leqslant x \leqslant x_0 + r$ and $g = 0$ elsewhere. The equations formed by inserting these values into eqn. (11.1) have to be solved subject to the boundary conditions that Δp and $\partial \Delta p/\partial x$ are continuous at $x = x_0 \pm r$ and that $\Delta p = 0$ at $x = 0$ and $x = l$ (ohmic contacts). Once Δp is known as a function of position it is convenient to define $\Delta p_{\max}$ by replacing the actual distribution by the idealized distribution shown in figure 11.1(b). Munakata estimates

$$\Delta p_{\max} = \left(\frac{E_0}{E_i}\right)\left(\frac{I_p}{q}\right)\left(\frac{l}{y_0z_0\mu_pKT}\right)\left(\frac{L_p}{2l}\right)$$
$$\left[1 - \frac{\sinh(x_0/L_p) + \sinh(l - x_0)/L_p}{\sinh(l/L_p)}\right]$$

$$= \left(\frac{E_0}{E_i}\right)\left(\frac{I_p}{q}\right)\left(\frac{l}{y_0 z_0 \mu_p KT}\right)\left(\frac{L_p}{2l}\right) F(x_0) \qquad (11.2)$$

$F(x_0)$ has the form shown in figure 11.1(c). Using the analysis of the corresponding light-spot case [3] Munakata calculates that the beam-induced voltage, $\Delta V(x_0)$, is given as a function of position by

$$\Delta V(x_0) = \left(\frac{d\rho}{dx}\right)^2 \left(\frac{E_0}{E_i}\right)\left(\frac{I_p}{q}\right)\frac{L_p^2}{y_0 z_0} F(x_0) \qquad (11.3)$$

Munakata has developed this equation in special cases corresponding to sinusodial, linear and abrupt changes in ρ. We have to consider what happens when only a small fraction, f, of the specimen cross-section is irradiated by the beam. In this case, the specimen acts in the manner of the equivalent circuit given in figure 11.1(d). The voltage generated is given by $\Delta' V(x_0) = \Delta V(x_0)/f$ in series with a resistance $R_0 = (R/f)$. Unfortunately the remaining bulk acts as a shunt resistance and only a fraction $R/R_0 + R \sim f$ of $\Delta' V(x_0)$ is available externally. Thus eqn. (11.3) is still valid in the more realistic case and can be used to estimate the expected magnitude of the beam-induced voltage. Taking $I_p \sim 10^{-8}$ amps, $E_0/E_i \sim 6 \times 10^3$ (corresponding to a 20 keV beam incident on Si), $y_0 = z_0 = 1/10$ cm, $\tau_p \sim 10\mu$ sec (giving $L_p \sim 3 \times 10^{-2}$ cm) we obtain $\Delta V(x_0) \approx 10^{-5}$ $(d\rho/dx)F(x_0)$. With $F(x_0) \sim 1$ a value of $d\rho/dx \approx 10\Omega$ produces a voltage $\sim 100\mu$V. Assuming the analysis to be valid for resistive materials (for semi-insulating GaAs for example) with $\tau p \sim 10^{-8}$ sec $(L_p \sim 9 \times 10^{-4})$ we again obtain $\Delta V(x_0) \approx 100\mu V$ with $d\rho/dx \sim 10^6\Omega$. Experimentally no difficulty is experienced in measuring voltages ~ 10 to 100μV. Theoretically the analysis needs to be extended to two dimensions by considering transverse diffusion currents and by removing the neglect of current flow arising from the presence of local electrical fields. This neglect of drift flow effectively limits the range of validity of Munakata's analysis to

$$(L_p/\Delta x)|\ln\left[\rho(x_0 + \Delta x)/\rho(x_0)\right]| \leqslant |$$

where $\rho(x_0 + \Delta x)$ and $\rho(x_0)$ are resistivities at $(x_0 + \Delta x)$ and x_0 respectively. It has been shown [4] that the theory predicts voltages of the order of those observed experimentally and the qualitative agreement is good. Since $\rho\alpha \int d\rho/dx \, dx \, \alpha \int \Delta V(x_0) \, dx$ the integrated voltage over the specimen length gives an estimate of relative resistivity variations which can be compared with estimates obtained by more conventional methods. One such comparison is shown in figure 11.1(*e*). It will be of interest to see how useful this technique becomes in the future for diagnostic studies of compound semiconductors, in thin film or bulk form.

The above analysis is concerned with one contribution to a voltage induced in a bulk specimen by an electron beam. In the analogous situation in which light is used to create a photovoltage there are two contributions: (*i*) the 'chemical' e.m.f., is that considered above and arises from a spatial variation in free carrier concentration in the

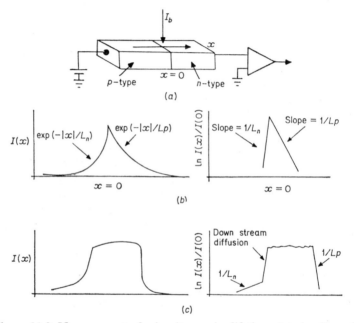

Figure 11.2. Measurement of minority-carrier lifetime: (*a*) circuit used; (*b*) typical results with narrow depletion layer; (*c*) complications introduced by wide depletion layer with non-uniform field distribution.

starting material, i.e. it arises from resistivity variations; (*ii*) the photo-e.m.f., is called the diffusion or Dember [5] potential and arises in materials in which the holes and electrons have unequal mobilities. In addition, Buimistrov [6] has shown that a photovoltage can be generated by the illumination of a material which contains variations in minority carrier lifetimes. Esposito *et al* [7] have examined the beam-induced voltages due to the Dember and Buimistrov effects arising from high energy (3 MeV) electron-beam bombardment in Si.

It is to be stressed that these photo-effects are not limited to bulk effects but can occur at surfaces as well. The 'photovoltages' induced between the specimen surface and the bulk are often used to diagnose surface properties (see Many *et al.* [18]). With the increasing evidence [17] that electrons within the range of those used in the SEM can create defects at surfaces or interfaces, it is possible that a combination of localized electron-beam bombardment and a static light beam may be useful to diagnose the spatial distribution of the defects formed, i.e. to examine which regions of a given device are particularly susceptible to irradiation damage.

11.3.2 *Measurement of carrier lifetime*
This is obviously a big topic and it is ready for considerable extension; but we shall limit ourselves here to a discussion of the published observations. Several observations [9, 10, 11, 12] of carrier lifetime or, more correctly, of the diffusion lengths, have been reported. Higuchi & Tamura [19] showed how, by using the circuit shown in figure 11.2 with a specimen containing a junction at right angles to the scanned surface, the minority carrier lifetime on both sides of the junction can be obtained by measuring the charge-collection signal as a function of position. Wittry & Kaiser [10] have shown how, in electroluminescent materials, other mechanisms (probably photon-coupling) can contribute to the observed current. Other studies [11] have shown how, in the case where the junction field is not a step distribution, the analysis is more complicated because the situation corresponds to 'down stream' diffusion, i.e. the minority flow occurs by diffusion aided by a drift component. Initial applications [13] to *p-i-n* structures have shown that a statial resolution of $\sim 1,000$ Å can be obtained. The most detailed study reported to date is that made by Czaja [12] using large-area diodes made in Si and GaP. The idea of these studies was to examine the possibilities of determining the carrier lifetimes on both sides of a junction by measuring the charge-collection current as a function of beam voltage.

These experiments are illustrative of the complexities that have to be faced and of the nature of the assumptions that are currently introduced and so merit considerable study. We shall begin by con-sidering the theoretical side of the problem. In terms of the notation adopted in Chapter 9 and of the parameters defined in figure 11.3,

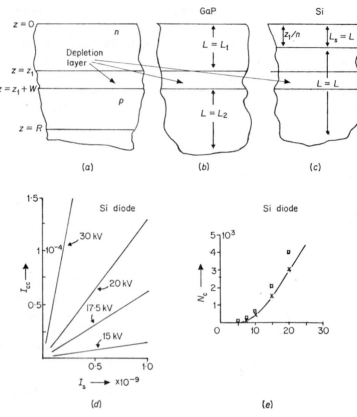

Figure 11.3. Data obtained by Czaja [12]: (a) definition of general parameters used; (b) lifetime distribution assumed for GaP diode; (c) corresponding distribution for Si diode; (d) charge collection, I_{cc}, as a function of specimen current, I_s, and beam voltage; (e) number of pairs collected by junction as function of beam voltage, □ uncorrected, × corrected as described in text, — theoretical curve.

the number of carrier pairs collected by the junction is given by

$$N_c = \int_0^{z_1} N(z) \exp\left[(z - z_1)/L_1\right]dz + \int_{z_1}^{z_1 + W} N(z)dz$$

$$+ \int_{z_1 + W}^{R} N(z) \exp\left[(z_1 + W - z)/L_2\right]dz \qquad (11.4)$$

if the diffusion length in the upper layer is L_1 and L_2 is the corresponding length in the lower layer. Czaja argues that this case is applicable to GaP diodes, but for Si diodes it is necessary [14] to assume a distribution of carrier lifetimes in the upper (diffused) layer. To take account of this surface 'dead space' it is assumed that

$$L_1 = L_s \qquad 0 \leqslant z \leqslant z_0 = z/n$$

$$= L \qquad z_0 \leqslant z \leqslant z_1$$

The next problem is to determine the form of $N(z)dz$ which is the number of pairs created between z and $z + dz$. Czaja accepts Makhov's empirical expression (see Chapter 4) and to simplify the integration, take as an approximation to this expression

$$N(z) = \frac{E_0}{E_i}(3/R)\exp(-3z)/R \qquad 0 \leqslant z \leqslant 0.3R$$

$$= (7/4)\left(\frac{E_0}{E_i}\right)(5/R)\exp(-5z)/R \qquad 0.3R \leqslant z \leqslant R$$

where R is the electron range. In the case of Si, R is taken as $R = 2.82 \times 10^{-6}(E_0)^{1.65}$, which, with E_0 in keV gives R as the maximum range [15] in cm. For GaP the empirical expression [16] $R = 1.3 \times 10^{-6}(E_0)^2$ is used. Within these limitations we then have a theoretical expression for the number of pairs collected per absorbed electron for comparison with experimental data with L_s, L, n or L_1, L_2 as variable parameters.

The experiments consist of measuring the diode short-circuit current as a function of specimen absorbed current, i.e. the current that flows to earth through the specimen (this is equal to the beam current less the secondary electron and reflected primary currents) for various beam voltages. From the essentially constant slope (see figure 11.3(d)) of these data, estimates of the collected pairs/absorbed primary electron, N_c', can be obtained. Czaja argues that these estimates have to be corrected before comparison can be made with theory. The basis for this correction is twofold: (i) some of the collected carriers arise from reflected electrons and (ii) some primary electrons give rise to secondary electrons and so are not counted in the specimen absorbed current and yet lose all their energy in the creation of electron-hole pairs. The correction for the second effect can be simply written as $-\sigma N_c'$ where σ is the secondary electron yield at the beam voltage used. The correction for the first effect can be made as follows: if $F(E_0)E_0$ is the mean energy of the reflected electrons, then each electron *creates* $[1 - F(E_0)]E_0/E_i$ pairs, of which a fraction $f(E_0)$ is collected. By writing $E_i/f = E_i^*$ where E_i^* represents the average energy expended per pair *collected* we can, according to Czaja, write the corrected number of collected pairs per absorbed electron as

$$N_c^{\text{corr}} = N_c'(1 - \sigma) - \eta\,(1 - F(E_0))E_0/E_i^*$$

where η is the back-reflection coefficient. For a beam energy of E_0, Czaja writes $E_i^* = (E_0/2)[N_c'(E_0) - N_c'(E_0/2)]^{-1}$ and suggests that this approximation is reasonable as the introduction of E_i^* represents a correction to a correction term. By carefully estimating η and σ and taking Sternglass's estimate of $F(E_0)$ ($\approx 0\cdot45 + 2 \times 10^{-3}\mathscr{Z}$ [17]), Czaja obtains the estimates shown in table 11.1.

Table 11.1. *Data on Si and GaP diodes taken from reference* [12]

(a) *Dislocation free Si* [N^{calc} determined using $L_s = 0\cdot2\mu$; $L = 8\mu$; $n = 3$]

E_0(keV)	N_c'	E_i^* (eV)	$\eta(\%)$	σ	N_c^{corr}	N_c^{calc}
5	84	29·8	16·2	0·400	36·2	24·1
7·5	273	13·7	,,	0·278	151	74·2
10	610	9·5	,,	0·208	394	313
15	2050	4·22	,,	0·133	1475	1440
20	3930	2·96	,,	0·103	2950	2790

(b) *Si diode with pronounced diffusion induced slip*
Agreement obtained with $L_s = 0\cdot1\mu$, $L = 3\cdot5\mu$, $n = 3$.

(c) *GaP diode*
Agreement obtained with $L_1 = 1\mu$, $L_2 = 6\cdot5\mu$.

The analysis is sensitive to small changes in the calculated parameters and it can be extended to studies of localized variations in properties. The measure of agreement is remarkable when it is realized that the data obtained depend on five separate experimental estimates (σ, η, $F(E_0)$, R as $f(E_0)$, I_D as $f(I_b)$) and on the extrapolation of an empirical law. Because of the very nature of the problem the assumptions are fairly numerous and have to be assessed for reliability at each stage. This is often difficult and as a result, it is not easy to achieve a self-consistent approach. For example, it is problematical whether the assumptions used above are self-consistent. It has been stressed that it is necessary to correct the data because of the contributions arising from back-scattered electrons and from electrons which give secondary electrons. And yet, the Makhov 'law' is used for $N(z)$. This

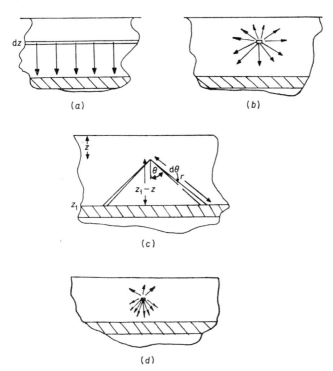

Figure 11.4. Assumptions used to describe beam-induced carrier diffusion: (*a*) laminar flow case; (*b*) isotropic flow case; (*c*) definition of parameters used; (*d*) more realistic immediate case.

relationship is based on measurements of the transmitted fraction of the *incident* beam current as a function of depth. No distinction is made between loss to the transmitted beam by absorption or back-scattering. It may, therefore, be argued that the use of the Makhov expression includes the contribution from back-scattered electrons and so the correction for this contribution (effect (1)) is not required. This view, if it is upheld, would still give acceptable (within a factor of two) agreement. Two other points should be made, one experimental and the other theoretical. The experimental point arises because of the contamination film that is evident on the micrographs. Some doubt arises, therefore, as to the physical origin of the 'dead-space' observed on the Si diodes. On the theoretical side the approach suffers from its one-dimensional nature. The assumption is made that the diffusive flow is 'laminar' as shown in figure 11.4(a), whereas in fact some transverse flow takes place in the manner shown in figure 11.4(b). A realistic solution of the diffusion equation in this situation is not known to the author, but if we take the opposite extreme approximation and assume that the pairs created in a given element diffuse radially outwards with equal probability, then the number of pairs collected per incident primary electron from the upper layer above the junction is given, in terms of figure 11.4(c), by

$$N_t = \int_0^{z_1} N(z)dz \int_0^{\pi} \sin\theta \, d\theta \exp\left[-(z_1 - z)/L_1 \cos\theta\right] \quad (11.5a)$$

as opposed to

$$N_t' = \int_0^{z_1} N(z)dz \exp\left[-(z_1 - z)/L_1\right] \quad (11.5b)$$

for the laminar case.

In fact the situation will lie between these two extremes because the density of electron-hole pairs is greatest near the surface and falls off exponentially with depth into the specimen. As a result the 'overpressure' of carriers at the surface leads to an increased diffusion into the specimen compared to the isotropic case. (See figure 11.4(d)).

11.4 Cathodoluminescent studies

11.4.1 *Use of scanning electron-beams*

The radiation induced by scanning electron-beams has been used to study the luminescent processes in ionic crystals [18, 19], commercially available phosphor powders [20, 21], and the radiative processes in the III-V compounds, particularly the Ga-As-P system [22, 23 and 24]. The most sustained studies have been made on GaAs and it is these that we shall use to illustrate the usefulness and limitations of the technique.

Wittry and Kyser [24] were the first to use a scanning electron-beam to study localized variations or inhomogeneities in GaAs. These workers showed that the presence of dislocations in Te-doped GaAs can be revealed by a localized change in CL efficiency near these defects. A similar variation also revealed the presence of growth striations [25] in pulled GaAs crystals and the importance of surface preparation was stressed by observing the decrease in CL efficiency associated with surface polishing. It proved possible to resolve the

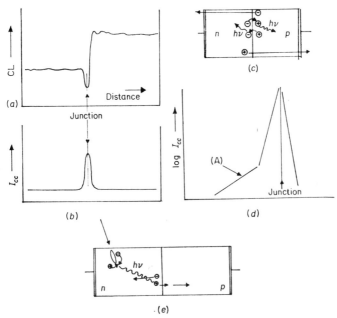

Figure 11.5. (a) Variation of CL signal near to a *pn* junction in GaAs; (b) corresponding charge-collection signal; (c) illustrating the competing mechanisms of minority-carrier injection giving CL and majority-carrier injections or charge-collection; (d) additional component, A, to CL signal observed at high-beam currents; (e) probable cause of additional component, the optical coupling mechanism.

general spectral distribution although some known details could not be resolved. Attempts to examine radiation emitted at wavelengths beyond the bandgap were unsuccessful. Wittry and Kyser also studied [26] laser structures by this method. These studies are of interest because they represent an early attempt to obtain quantitative information from this approach. It was found that the CL efficiency

U

fell off as the scanning electron-beam crossed the junction itself. At the same time the current generated in the device gave a peak (see figure 11.5). The most likely explanation is outlined in figure 11.5(c). In addition to minority-carrier injection at the junction which leads to radiative recombination, majority carriers can be injected, i.e. charge collection can occur. For example, electrons can drift from the *p*-type material into the *n*-type GaAs. The associated negative charge will be compensated by the non-radiative process of current flow through the electrode. Therefore, when the beam is near the junction, an additional part of the beam-induced energy is used non-radiatively and the CL efficiency falls. If the relative beam-induced current is plotted, figure 11.5(d), as a junction of beam position, x, from the junction and compared with an approximate theoretical expression, $I(x) \alpha \exp(-x/L)$, then L, the minority-carrier diffusion length can be estimated. Wittry and Kyser showed that such estimates were in order of magnitude agreement with previous estimates made by other methods. Finally in certain specimens it was found that, at high beam currents, the charge-collection current on the *n*-type side can be represented as the sum of two terms, $I(x) \alpha \exp(-x/L) + \exp(-x/L_0)$. The second, more slowly varying term gives an apparent diffusion length $L_0 \approx 10L$. The most likely explanation of this second term is illustrated in figure 11.5(e). Photons created by the beam travel through the specimen until reabsorbed in the neighbourhood of the junction. The carriers so created can contribute to the current flow. In comparison with the theoretical approach a value of the absorption coefficient of 330 cm^{-1} is obtained. Such a value implies a low, but not unacceptable, value of the photon energy.

Casey and Kaiser [27] have also studied radiative processes in GaAs and have stressed the ability of the SEM to study localized variations. These workers examined the spectral distribution near the bandedge as a function of the free-electron concentration and were able to show that, over a limited range (5×10^{17} to 7×10^{18} cm^{-3}), measurements of the spectral width can be used to predict the electron concentration to within 10%. This technique may be used to relate variations in CL efficiency with changes in electron concentration with a spatial resolution $\sim 2\mu$. Casey [28] applied these ideas to the investigation of the growth striations and dislocation effects in Te-doped GaAs. Shaw and co-workers [29] have studied these defects over a range of temperatures after eliminating the oil contamination problem and with improved resolution. Similar studies have shown that Se and Si, when used as dopants in GaAs, interact with dislocations to a far lesser degree than Te and have illustrated the interaction between Zn and amphoteric Si when used as double dopants in GaAs. In these studies the use of low (100 to 120°K) temperatures increased the signal under constant excitation by a factor of between 6 and 10.

Two other techniques have been used which are of general application. One of these is shown in figure 11.6 in which a scintillator-light

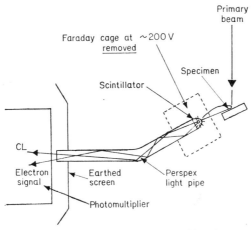

Figure 11.6. Use of scintillator-light pipe combination to observe CL signal and emissive signal simultaneously.

pipe combination is used without a Faraday cage. This system utilizes electrons emitted from the specimen to give a micrograph of the surface details and, at the same time, uses a fraction of the emitted radiation to form a CL micrograph. Thus CL data can be superimposed on the surface features. This method is useful, for example, when relating the variations in CL efficiency to the presence of dislocations, microcracks, surface films and *pn* junctions, etc. The second technique involves the use of a comparator circuit. Such a circuit, when incorporated at the amplifier output, rejects all signals except for those in a narrow band ΔV about a preset voltage V_0. In this way contours of constant CL efficiency can be obtained with flat specimens. Such a circuit has been used [30] to study the interactions between impurities, dislocations, growth striations and surface and diffused junctions. Finally, Sulway *et al.* [23] have shown how a multi-mode use of the SEM can be exploited to study electroluminescent devices quickly at high resolution. The type of information obtained included the nature of the field distribution at the contacts and the manner in which this distribution affects the CL efficiency, the presence, extent and nature of inhomogeneities, the presence of insulating precipitates in subgrain boundaries and the relative radiative efficiencies of the n- and p-type layers as a function of doping.

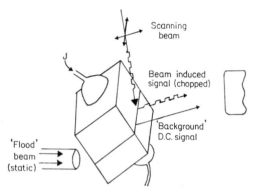

Figure 11.7. Schematic diagram showing the possible use of static electron beam in conjunction with modulated scanning electron beam to give high differential CL efficiency.

11.4.2 *Use of stationary electron-beams*
So far we have emphasized the use of finely focussed beams to study localized variations. We should also stress the role played by stationary electron-beams of somewhat greater spot-size but having a larger current and therefore giving a larger signal. Cusano [31], for example, has shown how a stationary beam can be used to study the complexities which exist in the spectra from highly doped GaAs as a function of dopant type and density. The very useful data shown in figure 10.8 were obtained by this method [31]. An instrument having a highly focussed beam and a stationary flood beam is a very powerful diagnostic tool.

11.4.3 *Future possibilities for qualitative studies*
Although the data discussed here are limited to the GaAsP system the methods used are not. So long as the material or device studied falls within the limitations implied by the calculations given in

section 10.4 then such methods can be used. In general, these limitations can be summed up by saying that specimens emitting radiation of wavelengths between 0.3 and 3μ to 4μ with efficiencies greater than about 10^{-4} to 10^{-5} may be studied. Within these limitations more sophisticated experiments can be made. For example, one approach to the investigation of the effect of material inhomogeneities in both lasing and non-lasing modes of injection lasers would be to bring a suitably cooled laser almost to the laser threshold either by injecting carriers through the contacts or by the use of a second static electron beam (typically, 1μ amp at 50 kV would be required) and using the scanning electron-beam to study localized variations in efficiency, see figure 11.7. Under suitable conditions of chopping and bandwidth limitation incremental efficiency of the scanning beam

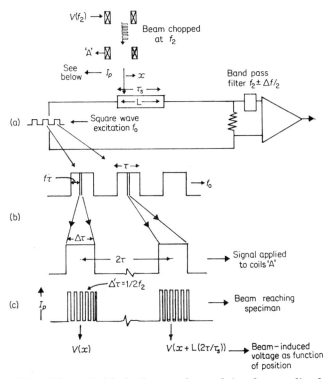

Figure 11.8. Schematic block diagram for studying fast, cyclic phenomena; (a) circuit diagram; (b) definition of sampling parameters used; (c) signal arriving at specimen surface.

can be very high ($\sim 50\%$) and the stationary beam-induced signal completely rejected.

Another example of current interest concerns a.c. electrolumines-cence, which is usually studied at frequencies of ~ 1 to 10 kHz. Therefore, the local field distribution, the local radiative efficiency and the current flow all vary at this frequency. But by strobing and/or chopping the system it should be possible to build up micrographs of the specimen behaviour at a given instant in the cycle. For example, the system blocked out in figure 11.8 can, in principle, be used to obtain such micrographs. The example shown assumes that the 'photovoltage' induced by the beam is measured as a function of position down the specimen at a fixed point in the cycle. The a.c. bias is applied to the specimen at a frequency ~ 1 kHz, a trigger pulse of width $\Delta\tau$ is taken at a time $f\tau$ ($0 \leqslant f \leqslant 1$) and used to control the beam current which is already being chopped at ~ 1 MHz. Thus the beam current arriving at the specimen has the form shown in figure 11.8(c). Therefore, with a frequency-selective amplifier centred on 1 MHz, the beam-induced voltage is obtained as a function of position at a fixed time in the duty cycle. By a suitable choice of $L(\tau/\tau_s)$ relative to the spot-size a continuous trace can be obtained.

11.4.4. *Quantitative studies*

A major difficulty here is the absence of a rigorous analysis of the minority-carrier concentration introduced by the beam, and the subsequent diffusion behaviour. We have stressed this point in sections 10.2.2 and 11.3.2. The basic problem is two-dimensional and allowance for lateral diffusion of the beam-injected carriers should be made. The existence of surface recombination must be considered and also, under certain conditions, the existence of the optical coupling mechanism and the presence of electric fields. There is no two-dimensional analysis of the problem known to the author. Several one-dimensional approaches have been made [32] in which it is assumed that the carriers once created diffuse 'laminarly' towards the junction, as depicted in figure 11.4(a). In this case the minority-carrier continuity equation can, in the absence of electric fields, be written as, for example,

$$D_p \frac{d^2\Delta p}{dz^2} - \frac{\Delta p}{\tau_p} + N(z) = 0 \qquad (11.6)$$

where $N(z)$ is the carrier generation rate as a function of depth. This equation has to be solved subject to the boundary condition

$$D_p \frac{d\Delta p}{dz} \bigg|_{z=0} = S\Delta p(0)$$

where S is the surface recombination velocity. The function $N\ (z)$ has to be chosen so that

$$\int N(z)dz = \frac{JE_0}{q^2 E_i}\left(1 - \eta \frac{\bar{E}}{E_0}\right)$$

where J is the current density, η is the back-scattering coefficient and $\bar{E}$ is the mean energy of the back-scattered electron. Kyser and Wittry argue [33] that a Guassian form for $N(z)$, i.e.

$$N(z) = N(o) \exp\left[-a(z - z_0)^2\right] \qquad (11.7)$$

is a good approximation in that it has proved its validity in the

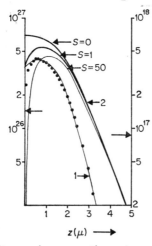

Figure 11.9. Minority carrier generation-rate according to Kyser and Wittry [33] in n-type GaAs; Curve (1) generation rate according to Guassian law; ● generation rate according to transport theory; curve (2) hole-concentration as function of surface recombination velocity.

corresponding problem of characteristic x-ray production and that it agrees with the predictions of solutions of the transport equation. By solving eqns. (11.6) and (11.7) Kyser and Wittry [33] obtain the data shown in figure 11.9. Implicit in such estimations are the follow-ing assumptions: (i) that τ_p is a constant not affected by the irradia-tion and is independent of Δp. This limitation effectively limits the analysis to the case where $\Delta p \ll n_0$, where n_0 is the equilibrium

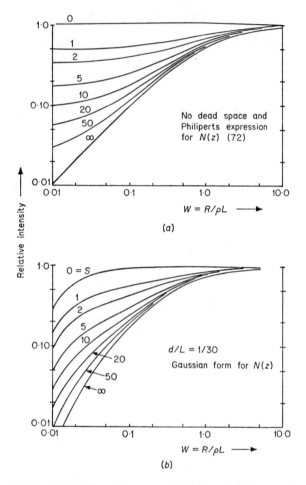

Figure 11.10. Calculations of emitted CL intensity from direct-gap semiconductors [34] as a function of surface recombination velocity, S, expressed in reduced form i.e. $S \times \tau/L$; (a) with no dead space and assuming the Philibert expression [72] for $N(z)$; (d) with a dead space of width, d, and a Gaussian form for $N(z)$.

electron concentration, (*ii*) S is constant and not affected by the electron-beam. This assumption implies that the occupancy of the surface states or the residual surface charge in any insulator layer present is unchanged during the irradiation. The tacit assumption that the irradiation creates no new surface states is also made. Finally, the assumption that eqn. (11.6) is valid for all z implies that there is no high-field region at the specimen surface.

Wittry and Kyser [34] have extended this treatment in a slightly different way in order to exploit the fact that, as the primary beam voltage is increased, the surface recombination velocity has a decreasing effect on the CL yield. These workers apply the Van Roosbroeck analysis [35] of surface recombination to calculating the relative CL yield as a function of beam voltage. The resultant expression for the yield includes as parameters the minority carrier diffusion length, L, the dead-space width, d, and the surface recombination velocity S. The relative intensity under conditions of constant-beam energy takes the form shown as a f $(L,d/L$ & $S)$ in figure 11.10. In these figures the absissca is $\rho R/L$, where R is the maximum electron range and is determined from $R = $ constant V_0^n with n taken as 1·7 and the constant found by a suitable integration of the Bethe law. By fitting the experimental observations to such curves until the best fit is obtained approximate estimates of L, d and S can be obtained. Some ambiguity results from this method which suffers from oversimplifying assumptions, the use of semi-empirical data and the uncertainty arising from the presence of oil contamination. But there is no reason why careful calibration experiments conducted in an oil-free environment with, if possible, some means of cleaning the surface and subsequently altering the surface recombination velocity should not produce a very useful method of material analysis, particularly if good theoretical treatments of the situation are available.

11.5 Metallurgical studies

11.5.1 *Deformation studies*

It was realized early on that the great depth of focus inherent in the SEM, together with its resolution capability (nowadays 100 to 200 Å in situations of high contrast), made it an ideal instrument for studying fracture, twinning, stress-induced transitions, fatigue extrusion and the effect of different ambients on deformation processes.

Tipper, Dagg and Wells [36] studied cleavage fracture of iron by both transmission and scanning electron microscopy, thus getting the best possible method. These authors stressed the ease of making the SEM observations and of using stereopairs to study the crystal and fracture morphology. McGrath, Buchanan and Thurston [37] have similarly examined fatigue and ductile fracture. Oxidation studies have been made by Pease and Ploc [38]. Iron specimens were heated to ≈ 500°C at atmospheric pressure in the specimen chamber, cooled and examined after the system had been pumped out. By repeating the process, details of nucleation, whisker growth inter-actions between oxygen and regions of mechanical stress, were studied. Similarly the effect of gaseous or vapour contamination on the strength of materials can be studied by cleaving, or polishing and then etching the specimen cross-section [39]. What has not been done yet is to observe the deformation directly in the SEM. The reason is apparent – the need for an ingenious (and probably costly) specimen stage. Typically (ignoring 'extreme' needs) workers in the deformation field may want to deform up to 100% a specimen 1 in. in length with loads up to 100 kg between 77°K and 600°C. The area to be examined has to be kept under the electron-beam, i.e. the whole deformation jig has to be movable across an area of the total elongated length × cross-sectional diameter. Finally the emitted current of secondary and reflected electrons has to be detected and the electronoptics has to be protected from inadvertent shock resulting from unexpected failure or specimen fracture. The problems are eased if compression or four-point loading can be used. However, with sufficient need, such stages should be forthcoming.

11.5.2 *Compositional variations*

With well-polished surfaces of the type used in metallography to study microstructure the use of reflected electrons to give composi-tional contrast in the manner pioneered by Kimoto and Hashimoto [40] comes into its own. We can already make a reasonable assessment of the qualitative potentialities of the method. Kimoto and Hashimoto established that spatial resolutions of the order of 1μ can be obtained and that the method is sensitive to changes in atomic number. Shaw [41] has recently reported more detailed studies in which thin films of various metals were evaporated onto Si, Au, or Pt substrates. The results can be summed up as follows:

(1) Provided the film thickness is $\geqslant \frac{1}{4}$ to $\frac{1}{3}$ of the beam penetration distance it is possible to distinguish between metal films of adjacent

atomic number over a wide range of atomic number. Mg[$\mathscr{Z} = 12$] and Al[$\mathscr{Z} = 13$] gave a measurable difference in signal, so did Al and Si[$\mathscr{Z} = 14$]. The same is true of Co[$\mathscr{Z} = 27$] and Ni[$\mathscr{Z} = 28$]; Ni and Cu[$\mathscr{Z} = 29$]; Cu and Zn[$\mathscr{Z} = 30$] and Pt[$\mathscr{Z} = 78$] and Au[$\mathscr{Z} = 79$].

(2) Even if the films are very thin (~ 50 Å) they can be detected, provided low beam voltages are used since the compositional contrast increases at low beam voltages. See figures 11.11(a) and (b).

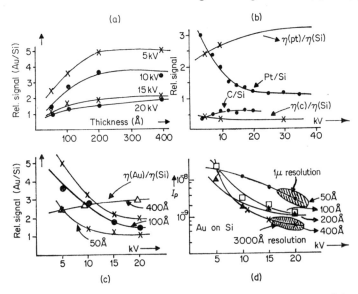

Figure 11.11. Use of reflected electrons to determine compositional differences [30]: (a) signal from Au on Si as function of thickness and beam voltage; (b) relationship between compositional signal and relative back-reflection coefficients for Pt on Si and for C on Si; (c) data corresponding to (b) for Au on Si as function of film thickness; (d) indication of the beam currents required and the resolution obtainable.

(3) These measurements showed that the contrast observed as a function of film thickness is not simply related to the relative back-scattering coefficients (see figures 11.11(c) and (d)) i.e. the variation in angular distribution of the reflected energy appears to be important.

(4) By the use of low beam currents resolutions of 3,000 Å can be obtained in favourable cases. See figure 11.11(d).

(5) Although there were differences in surface topography between
the films used they were small and it is very unlikely that they can
account for the effects described above.

11.6 Observations of magnetic and ferro-electric domains

So far as is known to the author there are no published SEM observations of magnetic domains*. The current belief is that it is probably
easier to observe magnetic domain effects by electron mirror microscopy as the forces involved are small and produce a maximum
deflection for very slowly moving electrons. It must be remembered
that transmission electron microscopy has already been exploited in
this field [42, 43]. Robinson and White [44] have observed contrast
in the SEM arising from the presence of ferro-electric domains in
$BaTiO_3$. This contrast arises from secondary effects associated with
the ferro-electric properties. At room temperature this material has
a tetragonal symmetry with the a-axis cell dimension slightly smaller
than that along the c-axis. In crystals which contain a mixture of c
domains (with the polarization parallel to the surface) the domain
structure will therefore be revealed by a change in surface height.
Robinson and White [44] have shown that this surface structure
leads to sufficient contrast in the SEM at the domain edges to reveal
the domains. By using $BaTiO_3$ with an evaporated metal film to
avoid charge-up these workers confirmed that the observed contrast
was associated with the domain structure in three ways: (i) By
heating the specimen above the Curie temperature it was possible
to cause the observed contrast to disappear. (ii) The contrast in the
SEM was compared with the domain structure as revealed by
simultaneous observation with an optical microscope using crossed
polarizers and found to be coincident. (iii) The contrast in the SEM
could be enhanced by etching in HCl. The observed changes in contrast
were in accord with the known etching properties of the c- and a-
domains.

Additional studies revealed the known surface layer that exists
on as-grown crystals. Finally it was found that exposure to higher
beam currents (10^{-7} amps/cm^2 at 25 kV for a period of minutes)
causes a movement of the domain boundaries. Again this is in accord
with the known properties that a local field in excess of 10^3V/cm can
nucleate an a-domain in a region of c-domain material. Thus the

* However, see J. R. Banbury and W. C. Nixon, [*J. Sci. Inst.*, **44**, 11,
(1967)] who have recently observed magnetic contrast.

domains can be studied without affecting their properties at low-beam currents and then studied after alteration at high currents. It would be of interest to extend these studies by the use of cine-techniques and lower beam voltages.

11.7 More general applications

There are, of course, many observations in a far wider field than is covered by the scope of this book. In the related fields we may mention the early application of the SEM to the study of paper and wood topography, processing and deformation, by Smith and others [45, 46, 47]. Similarly, Wells [48] made early use of the instrument to examine, in particular, the internal structure of nylon spinneret holes. In the chemical field controlled decomposition of explosive crystals have been studied [49] by heating during examination in a SEM and the beam-induced decomposition of sucrose has been observed [50]. In the field of crystal growth, the cellular structure associated with certain types of graphite has been examined [51], the formation of iron whiskers has been studied and so has the mechanism of the VLS crystal growth method [52]. In ceramics and glass technology the SEM is finding ready application to the study of glasses, cements [53] and ceramics [54] in general. Diamond grinding powders have been examined [55]. Studies of the growth of oxide films on Fe began early [Knoll, 56] and are continuing [57].

Scanning electron microscopy is finding continued application to the detailed study of thermo-ionic cathodes [58]. Studies of arc-erosion and of wear on field-emitting structures have also begun [59]. The geological possibilities are being exploited and the use of selectively absorbed dyes in organic material to give cathodoluminescence and contrast in the SEM has already been pioneered.

With this mention of organic material we must stop. The use of the SEM in the biological and related fields is developing rapidly with encouraging and fascinating results. For a bibliography of the relevant literature the reader is referred to the bibliography published by Wells [73].

11.8 Special techniques: (I) ion-beams

Here we shall limit the discussion to those aspects of the technique concerned with materials problems. The use of ion-beams in device fabrication is discussed in Chapter 13. The problems we shall discuss here are:

(1) Use of ion-beams as a diagnostic tool in surface physics.

(2) Application of ion-beams to the cleaning of the surfaces of specimens.

(3) The enhancement of contrast and revealing of precipitates by ion-etching.

11.8.1 *Ion-beams as a surface diagnostic and as a means of surface cleaning*

No reported studies using a SEM for this purpose are known to the author. There are, however, indications of the possibilities inherent in the method from other studies. Estrup [60] used the simple system shown in figure 11.12 and measured the increase in conductance resulting from ion bombardment from the discharge. The effect of gaseous ambient and the decay of the excess conductance after the discharge is turned-off were studied. The type of information obtained is illustrated in figures 11.12(c) and (d). The decay of the excess charge

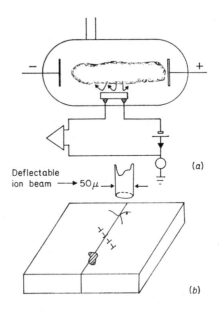

Figure 11.12. Ion-beams used to vary surface properties: (a) arrangement used by Estrup [60]; (b) arrangement capable of incorporation in SEM; (c) surface leakage as function of ion current and time; (d) relaxation of ion-induced changes. Curve (a) normal relaxation, curves

can be quickened by exposure to an electron beam (curves (b) and (c)). This exposure induces a memory effect in the sense that it increases the sensitivity of further ion-beam bombardment (curves (d) and (e)). This type of study can be refined by the SEM in the way shown in figure 11.12(b). Localized ion-beam bombardment can be exploited to investigate the effects of ambients on surface defects. By using a combination of ion-beam bombardment to change the surface properties and an electron beam delivering slightly smaller current

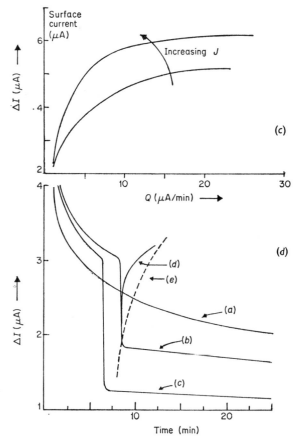

(b) and (c) enhanced relaxation on exposure to electron beam; curve (d) behaviour on further exposure to ion-beam showing memory effect; Curve (e) behaviour on re-exposure to ion beam if no memory effect present.

it should be possible to control the rate at which the surface leakage builds up and so observe it as it does.

Likewise, with regard to surface cleaning we cannot refer to any SEM studies and must rely on other work. In this context recent Russian work [61] has shown that the prior ion bombardment of SiC can increase the electro- and cathodoluminescence efficiency of the material. Similar work has shown that the same general behaviour is observed on CdSe [62]. Sulway *et al* [23] have shown by using the cathodoluminescent mode that GaP crystals often have a surface layer which is of low luminescent efficiency. Possibly the same situation occurs in SiC and the surface layer is removed by the ion bombardment. It should also be noted that previous attempts to use ion-beams to clean specimen surfaces have usually used ions which are incident on the surface at normal or near-normal incidence. It may be possible by using ion-beams at glancing incidence to obtain an efficient clean-up of the surface without introducing surface damage.

11.8.2 *Enhancement of contrast*
The enhancement of contrast by ion-etching has already been actively exploited. Stewart [63] and Stewart and Boyde [64] used the method to reveal detail in surface structure. Stewart also showed that inclusions of a lower sputtering rate than the bulk can be revealed by ion bombardment. Broers [65] has shown that slip planes and other mechanical defects in Al can be preferentially etched by ion-bombardment. There is some evidence relating the selective chemical and ion-etching of mechanical defects in a variety of materials [66, 67, 68]. In general there is a fairly close relationship between the selective etching at mechanical defects caused by chemical etching and that caused by ion-beams. What is less clear is how the etching occurs. It is not known whether the ion-etching occurs preferentially at dislocation sub-boundaries because of some inherent property of the dislocations themselves or because of some secondary effect arising, for example, from the presence of a second phase which occurs preferentially at the boundary. Independent of these interpretative difficulties involving the detailed mechanisms the method is already of practical use. Figure 11.13 (Plate) shows some ion-etching studies of GaP. One of the problems with this material arises from its method of preparation and this is the existence of inhomogeneities. Figure 11.13(*a*) (Plate) shows an ion-etched sub-grain boundary in GaP.

Two defects which do not occur in the bulk crystal are revealed. One type of defect is an insulator precipitate which gives a characteristic cone structure (see below) because its sputtering rate is lower than the adjacent material. The other type of defect has a rounded 'hillock' structure and is associated with regions of poor CL efficiency. Thus inclusions, detrimental to the performance of the material, are exposed for chemical analysis by x-ray microanalysis. One of the

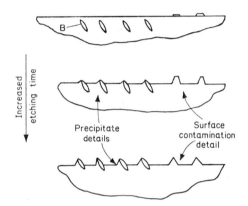

Figure 11.14. Sequence showing possible difficulty in distinguishing between 'spikes' due to internal precipitates and those due to surface contamination.

difficulties sometimes experienced is illustrated in systematic form in figure 11.14. A specimen contains precipitates, figure 11.13(*b*) (Plate), which are to be examined and small regions of insulating surface film. As the bombardment proceeds, the structure will take the form shown in the figure and it may be difficult to distinguish between the details arising from bulk material protected by the surface insulator. One way in which the distinction can be made is by 'compositional contrast', using a pair of detectors.

One of the main problems currently facing a full use of this method is the existence of uncertainties in interpretation. For example, in figure 11.13(*a*) (Plate), there are shallow pits around the bottom of the insulator cones. Are these pits evidence of some chemical interaction or diffusion between the precipitates and the surrounding matrix which increased the local etch-rate? Or have ions incident on the cone been scattered into this region so that a nett increased flux occurred with an increased etching rate?

x

11.9 Special techniques: (II) stereomicroscopy

We have stressed the ability of the SEM to examine surface topography at good resolution with large depth of focus and with sufficient degrees of specimen movement, to obtain views of the surface from many directions. Stereopairs can also be formed by taking two micrographs at an angular separation corresponding to that of the eyes and thus obtaining with a suitable projection system an integrated image with an illusion of depth. This technique is useful in cases where it is difficult to judge whether the detail being examined protrudes from the surface or is a narrow groove or pit in the surface. A stereopair will obviate this kind of uncertainty. The technique can also be used [36] to obtain quantitative estimates of surface angles by making measurements on two micrographs taken at a known difference in direction. The errors involved have been studied by Garrod and Nankivell [69] and Wells [70] has indicated how two of the major errors can be eliminated and how the uncertainty of the remaining errors can be calculated. Wells lists three main sources of error: (*i*) a 'tilt' error introduced when the axis of the electron column does not intersect the axis about which the specimen is tilted, (*ii*) a 'perspective' error introduced because of the variation of magnification between the fore- and back-ground in a micrograph and (*iii*) errors in making measurements on the micrographs. Wells shows how it is possible to eliminate (*i*) because *four* measurements of a given position are available (two from each micrograph) and only *three* co-ordinates are needed to locate a given element, i.e. the redundancy is used to estimate (*i*) by trial and error. Unless computorized, the calculations may be somewhat lengthy.

11.10 Special techniques: (III) Ciné-techniques

It is sometimes necessary to record the behaviour of specimens which give time-dependent behaviour. In this application the resolution required is often minimal as it is usually required to examine relatively large areas of the specimen. Because of the finite time necessary for the completion of a frame-scan the events that can be followed are relatively slow, i.e. the details change significantly only in a time of $\sim 1/10$ second or longer. The type of problem in which ciné-techniques are important are charge-up and discharge effects in insulators, growth of inversion layers, specimen melting and evaporation, etc. Although some of these effects can be slowed up by the use of low beam currents, it is still difficult to examine events which occur quicker than 1/10 second unless they are repetitive. Within this limitation the use of ciné-techniques presents no real problem. To obtain complete frames it is necessary to synchronize the frame scans and the ciné-film movements. This can be done, in principle, by arranging a control circuit which uses a camera on single-shot operation and which (*i*) allows the fame to be scanned in 0·5 seconds, (*ii*) moves the film during the frame flyback time during which the signal is blanked-off and (*iii*) repeats the cycle at the operator's command or automatically. The frame flyback time has to be $\sim 1/10$ second to accommodate the inertia in the mechanical movement.

A simpler method involving minimal extra equipment is possible. The scan coil which controls the frame-scan of the record tube is removed from the scan-generator load and replaced by an equal resistance. As a result the beam still scans a full raster on the specimen and on the visually observed CRT's, but the complete raster is superimposed (time sequentially) on the same line scan on the record tube. The data are recorded on a film which moves at a constant speed across the camera image plane. If the relative speeds of the film movement and the frame-scan are correctly chosen the complete frame is recorded as viewed on the visually observed CRT, i.e. without geometrical distortion. By a further adjustment of the relative speeds it is possible, in principle, to use this technique to remove any distortion arising from the inclination effect discussed in section 8.4.

REFERENCES

[1] J. TAUC, *Czech. J. Phys.*, **5**, 178, (1955)

[2] C. MUNAKATA, *J. Appl. Phys. of Japan*, **5**, 756, (1966)

[3] See ref. [1] and J. TAUC, *Photo- and Thermo-electric Effects in Semiconductors*, Pergamon Press, (1962)

[4] C. MUNAKATA, *J. Appl. Phys. of Japan*, **5**, 336, (1966)

[5] H. DEMBER, *Phys. Z.*, **32**, 554, 856, (1931) and **33**, 207, (1932)

[6] V. M. BUIMISTROV, *Fiz. Tverd. Teta*, **5**, 481, (1963)

[7] R. M. ESPOSITO, J. J. ROFERSKI and H. FLICKER, *J. Appl. Phys.*, **38**, 825, (1967)

[8] A. MANY, Y. GOLDSTEIN and N. B. GROVER, *Semiconductor Surfaces*, Chapter 7, North Holland Publishing Co., Amsterdam, (1965)

[9] H. HIGUCHI and H. TAMURA, *J. Appl. Phys. of Japan*, **4**, 316, (1965)

308   *Scanning Electron Microscopy*

[10] See references [26] and [27]

[11] P. R. THORNTON, K. A. HUGHES, D. V. SULWAY and R. C. WAYTE, *Microelectronics and Reliability*, **5**, 291, (1966)

[12] W. CZAJA, *J. Appl. Phys.*, **37**, 4236, (1966)

[13] P. R. THORNTON, I. G. DAVIES, K. A. HUGHES, N. F. B. NEVE, D. A. SHAW, D. V. SULWAY and R. C. WAYTE, *Proc. of 2nd Inter. Conf. on Ion and Electron Beams in Science and Technology, New York*, (1966)

[14] R. L. WILLIAMS and P. P. WEBB, *I.R.E. Trans. Nucl. Sci.*, **5-9**, 160, (1962)

[15] V. E. COSSLETT and R. N. THOMAS, *Brit. J. Appl. Phys.*, **15**, 1283, (1964)

[16] C. FELDMAN, *Phys. Rev.*, **117**, 455, (1960)

[17] E. J. STERNGLASS, *Phys. Rev.*, **95**, 345, (1954)

[18] F. DAVOINE, P. PINARD and M. MARTINEAN, *J. Phys. Radium*, **21**, 121, (1960)

[19] F. DAVOINE, R. BERNARD and P. PINARD, *Proc. Europ. Reg. Conf. on Electron Microscopy, Delft*, (ed. A. L. Houwick and B. J. Spit), (1960)

[20] R. BERNARD, F. DAVOINE and P. PINARD, *Compto Rindui Acad. Sci.*, **248**, 2564, (1956)

[21] D. A. SHAW, R. C. WAYTE and P. R. THORNTON, *Appl. Phys. Letters*, **8**, 289, (1966)

[22] *C. Z. LEMAY, *J. Appl. Phys.*, **34**, 439, (1963)

[23] D. V. SULWAY, HTIN KYAW and P. R. THORNTON, *Solid-State Electron*, **10**, 545, (1967)

[24] D. B. WITTRY and D. F. KYSER, *J. Appl. Phys.*, **35**, 2439, (1964)

[25] *D. F. KYSER and D. B. WITTRY, *The Electron Microprobe*, (ed. McKinley, Heinrich and Wittry), Wiley, New York, (1966)

[26] D. B. WITTRY and D. F. KYSER, *J. Appl. Phys.*, **36**, 1387, (1965)

[27] H. C. CASEY, JNR. and R. H. KAISER, *J. Electrochem. Soc.*, **114**, 149, (1967)

[28] H. C. CASEY, JNR., *J. Electrochem. Soc.*, **114**, 153, (1967)

[29] D. A. SHAW, D. V. SULWAY, R. C. WAYTE and P. R. THORNTON, *J. Appl. Phys.*, **38**, 887, (1967)

[30] D. A. SHAW, M.Sc. Thesis, Bangor U.C.N.W., (1967)

[31] D. A. CUSANO, *Solid-State Comm.*, **2**, 353, (1964)

[32] See references [12], [2], [4], [9], [11] and [34]

[33] D. F. KYSER and D. B. WITTRY, *Proc. I.E.E.E.*, **55**, 733, (1967)

[34] D. B. WITTRY and D. F. KYSER, *J. Appl. Phys.*, **38**, 375, (1967)

[35] W. VAN ROOSBROECK, *J. Appl. Phys.*, **26**, 380, (1955)

[36] C. F. TIPPER, D. I. DAGG and O. C. WELLS, *Proc. Iron & Steel Institute*, **193**, 133, (1959)

[37] J. T. MCGRATH, J. G. BUCHANAN and R. C. A. THURSTON, *J. Inst. Metab.*, **91(I)**, 34, (1962)

[38] R. F. W. PEASE and R. A. PLOC, *Trans. Met. Soc. of A.I.M.E.*, **233**, 1949, (1965)

[39] J. E. CASTLE and H. G. MASTERTON, *Corrosion Science*, **6**, 93, (1966)

[40] S. KIMOTO and H. HASHIMOTO, *The Electron Microprobe*, (ed. McKinley, Heinrich and Wittry), Wiley, New York, (1966)

[41] D. A. SHAW. To be published

[42] R. D. HEIDENREICH, *Fundamentals of Transmission Electron Microscopy*, Wiley, New York, (1964)

[43] See *Electron Microscopy*, Vol. I, (*Proc. of 5th Inter. Conf. on Electron Microscopy*, Philadelphia), ed. S. S. Breese, Jnr., Academic Press, New York, (1962)

[44] G. Y. ROBINSON and R. E. WHITE, *Appl. Phys. Letters*, **10**, 320, (1967)

[45] K. C. A. SMITH, *Pulp and Paper Mag. of Canada*, **60**, T366, (1959)

[46] K. C. A. SMITH and J. G. BUCHANAN, *Proc. Europ. Reg. Conf. on Electron Microscopy, Delft*, (editors, A. L. Houwmk and B. F. Spit), (1960)

[47] J. G. BUCHANAN and O. V. WASHBURN, *Pulp and Paper Mag. of Canada*, **63**, T485, (1962)

[48] O. C. WELLS, *J. Electron. and Control*, **7**, 325, (1959)

[49] F. B. BOWDEN and J. H. L. MCAUSLAN, *Nature*, **178**, 408, (1956)

[50] D. V. SULWAY. Private Communication

[51] I. MINKOFF and W. C. NIXON, *J. Appl. Phys.*, **37**, 4848, (1966)

[52] P. R. THORNTON, D. W. F. JAMES, C. LEWIS and A. BRADFORD, *Phil. Mag.*, **14**, 165, (1966)

[53] S. CHATTERJI and J. W. JEFFREY, *Nature*, **214**, 559, (1967)

[54] R. F. M. THORNLEY and L. CARTZ, *J. Amer. Ceramic Soc.*, **45**, 425, (1962)

[55] Author's unpublished results

[56] M. KNOLL, *Phys. Z.*, **42**, 120, (1941)

[57] N. J. THEMELIS and W. H. GAUVIN, *Trans. Met. Soc. of A.I.M.E.*, **227**, 290, (1963)

[58] H. AHMED, Ph.D. Thesis, Cambridge, (1962) and H. AHMED and A. H. W. BECK, *J. Appl. Phys.*, **34**, 997, (1963)

[59] P. E. SECKER, Private communication

[60] P. J. ESTRUP, *Solid-State Electron.*, **8**, 535, (1965)

[61] V. V. MAKAROV and N. N. PETROV, *Sov. Phys. Solid-State*, **8**, 1272, (1966) and V. V. MAKAROV, *Sov. Phys. Solid-State*, **9**, (1967)

[62] T. YA SERA and G. G. GHEMERSYUK, *Sov. Phys. Solid-State*, **6**, 104, (1964)

[63] A. D. G. STEWART, *Proc. of 5th Inter. Conf. on Electron Microscopy, Philadelphia*, Academic Press, New York, (1962)

[64] A. D. G. STEWART and A. BOYDE, *Nature*, **198**, 1102, (1963)

[65] A. N. BROERS, Ph.D. Thesis, Cambridge, (1965)

[66] G. K. WEHNER, *Phys. Rev.*, **102**, 690, (1958)

[67] R. C. WAYTE, Unpublished results on GaP.

[68] G. J. OGILVIE and M. J. RIDGE, *J. Phys. Chem. Solids*, **10**, 217, (1959)

[69] R. I. GARROD and J. F. NANKIVELL, *Brit. J. Appl. Phys.*, **9**, 214, (1959)

[70] O. C. WELLS, *Brit. J. Appl. Phys.*, **11**, 199, (1961)

[71] E. H. SNOW, A. S. GROVE and D. J. FITZGERALD, *Proc. I.E.E.E.*, **55**, 1168, (1967)

[72] J. PHILIBERT, *X-ray Optics and X-ray Microanalysis.*, (ed. H. H. Pattee, *et al.*), Academic Press, New York, (1963)

[73] O. C. WELLS, *Proc. of I.E.E.E. 9th Annual Symp. on Electron, Ion and Laser Technology*, Berkeley, Calif., (1967)

CHAPTER 12

Applications of the SEM: (II) To Device and Surface Physics

12.1 Introduction

As devices get smaller and smaller, device physics becomes increasingly identified with surface physics. Present-day microcircuits are very dependent on surface or interface properties, either because faulty control of the surface properties can lead to a degradation of the device properties, or because the device operation depends completely on some surface-controlled process. Ample evidence of this fact has been given in previous chapters. Up to the present the SEM has not been applied in any sustained way to fundamental surface-physics problems, but a wealth of data in the device field is available. These device studies are indicative of the type of data that can be obtained in the more general surface-physics field. It is suggested that the following sections be read with this point in mind. It will be seen that a current difficulty in exploiting the SEM in these interrelated fields arises from the fact that the electron-beam bombardment inherent in the SEM can alter the device or surface properties. This alteration may arise because of oil-induced contamination, which can be eliminated, or because of some 'irradiation damage' introduced into the examined surface by the beam even in a clean environment. These beam-induced changes sometimes complicate the interpretation of surface effects, sometimes they help. In order to illustrate these points in relation to the capabilities of the SEM in this field the author has selected a series of studies of what might be called 'device failure', provided a somewhat wide definition of device failure is adopted. The main reason for this selection is that it is in the field of device process control and failure analysis that the SEM has been most usefully employed to date in semiconductor work. The other, more long-term, application to device fabrication is considered in the next chapter.

12.2 The application of the SEM to device-failure problems

12.2.1 *Introduction*

In general terms failure can be said to take one of three forms: (*i*) The device can fail to come up to the required specification because of failure to control sufficiently some one or more of the processes used to make it. This is relatively common during the early development of a device. (*ii*) A device may, as a result of storage, become degraded because of slow physical and chemical changes occurring in the device. (*iii*) The actual running of the device can lead to failure particularly when the devices are operated at high power or in environments in which they are irradiated.

The main causes of device failure are:

(1) '*Materials*' *faults*, i.e. faults or variations in the initial starting materials.

(2) '*Process*' or '*fabrication*' *faults*. In preparing the polished and etched slices which are subsequently diffused, microcracks and surface scratches and contamination may be introduced. The subsequent diffusion itself can be the source of further variations in properties. Faulty photo-resist techniques may lead to further complications. Finally, faulty line-up and bonding techniques can lead to a variety of problems.

(3) *Insulator faults*. Strictly speaking, this type of fault should be included in fabrication faults, but, because of their rather unique characteristics, we shall consider them separately. The passivating layer (either oxide or nitride) can lead to difficulties arising from the presence of defect states at the outer surface, at the insulator-semiconductor interface and in the insulator bulk. We have already mentioned that reactive ions can be mobilized by a combination of suitable bias and heat treatment. Pinholes in the insulator layer cause diffused regions in unwanted places, inadequate passivating and a severe limitation on the voltage that can be applied across the insulator before it breaks down. If silicon nitride or silicon oxide-nitride layers are used, considerable hysteresis may be introduced.

These faults can lead to

(1) Unwanted inversion and/or surface depletion layers.

(2) Excess noise.

(3) Localized avalanche breakdown.

(4) Excess current due to free-carrier tunnelling.

(5) Surface breakdown.

If we add failure mechanisms in which heating occurs such as thermal runaway [1] and second breakdown [2] we have a complete list of the major failure causes. The basic problem of failure analysis is to relate these electrical faults to the underlying causes arising from structural and/or fabrication faults. To investigate these effects we have the usual electrical measurements which give the electrical properties integrated over the whole device and we have the transmission electron microscope, the x-ray microanalyser and the SEM which provide complementary localized information.

There are two situations in which the failure of devices has to be examined. The first occurs when the yield of an established device drops and it is necessary, for urgent economic reasons, to locate the fault quickly (albeit empirically) and restore production without necessarily investigating the detailed cause. The other situation, which is more applicable to the research and development laboratory, is long-term and seeks to trace the details of each electrical fault back to the exact, initial defect and hence determine which of the initial defects it is most essential to eliminate. In this case it is often useful to make a special structure to facilitate the study of device faults [3]. This simple structure can thus serve for an examination of the fabrication processes used to make the more complicated device without any of the difficulties due to parallel devices, parallel leakage paths and a multiplicity of faults. We will now see how the SEM may help in both these situations by beginning with what is probably the most worrying fault in present-day microcircuits – the occurrence of unwanted inversion layers.

12.2.2 *Detection of inversion layers*

(1) *General.* We are concerned here with unwanted regions or irregularities in the required inversion layers. Such faults arise from an unwanted fixed charge, associated with the surface in any one of the ways outlined in Chapter 6. Two types of electrical measurement are usually used to study inversion layers. Surface conductivity and recombination studies indicate the leakage currents carried by such layers and capacity plots as a junction of bias and frequency can tell us about the capacity associated with inversion layers, and, within limitations, indicate the density and nature of the stored charge density. In addition, the noise properties of surface layers can be

used to diagnose their existence and properties. Recently, pioneering studies in the microcircuit field, mainly by the Westinghouse group [4, 5,6], have shown how the SEM can augment these techniques by providing localized information about the position and extent of the inversion layer. This information is best obtained by observing the charge collection from the underlying depletion layer which must be present if the surface is inverted. This fact demonstrates the first limitation in the technique. A straightforward inspection in the SEM of a 'stray' or 'unwanted' region of charge collection does not allow a distinction to be made between an inverted surface or a depleted surface. At present, only if the SEM is used in conjunction with the VI characteristic can the area under consideration be identified as an inversion layer. In this context it is well to stress the range of leakage currents that we are concerned with here. We have seen in Chapter 6 that the range of leakage currents can vary from $\sim 10^{-12}$A to 10^{-9}A when the surface recombination rate in a narrow region in the immediate neighbourhood of the junction is increased by a change in fixed, surface charge-density in this region. We also know that an inversion layer acting as a channel shorting out the base of a transistor, for example, can carry up to 10^{-3}A of leakage current. In diagnosing device faults we are interested in the extent of the excess region, the leakage current it adds to the structure, and in the increase in capacity associated with it.

To determine the extent and position of the region which gives the excess leakage we can proceed in one or more of three ways:

(1) Rely on our knowledge of the device, in particular on our knowledge of the geometry and position of the diffused junctions relative to the surface structure, and then examine any areas of unpredicted charge collection in relationship to the electrical fault.

(2) Make a straightforward comparison with a good device by including two specimens (one faulty, one acceptable) and examine them in turn under the same conditions.

(3) Undertake experiments in which the channel or surface fault is examined, removed, the device examined with the fault removed and finally with the fault restored.

Often the inversion layer has to be observed against the background of some other junction. For example, an inversion layer over a transistor base-region has to be observed against the charge-collection signal from the diffused base-collector function. To minimize the charge collection from the underlying junction it is best to work at a low beam kV so that, if possible, the beam-injected carriers do not penetrate to the underlying junction. The circuit used to investigate the presence of unwanted inversion layers is also important and should be carefully chosen.

It is possible that the leakage path under study will not occur until a finite bias is applied across the device. Therefore to establish the presence of all the possible faults it is necessary to apply a bias to

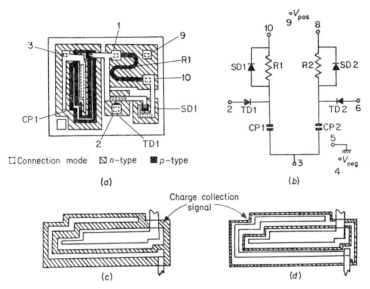

Figure 12.1. (*a*) Layout and (*b*) circuit of steering circuit discussed in the text; (*c*) a faulty transistor with an inversion layer over the base region; (*d*) a good transistor giving a charge-collection signal from the diffused junctions only. See plates for (*e*) to (*j*).

the device. This cannot always be done by applying a bias directly directly to the device but only by applying a voltage to some voltage 'rail' in the complete circuit. This voltage not only biasses the device in question but alters the voltage across other elements. As a result the charge-collection signals from the complete device can go through a series of changes of the type outlined in section 9.5 and the presence of an unwanted inversion layer has to be detected against the background of these changes. In this case the VI characteristic and a comparison with a 'good', i.e. non-leaky, device are of considerable help. A final complication arises from the fact that the underlying cause of the inversion layer may be removed or augmented during the examination in the SEM.

We may illustrate the detection of inversion layers by considering a case in which examination in the SEM tends to alter the device properties.

(2) *Instabilities caused by irradiation in the SEM.* The type of situation that can arise is shown in figure 12.1. The circuit examined [7] was an early developmental model of a Mullard steering circuit. The circuit is shown in figure 12.1(*b*) and the device consisted of two identical chips of the structure shown in figure 12.1(*a*). The transistor incorporated on each chip is used as a condenser by joining the emitter and collector together to form one contact while the base is used as another. In the examples examined a leakage current of the order of several microamps existed across this capacitor. By examining the charge-collection map obtained from pin (10) with pin (3) earthed it was found that a near-continuous 'white' signal existed over the whole of the base region as shown in figure 12.1(*c*). After prolonged exposure to the beam this uniform white signal altered to the signal characteristic of a good device, as indicated in figure 12.1(*d*). At the same time the *VI* characteristic improved. More systematic studies of the type shown in table 12.1 indicated an inversion layer over the base region which connected both emitter and collector to the base contact and that this layer is removed for a short time by exposure to the beam. (See plate figure 12 (*e*) to (*j*).

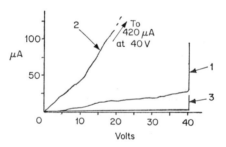

Figure 12.2. The time dependence of the reverse characteristic of a diode with an inversion layer over the *p*-type region as a function of dosage. Curve (1) is the characteristic prior to irradiation; curve (2) is the characteristic just after start of irradiation; curve (3) is the final characteristic after considerable irradiation.

Table 12.1. *Exposure sequence for the capacitor described in the test. No voltage was applied during the exposure and the leakage currents measured with V = 3 volts* [7]

Time (min)	Exposure	Leakage current and comments
0	—	Initial leakage $5 \cdot 15 \mu$A prior to exposure
6	4 min exposure to 1×10^{-10} A at $\times$ 100	Slight increase in leakage during this period to $5 \cdot 9 \mu$A which gradually decays if beam switched off
$9\frac{1}{2}$	$1\frac{1}{2}$ min exposure to 1×10^{-10}A at $\times$ 100	Rapid drop to $1 \cdot 2 \mu$A caused by this exposure
$14\frac{1}{2}$	,, ,,	Further drop to $0 \cdot 37 \mu$A.
18	,, ,,	Drop in current to $0 \cdot 25 \mu$A.
$21\frac{1}{2}$	,, ,,	Drop to $0 \cdot 17 \mu$A.
$24\frac{1}{2}$	,, ,,	Drop to $0 \cdot 09 \mu$A.
27	,, ,,	Drop to $0 \cdot 085 \mu$A.
31	$1\frac{1}{2}$ min exposure to 2×10^{-10}A at $\times$ 100	Drop to $0 \cdot 058 \mu$A.
39	,, ,,	Drop to $0 \cdot 050 \mu$A.
45	$1\frac{1}{2}$ min exposure to 2×10^{-10}A at $\times$ 1000	Small region exposed at high current. Leakage drops to $0 \cdot 038 \mu$A.
48	—	Specimen allowed to 'rest' without exposure to beam, leakage increases to $0 \cdot 041 \mu$A.
52	$1\frac{1}{2}$ min exposure	Leakage drops to $0 \cdot 038 \mu$A.
55	$1\frac{1}{2}$ min exposure to 6×10^{-10}A at $\times$ 300	Leakage drops to $0 \cdot 037 \mu$A.
58	3 min exposure to 6×10^{-10}A at $\times$ 100	Leakage drops to $0 \cdot 033 \mu$A.

Table 12.1 shows two features which are often observed with inversion layers on p-type Si. There is an initial increase in leakage during the first part of the exposure followed by a subsequent decrease. The magnitude of the changes can vary greatly from one device to another and depends on whether the device is biassed during the exposure. Figure 12.2 shows just how large a change can be induced when the device is under bias during the exposure. These studies show how the SEM can be used to detect inversion layers and how sensitive the method can be. We shall consider the limitations and possible extensions of the method later in section 12.7, but first we will see how the SEM can be used to study avalanche breakdown.

12.3 Detection of current multiplication in the SEM

12.3.1 *Introduction*

In the present context our main interest in current multiplication is in the excess leakage current associated with the effect and in the degradation of the breakdown characteristics that results when material inhomogeneities or geometrical factors enhance the local electric field. We shall discuss these aspects but it should be remembered that the methods discussed also have a wider application. For example, they are applicable to insulating materials for which the emphasis will be on the dielectric strength of the material and to semiconducting materials in which the interests are more varied – ranging from high-field studies and light emission properties to the production of fast avalanche diodes. In the semiconductor field, observations on current multiplication and avalanche breakdown have been reported on Si, Ge, $GaAs_xP_{1-x}$, InAs, ZnS and SiC [8, 9, 10, 11, 12, 13, 14]. In other materials effects very similar to these have been observed over a wide range of temperatures ($4\cdot2°$K to $\sim 500°$C).

Obviously current multiplication and avalanche breakdown are quite general phenomena. These can be either bulk effects extending more or less uniformly over the whole active area of the device or they can be localized effects arising because some imperfection has enhanced the field and caused localized current multiplication at an applied voltage which is below that required to give bulk multiplication. We need to study both forms over the relevant voltage range, that is, from the voltages at which the current multiplication factor, M, is just beginning to exceed unity up to voltages at which the structure has completely broken down and is passing a large current. And we wish to do this over a range of temperatures without degrading the device. We shall illustrate the present ability of the technique by considering four applications:

(1) The traditional 'microplasma' [8], or very localized breakdown in unpassivated Si diodes.

(2) Scratch-induced breakdown in unpassivated diodes [15].

(3) Localized breakdown in integrated circuits [16, 17].

(4) Bulk breakdown in passivated diodes [18, 19].

We shall be almost exclusively concerned with the conductive mode as this is the most direct way of detecting current multiplication, although the emissive mode is used extensively to relate the observed regions of current multiplication to surface features. Experimentally the system used in that described in previous sections with only minor changes, such as the incorporation of signal attenuators and a somewhat extended current 'back-off' facility.

Let us imagine a diode of active area A_d that is biassed to a voltage V_b at which it passes a d.c. current of I_D. The magnitude of I_D can vary from $\sim 10^{-12}$A for a good passivated device at low voltages to ~ 20mA for a small-area device that is breaking down. This d.c. current is 'backed-off' to within a limit of ΔI_d and the charge-collection signal observed against this background. As the bias is increased, the diode can either breakdown locally or uniformly. The instantaneous signal-to-noise ratio from a given element of the diode on a charge-collection map is

$$I_p(E_o/E_i)f(V_b)M(V_b)/\Delta I_d(A_o/\Delta_d)$$

where $f(V_b)$ is the bias-dependent fraction of the created carriers that are collected by the junction, $M(V_b)$ is the current multiplication and A_o is the area from which the current multiplication occurs ($\gtrsim$ the spot area). At zero bias, $M(V_b) = 1$ and the contrast is largely determined by variations in $f(\text{o})$. This behaviour may persist up to voltages $\gtrsim 4$ volts at which voltages the current multiplication may begin to increase near linearly with increase in voltage (see figure 9.12). After further increase in bias a sudden and large increase in signal in a localized region may occur, necessitating a large decrease in system gain if the signal is to be completely accommodated. Further increase in diode voltage may well see extensive current multiplication occurring reasonably uniformly over the whole diode area. This typical sequence establishes the basic requirements of the system for this kind of study: (*i*) The ability to locate the zero signal condition against the standing current which is backed off to a convenient but arbitrary degree. (*ii*) The need to accommodate a wide range of signals. (*iii*) Accurate control of diode voltage (to within 2 mV for diodes breaking down at 6 to 20 V) and (*iv*) A back-off facility capable of fine control up to ~ 20 mA.

We may now illustrate the method by considering specific examples.

12.3.2 *Localized breakdown in devices*
Neve [20] has shown that the SEM can be used to give the same

type of information about current multiplication at microplasmas that light-spot studies can give, but with increased resolution, considerably quicker and with a high sensitivity to small changes in current multiplication. Regions of localized current multiplication can be related to the leakage current as a function of bias and to the noise properties. The method is quite general and has been applied up to the present to Si, Ge, GaAs, GaP, SiC, and microcircuits [21]. Several difficulties may sometimes be encountered in such studies. When we are concerned with examining one group of microplasmas over a wide voltage range in a diode containing thousands of such regions all with differing 'half-on' voltages, the noise inherent in the microplasmas not being examined can tend to obscure the signal from those being studied. Considerable skill is sometimes needed to locate a given microplasma and correlate it with the corresponding set of noise pulses on the VI characteristic, because the area of high multiplication is very small ($\geqslant 1\mu$) and the range of diode voltage over which a microplasma gives a rapid pulse rate is very limited (typically 50 mV centred on an unknown voltage). At high diode currents the device characteristic is not always stable because of heating effects. One other warning is appropriate. It is possible, by overenthusiastic use of high magnifications and line scans, to permanently alter the properties of some microplasmas. The usual effect is to 'put out' the microplasma by the sustained use of high current densities, i.e. the noise pulses, the current multiplication and the light emission properties are virtually eliminated. This can be avoided by exercising due care, i.e. by keeping the beam current low and by using fast scan-rates. Often the damage is done when the device is photographed using a 100-second, frame-time. This can be avoided by superimposing ten, 10-second, frame-time exposures.

The technique can be used in conjunction with the x-ray microanalyser to diagnose the chemical nature of any contaminant associated with the microplasma and, possibly, in conjunction with ion-etching to establish the structure in three dimensions or to reveal precipitates. The method has also been used to examine localized surface breakdown [15, 20]. When used in conjunction with the pn contrast mechanism it was possible to observe the field ionization of neutral impurities associated with surface scratches across a pn junction in silicon. And it was possible to observe such effects at low voltages (4 to 6 volts) compared to the voltages (16

PLATES

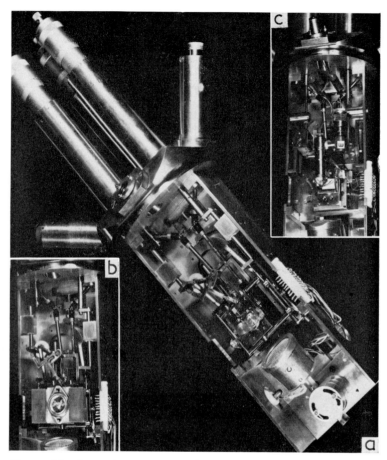

Figure 7.1. A specimen stage suitable for semiconductor work; (a) general view showing how two specimens can be incorporated with five degrees of freedom; (b) use of a heavy heat sink; (c) incorporation of a miniature liquifier. (*Note:* In the last figure the wedge movement shown is the earlier, friction-bearing movement—see text.)

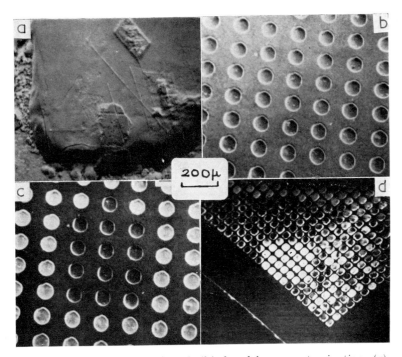

Figure 7.7. Typical examples of oil-induced beam contamination; (a) 'photoresist' action protecting GaAs specimens from etchant, (b) to (d) charge-up effects associated with oil-induced contamination obscuring pn contrast and charge collection signal from Ge photo-diode; (b) emissive micrograph taken with $V_b = 0$; (c) as (b) but with $V_b = 6$ volts; (d) conductive micrograph of similar diode showing contamination induced region of charge collection.

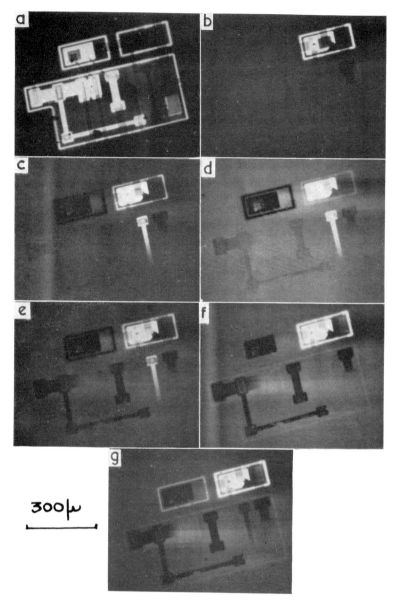

Figure 9.9. Charge collection micrographs of the circuit shown in figure 9.8. The micrographs shown were taken at the bias (V_4) values indicated in figure 9.10(a).

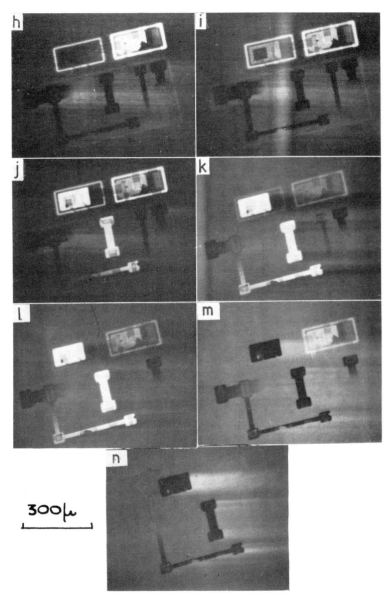

Figure 9.9. (*continued*).

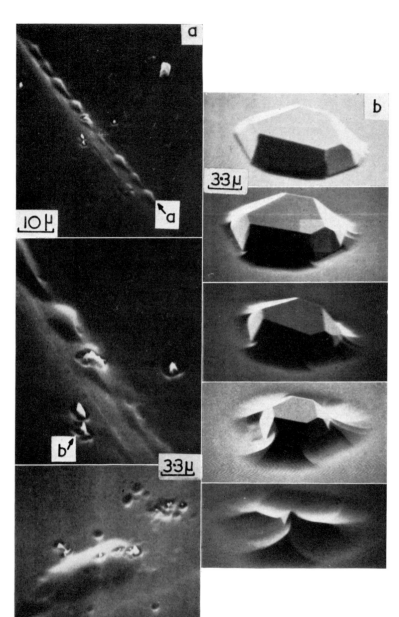

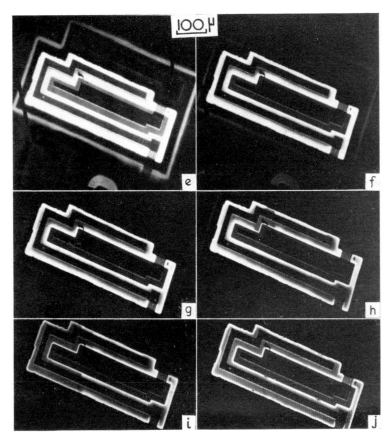

Figure 12.1. Actual conductive micrographs of a faulty planar microcircuit showing the gradual removal of the inversion by electron beam
bombardment. (e) to (j) correspond to leakage currents of $1\cdot2\mu$A,
$0\cdot17\mu$A, $0\cdot05\mu$A, $0\cdot038\mu$A, $0\cdot037\mu$A and $0\cdot033\mu$A respectively. (See page
315 for parts (a) to (d).)

Opposite
Figure 11.13. Ion-etching studies of GaP and epitaxially deposited Si:
(a) insulator precipitates [b] and 'hillocks' [a] revealed at subgrain
boundaries in GaP; (b) ion-etching studies of crystal growth on Si
(times of etching $\frac{1}{2}$, $1\frac{1}{2}$, $3\frac{1}{2}$, $5\frac{1}{2}$ and 8 hrs. respectively, ion current
density $\sim 10\mu$ amps/cm^2).

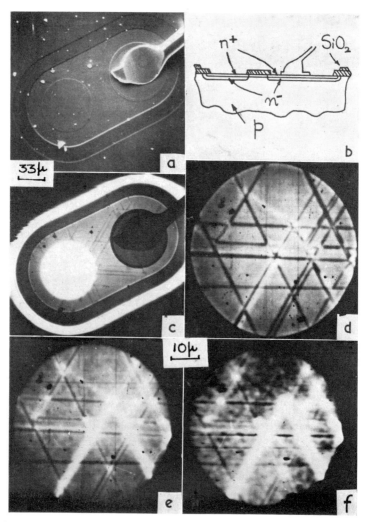

Figure 12.3. Avalanche breakdown in planar guard ring diodes containing diffusion induced dislocations. (*a*) Emissive micrograph of the diodes studied; (*b*) cross-section line diagram of the devices studied; (*c*) conductive micrograph of the general device structure at zero volts bias; (*d*) conductive micrograph of the active area at zero volts bias. (*e*) and (*f*) conductive micrographs of the active area at voltages of 5·72 and 8·43 volts respectively showing current multiplication at some dislocation nodes. (Diameter of active area = ∼ 60μ.)

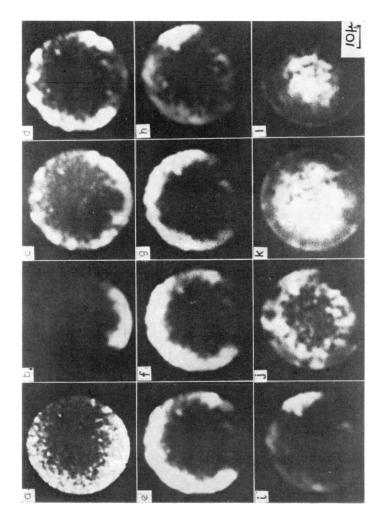

Figure 12.4. Studies of bulk avalanche breakdown at high currents (a) to (l) were taken at currents of 2·25, 80·0, 300, 450, 700, 900μA, 1·5, 2·0, 2·1, 3, 6 and 9 mA respectively.

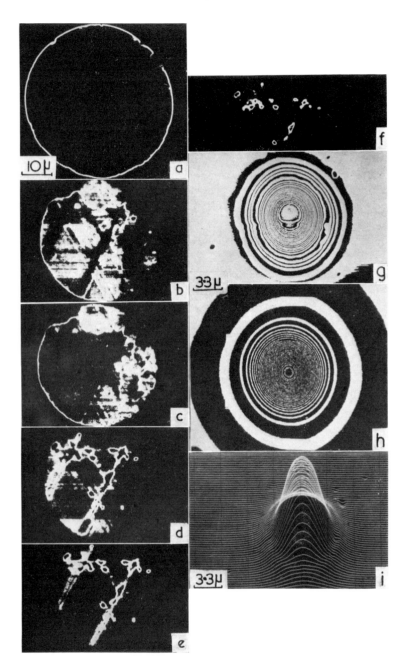

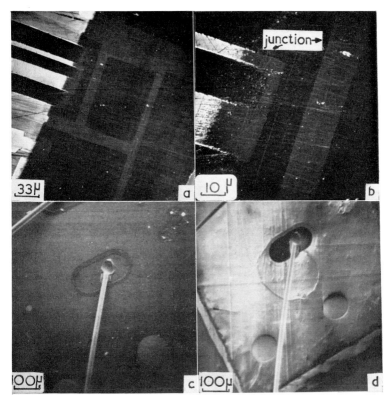

Figure 12.10. Application of the SEM to device inspection: (a) and (b) location of *pn* junctions on bevelled devices with no contacts and no chemical staining; (c) and (d) inspection of insulator fields, additional contrast revealed at low beam voltages. (c) Area of SiO_2 − Si device taken at $V_0 = 10$ kV; (d) same area taken at $V_0 = 3$ kV.

Opposite

Figure 12.5. Initial quantitative studies of current multiplication using a comparator circuit to determine regions of equal signal. The diode bias = 7·49 volts, (a) to (f) were taken at signal level settings of 0·2, 3·18, 3·23, 3·30, 3·40 and 3·52 volts respectively. (g) and (h) are multi-exposures taken with a comparator circuit. (g) comparator set at 0·38 volts then 0·1 volt steps to 2·8 volts at centre, $V_b = 10·0$ volts, (h) comparator set at 0·19 volts then 0·1 volt steps to 3·19 volts at centre, $V_b = 9·91$ volts; (i) is a deflection modulation display of a similar diode taken at $V_b = 0$.

to 24 volts) at which light emission occurred at the scratch regions.

Gaylord [16] has examined localized breakdown in planar micro-circuits and related the effects observed to pinholes in the passivating layer. Similarly the method can be used to examine breakdown in the SiO_2 layer itself. An insulator layer on a Si substrate is made into a condenser by evaporating a thin ($\lesssim 500$ Å) Au layer onto the top surface of a SiO_2 layer on a Si substrate and by subsequently bonding to this layer. This top contact not only allows a bias to be applied but eliminates the 'charge-up' effects observed in uncoated insulator layers. As the bias across the insulator is increased, high electric fields occur which are localized near 'pinholes', regions of contamination and other faults. Localized avalanche breakdown occurs above a certain critical bias voltage in each case and can be used to form a conductive micrograph which may be compared with the surface topography.

It is interesting to record that the transmission electron microscope has recently been used to study the breakdown of oxide layers [22].

12.3.3 *Studies of bulk breakdown: qualitative*

Figure 12.3 (Plate) shows an instructive sequence of conductive micrographs of a passivated guard-ring diode with the structure shown in figure 12.3(a) and (b). In the micrograph shown in figure 12.3(c) the charge-collection signal from the active area of the device and from where the guard-ring junction comes to the surface were allowed to saturate in order to photograph the device structure and to reveal the diffusion-induced dislocations at the n^+n inter-face. Figures 12.3(d) and (f) were taken with reduced gain and increased current back-off to reveal the effect these dislocations have on the device operation. These dislocations have been extensively studied [29, 30, 31] and, as indicated in section 9.3, are observed in the SEM because the enhanced carrier recombination-rate that occurs in the immediate neighbourhood of the dislocations interferes with the charge-collection by the junction field. As the diode bias is increased, the majority of the dislocation length remains a region of enhanced recombination. But some regions, particularly those where the dislocations cross (the dislocation 'nodes'), become regions of enhanced signal, i.e. current multiplication. The implica-tion is that, in general, the dislocation lengths do not give rise to localized breakdown, but that some special regions do. Possibly this breakdown arises because of the presence at these places of a second

Y

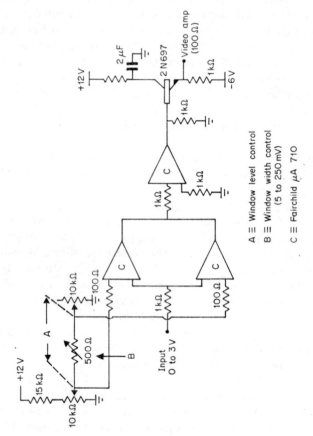

Figure 12.6. Comparator circuit used for the studies shown in figure 12.5 (*Courtesy K. A. Hughes*).

phase or precipitate which enhances the local field, i.e. the model suggested by Shockley may be applicable. Although these observations were obtained with relatively large bias voltages the diode current is relatively low ($\lesssim 100\mu$A). Figures 12.4(a) to (d) (Plate) show what kind of data can be obtained with large currents flowing in the device. Although the spatial resolution is not so good ($\sim 1\ \mu$ depending on structure) at high currents it is apparent that detailed information about the variations in current multiplication as a function of bias can be obtained. This kind of data can be obtained quickly from all relevant types of specimens over a wide range of temperatures and field strengths. From a quantitative point of view these data are unsatisfactory because the gain and 'back-off' are often varied to accommodate the large change in signals observed as the bias is changed.

12.3.4 *Studies of bulk breakdown: quantitative*

One way in which quantitative studies can be made is to work at constant (precalibrated) gain and to use a calibrated back-off unit (such as Tetronix type Z plug-in unit). The sequence shown in figure 12.5 (Plate) was taken by another approach using a comparator circuit of the type shown in figure 12.6. This circuit rejects any signal which does not fall within a narrow range (the 'gate-width') about a given, preset value. In the comparator used in these studies [19] the preset value could be altered from 0 to 5 volts and the gate width was 30 mV. Thus, by keeping the diode bias constant (as in the sequence shown) and varying the preset value, quantitative estimates of the relative charge-collection efficiency can be obtained. By repeating such studies as a function of diode bias in positions of interest on the diode surface estimates of the current multiplication can be obtained as a function of beam voltage (i.e. penetration distance) [19].

Quantitative studies can also be made by a modified deflection modulation system. The scan generator is used on a line scan and the 'end of line' blanking pulse used to trigger a voltage ramp or step generator. The output from this step generator is used to control the Y deflection of the CRT spot and synchronously to vary the diode bias. In this way the charge-collection signal over a line is plotted out as a function of V_b along the Y axis. If a chopped primary beam is used, quantitative measurements of the current multiplication can be obtained because the true signals can be determined, i.e. there is no uncertainty due to 'back-off'. Further refinement is possible. Obviously this kind of approach means that the specimen has to be examined in the SEM for a considerable time, and it is necessary to check that the device suffers no degradation or variation of properties during the examination otherwise the data obtained at the end of the run cannot be straightforwardly related to the data acquired at the start. This means that the contamination problem discussed in Chapter 7 has to be eliminated and spot-checks have to be carried out throughout the period of observation to ensure that no beam-induced changes of the type discussed in Chapters 6 and 7 have occurred.

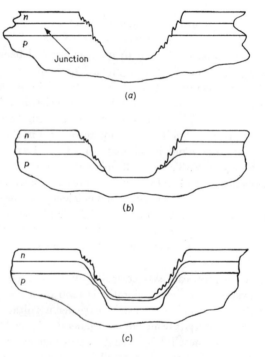

Figure 12.7. Diode structure with uncertain junction position in which it is difficult to determine the junction position: (*a*), (*b*) and (*c*) indicate the possible junction positions that may exist as a function of 'dimple' depth.

12.4 Use of voltage contrast mechanism

12.4.1 *Limitations and possible extensions*

We have already made the point that the voltage contrast mechanism is not completely understood in the sense that we cannot predict the best, i.e. most sensitive, conditions under which to examine a given device. As we have to rely on empiricism to determine the most sensitive conditions, it is well to consider what factors can impede or enhance the ability to detect voltage contrast, and we will begin by noting some of these factors.

(1) *Surface topography.* Most of the pioneering studies [23, 24, 25] have been made with simple structures, either isolated diode structures, bevelled or cleaved edges and planar microcircuits. Relatively few studies have been reported of junction location in cases where the surface roughness leads to rapid changes in contrast across the junction area and so tends to obscure the voltage contrast. The type of situation that can exist [26] is illustrated in figure 12.7. The junction (of unknown position and extent) is located in 'dimples' in the surface. Superimposed on this required surface shape there may be a more refined structure, such as that due to etching. In cases like this the 'voltage contrast' electrons can be lost by specimen modulation (see section 8.3). This loss, together with surface contrast, can make the location of the junction uncertain.

(2) *Reflected electrons.* Au, and more recently, Pt and Pb, are being used as bonding materials in micro-devices. Such high atomic-number materials have high back-scattering coefficients. If a fraction of back-scattered electrons from Au contacts are collected by the scintillator, they may give a large signal which obscures the detail (including the voltage contrast) from the remainder of the area examined.

(3) *Device construction.* We often have to examine device elements which are relatively low in position compared to the device container. Figure 12.8(*a*) illustrates the case of a 'flat-pack' container which stops some of the emitted secondary electrons from reaching the collector. Figure 12.8(*b*) shows another case in which a thermally bonded device is positioned so that the bonding posts with the stand-off insulators (I) are remote from the collector. If the insulators

charge up, they may affect the voltage contrast. Sulway [17] recently observed an apparent increase in voltage contrast as such a device was gradually heated to 200°C. It was found that this increase in sensitivity occurred at the temperature at which the insulators ceased to charge up, under the beam current used. Subsequent studies showed that if care was taken to shield the insulators from the effects of the primary beam then the voltage contrast was maintained at a sensitive level.

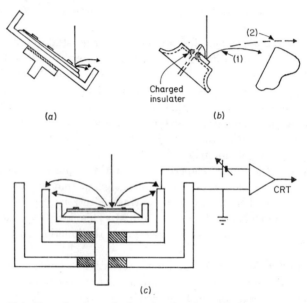

Figure 12.8. Examination of microcircuits: (*a*) and (*b*) two situations in which detection of voltage contrast can be difficult due to (*a*) loss of signal to container and (*b*) due to charge-up of near-by insulators, (1) before insulator charged up, (2) with insulator charged up; (*c*) use of collecting ring near to specimen to detect secondary electron signal [28].

(4) *Surface field effects.* Most of the reported observations of voltage contrast have been made on *pn* junctions with narrow depletion layers. Spivak and collaborators [25] were the first to show that surface fields, as opposed to differences in surface voltage, can play a role in determining the observed signal if the depletion layer is wide compared with the spot size. Similar effects are observed on

bulk materials [47]. It is not really known how the high field contrast arises. One possibility is that the surface fields affect the electron trajectories in the manner indicated in Chapter 8. Another possibility is that internal surface fields can cause variations in secondary electron emission in much the same manner as surface fields can aid photoemission [26, 27], by providing, in effect, additional energy to help in escaping through the crystal surface.

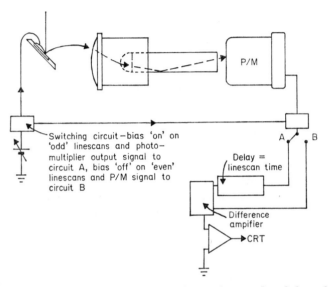

Figure 12.9. Block diagram suggesting how micrographs of the voltage distribution alone can be obtained. (Schematic).

Much can be done to avoid these complications. For example, the signal from the reflected electrons can be avoided by the use of a velocity-selective collector system such as the simple system shown in figure 8.14. The loss of emitted electrons to a nearby shield or to part of the structure can be exploited to obtain information by measuring the current flowing to earth through it when maintained at a positive voltage relative to the device. Potts [28] has improved the technique by using the collector system shown in figure 12.8(c) and obtained an ability to distinguish surface voltage differences ~ 100 mV, although with very limited spatial resolution. It is unlikely that this approach will give the required combination of high resolution and good voltage detectivity. The question of

surface topography has yet to be resolved. One possible approach
is outlined in figure 12.9. It is so arranged that the element being
examined is reverse biassed on 'odd' line scans and is either unbiassed or forward biassed on 'even' line scans. A given 'odd' line
scan is delayed by a time required to synchronize it with the following 'even' scan. These signals are compared by a difference amplifier
and the difference used to form an emissive micrograph. In this
way the contrast will, to a first approximation, be determined by
the voltage difference applied during the 'odd' and 'even' line scans.

With regard to the various mechanisms involved in 'high field'
contrast we can only reiterate that further work of a fundamental
nature is required to clarify how useful the effect can be and how
it can be eliminated in situations where it is a nuisance. Finally it
should be noted that small surface voltages become easier to detect
when the primary beam energy is lowered. This does not appear to
increase the limiting sensitivity of which a given collector in a
given position is capable, but it does make it less susceptible to
charge-up and to loss. Using an Everhart-Thornley collector system
or a channel electron multiplier without any velocity selection it
should be possible to detect 0·2 volts surface voltage difference in
most cases and still maintain a spatial resolution $\lesssim$ 1,000 Å.

12.4.2 *Quantitative surface voltage studies*

Ideally we should like to be able to plot out quantitative high-
resolution maps of surface potential with good voltage discrimination
in situations where we have no other methods of making such
measurements. So far as we have not attained this end, but some
pioneering studies have been made. MacDonald and Everhart [32]
have used the voltage contrast mechanism to study the depletion-
layer movement with applied bias of an abrupt junction exposed by
bevelling. By measuring the movement of the contrast as a function
of bias it was possible to predict the bulk resistivity of the material
on the more resistive side of the junction, and to obtain good
agreement with surface conductance measurements. So the method
gives reliable estimates in simple situations. The interesting possibility is that of using the conductive mode and the voltage-contrast
mechanism to diagnose surface field configurations in complex
situations. It has been shown [33] that in structures where the field
distribution is not abrupt the depletion layer movement as measured
by charge collection signal is not always simply related to the

changes observed in voltage contrast. By analysing the results of such combination studies, it may be possible to develop first qualitative models of the field distribution; finally we should aim for quantitative data.

12.4.3 *Applications of voltage contrast*

The useful application of the voltage-contrast mechanism to development studies of devices that have already been bonded is well documented in the literature [4, 32, 34], and needs no elaboration here. What is less well-established is the use of the method to examine devices that have not been bonded and to which electrical contact can be made only by the substrate. There are two situations of interest; one in which junction configurations at the surface have to be observed without making any bevel on the slice and the other in which the underlying sections of a junction have to be examined after bevelling. There are two difficulties facing the present bevelling and staining technique used to outline junction position. One is the difficulty caused by the gradual curvature of the bevelled edge when the junction depth is small ($\leqslant \frac{1}{2}\,\mu$), the other is the need to develop a selective etch which reveals the junction position with certainty, and not in a manner which depends on the etching time and/or solution concentration. The SEM cannot help with the first of these difficulties, but it can eliminate the second. Figure 12.10 (Plate) shows the junctions revealed by voltage contrast on the bevelled edge of a microcircuit with no contacts. The contrast arises because the collector system detects the nett voltage difference which exists across the junction under the combined action of the diffusion potential and the charge collection current. This method works best with relatively low beam voltages (5 to 10 kV). Junctions can be located to within $\pm$ 1,000 Å with ease on bevelled surfaces. A similar resolution can be obtained on well cleaved surfaces. Provided the cleave is made from the side opposite to that on which the junction is located it is possible to locate a junction of depth 2,000 Å below the surface to within $\pm$ 1,000 Å. Similarly, by using a capacitatively coupled signal in the manner described in section 9.8 to give a deflection modulation display, the beam-induced charge-collection can give a very useful display of the junction position with only one electrical connection to the substrate. Chang and Nixon [35] have studied unbevelled and unbonded transistors, both with and without oxide layers, by the voltage-contrast mechanism.

They conclude that on unpassivated devices it is possible to locate both emitter-base and base-collector junctions, provided the primary beam energy is chosen to give the correct degree of penetration relative to the junction depths. On passivated devices these workers show that the true potential difference across a junction can be obscured by charge-up of the oxide layers at low beam voltages. Thornley [36] has shown that this difficulty can be avoided by working at a beam voltage near to the second, cross-over point.

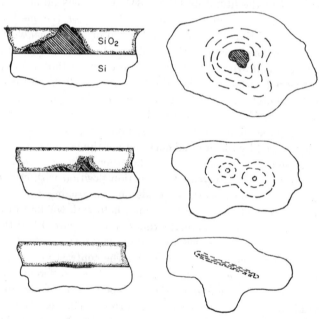

Figure 12.11. Diagrams showing the type of relationship observed between structural defects, the contrast observed at high beam voltages (shaded areas) the additional contrast at low beam voltages (dashed lines).

12.5 Insulator studies

There are very few published SEM studies [37, 38], of the properties of insulating layers and we have to rely on uncompleted studies and plausibility arguments to assess the possibilities. If we restrict our discussion for the present to the use of the SEM to study localized variations in oxide or nitride layers on Si or Ge we can make the following points:

(1) By using low beam voltages (2 to 5 kV for the film thicknesses appropriate to microcircuits) it is possible to observe additional contrast features over and above those observed when high beam voltages are used and the beam penetrates right through the insulating layer.

(2) The observed contrast takes a finite time to build up to its final equilibrium value under a given excitation. The magnitude of this build up time depends on the insulator properties, the beam voltage and beam current density.

(3) The effects are reversible in that they decay with time or with exposure to ambient gas.

(4) Often the features observed are associated with some surface marking or have the geometrical shape associated with scratches on the underlying Si, errors in photo resist, etc. For example the contrast observed at low beam voltage can take the form shown in figure 12.11. A pair of micrographs showing these effects is illustrated in figures 12.10(c) and (d) (Plate).

(5) There appears to be an optimum beam voltage to observe these effects. If the beam voltage is too low, the contrast is inadequate and the effects difficult to observe. If the voltage is too high, 'charge-up' effects tend to obscure regions of the surface.

(6) In the case of the silicon oxide specimens examined a relatively slow, but near permanent beam-induced change in oxide properties tended in time to remove these effects.

The detailed mechanisms leading to this low beam voltage contrast are not known, but the general behaviour can be rationalized in terms of how variations in oxide thickness and resistivity can lead to variations in surface voltage (see Chapter 5). These variations in surface voltage can affect the emission yield and the fraction of the emitted electrons which are collected by the detection system. Although we cannot fully assess the value of this application until we can understand the contrast mechanisms, the method is of use even in its present form, as these effects enable pinholes and buried defects to be found with ease because of enhanced contrast and it allows the comparison of oxides made by various methods.

Another possible use of the SEM in this context is as an extension to irradiation studies of materials and devices. At present irradiation studies are generally effected by flooding the whole device with the appropriate radiation. It is conceivable that it may be of value to irradiate only part of a device or circuits. Such experiments can be

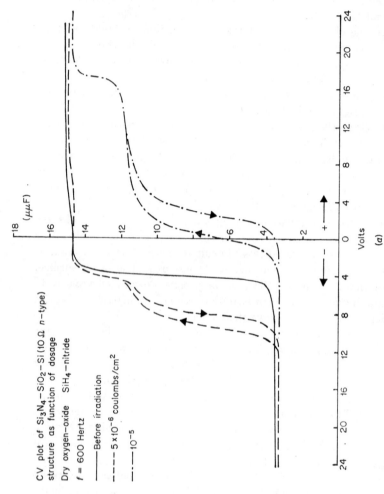

CV plot of $Si_3N_4-SiO_2-Si$ (10 Ω n-type)
structure as function of dosage

Dry oxygen–oxide SiH_4–nitride

$f = 600$ Hertz

—— Before irradiation

– – – 5×10^{-6} coulombs/cm^2

–·–·– 10^{-5}

Figure 12.12. (a) to (c) Irradiation studies of a metal – $Si_3N_4 - SiO_2 - Si$ 'sandwich' with n-type Si oxide formed by dry oxidation and nitride derived from SiH_4/N_2O.

332

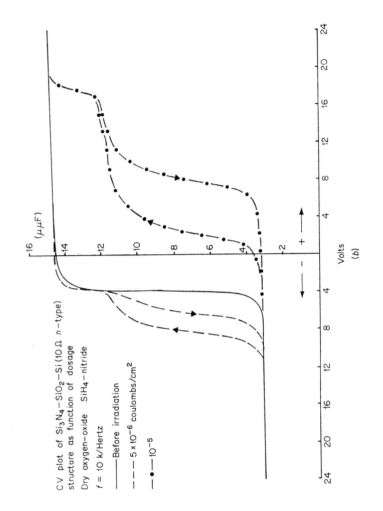

CV plot of Si_3N_4–SiO_2–Si (10 Ω n–type) structure as function of dosage

Dry oxygen–oxide SiH_4–nitride

$f = 10$ k/Hertz

—— Before irradiation

– – – 5×10^{-6} coulombs/cm^2

•—— 10^{-5}

16 $(\mu\mu F)$

Volts

(b)

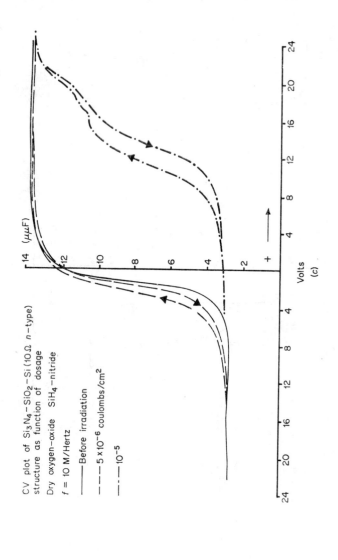

CV plot of $Si_3N_4-SiO_2-Si$ (10 Ω n-type) structure as function of dosage

Dry oxygen-oxide SiH_4-nitride

$f = 10$ M/Hertz

—— Before irradiation

— — — 5×10^{-6} coulombs/cm^2

— · — 10^{-5}

14 ($\mu\mu F$)

Volts

(c)

done in the SEM. The data shown in figures 12.12 and 12.13 illustrate initial studies of two types of composite Si_3N_4-SiO_2 sandwiches. In these experiments the whole of the active condenser formed by the substrate – insulator sandwiches – evaporated contract layers, was irradiated. It is apparent that a wide diversity of behaviour can be observed on irradiation. At the present time experiments are being designed to relate these changes to the initial properties of the layers and to study the variation with position on the slice.

12.6 Use of very low energy scanning electron beams in surface studies

An elegant use of a scanning electron beam of very low energy has been proved by Wolf and colleagues [39]. This low energy beam is used to determine surface potential variations quantitatively and to assess the properties and faults of devices made by ion implantation. The basic system is shown in figure 12.14. The current from a tungsten filament passes through an Einzel lens. In the final lens there is a very small aperture (7.5μ or, on occasions, 1μ). The acceleration voltages used are $\lesssim 200$ volts. After passing through the final aperture the electrons meet a high retarding field before impinging on the specimen, which can be 'floated' in potential relative to the source. The system is contained in an all-metal, vacuum system capable of 10^{-10} torr pressure after baking. In the earlier models the specimen was scanned manually, but later models incorporated electron-optical scanning. Facilities for a sputter clean-up were also included. This system is ideal for studying the very shallow junctions ($\gtrsim 0.1\mu$) formed by ion implantation and surface physics problems in general.

Wolf *et al.* [39] used the system to make three sets of measurements-static retarding potential studies, scanning potential and charge-collection studies, (see figure 12.15). In the retarding potential studies the cathode-target voltage difference was varied between 0 and 10 volts (both signs) and the collected beam current measured. In the scanning potential mode the target voltage was held near that corresponding to the 'knee' of the collected current voltage curve and the collected current measured as a function of position. This measures the potential distribution. In making charge-collection studies an accelerating field is used between the Einzel lens and the specimen. More recently the method has been used [40] to study imperfections arising in ion-implanted structures.

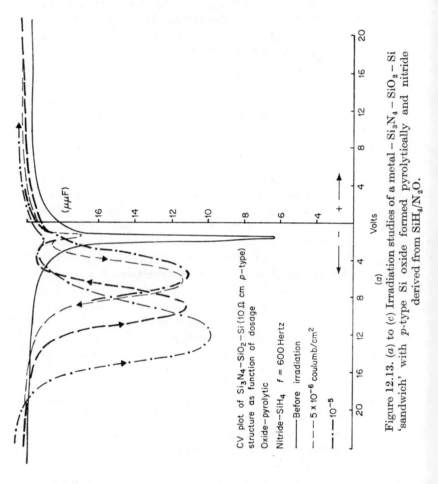

CV plot of Si_3N_4–SiO_2–Si ($10\,\Omega$ cm p–type)
structure as function of dosage

Oxide–pyrolytic

Nitride–SiH_4 f = 600 Hertz

——— Before irradiation

– – – 5×10^{-6} coulumb/cm^2

–·–·– 10^{-5}

($\mu\mu F$)

Volts

(a)

Figure 12.13. (a) to (c) Irradiation studies of a metal – Si_3N_4 – SiO_2 – Si 'sandwich' with p-type Si oxide formed pyrolytically and nitride derived from SiH_4/N_2O.

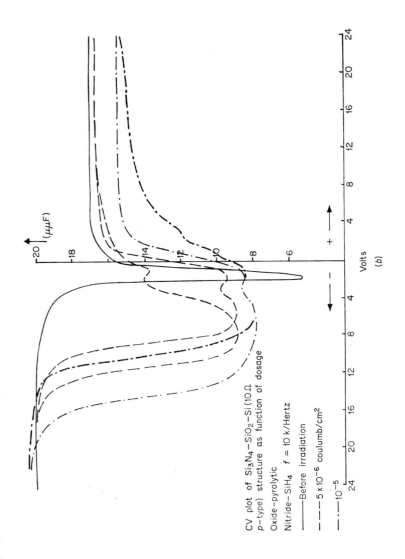

CV plot of Si_3N_4–SiO_2–Si ($10\,\Omega$ p-type) structure as function of dosage

Oxide–pyrolytic

Nitride–SiH_4 $f = 10$ k/Hertz

——— Before irradiation

——— 5×10^{-6} coulumb/cm^2

—··— 10^{-5}

Volts

(b)

z

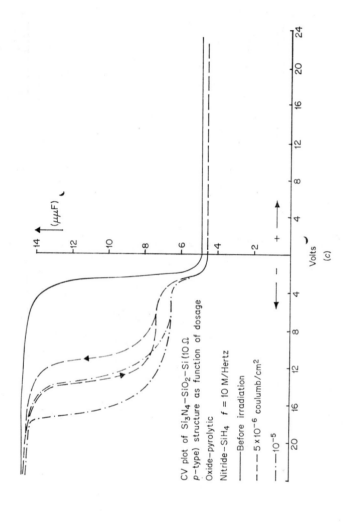

CV plot of Si_3N_4–SiO_2–Si (10 Ω p-type) structure as function of dosage

Oxide–pyrolytic

Nitride–SiH_4 f = 10 M/Hertz

——— Before irradiation

– – – 5 × 10^{-6} coulumb/cm^2

–·–· 10^{-5}

($\mu\mu F$)

Volts

(c)

The question naturally arises as to whether this technique can be incorporated in a more conventional, relatively high-voltage SEM. For example, can a low energy beam of good resolution be obtained with a cathode at − 5,000 volts and a specimen at a potential of between (− 900 to − 5,000 volts)? Studies made by Pease [41] are relevant to this query. A simple model suggests that the use of a retarding field between the final lens and the specimen may be

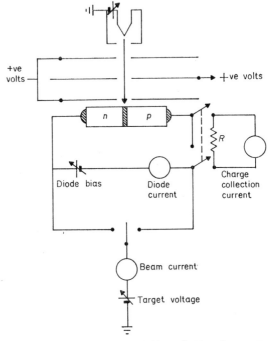

Figure 12.14. Apparatus used by Wolf *et al.* [39] for surface physics
·studies using a very low voltage electron beam.

capable of giving a resolution which should be within a factor of two of that obtained with the more conventional system. Initial experimental measurements bear out this prediction for a somewhat restricted specimen structure. One point is problematical. If such a system is to be used to give retarding potential studies then the control of voltage between cathode and target has to be ≲ 20 mV. If the cathode is to be at 5 to 2 kV, this requirement implies a voltage stability of ≲ 2·5 in 10^6. This is near the limit of stability of EHT supplies and so, together with restrictions on specimen geometry, may restrict the full use of the low voltage approach.

12.7 Discussion

We have already made the points that electrical measurements on inversion layers give 'averaged' information in which localized variations are smeared out and that an unambiguous interpretation cannot always be obtained. And we have seen how the SEM can locate the spatial variation of a given leakage path. This technique is already in use in development laboratories. What has not been developed to date is a technique whereby the SEM can be used to give information about the *causes* of the observed inversion layers, i.e. to determine the nature (donor, acceptor, etc.), position in the bandgap, position in the structure and the density of the defects causing the inversion. In other words, how can we use the SEM as a refined probe in the same way as a scanning light spot is used in surface physics to study surface properties and in the same way as ultraviolet excitation is used to investigate the distribution of a charge trapped in an oxide layer [42, 43]? Just as in the case of the light-spot so we can vary the penetration of the excitation by varying the beam voltage. The variation is somewhat more restricted (20 Å to 8μ in SiO_2 is feasible, see [46]) but the spatial resolution is considerably greater. The one important complication that we have to consider is the semi-permanent changes induced in the specimen by the beam; for example, the degradation of β in planar transistors [44] which is reversed by annealing in air at 250°C. Unless such effects are understood they cannot be exploited to diagnose surface and interface properties, nor can they be eliminated when they have to be avoided, in the inspection of production line devices, for example. Work is going on in many laboratories aimed at extending the technique in this direction.

Leaving aside the question of oil-beam contamination which can be minimized by a suitable choice of pumping oil or by heating the specimen and can be eliminated by the use of baked, ion-pumped systems, there remains the interaction with the specimen surface itself. The fact that many irradiation induced defects can be annealed out at 200 to 250°C suggests that SEM examinations carried out at temperatures of this order would result in little or no change. In addition, working at such temperatures reduces both the contamina-

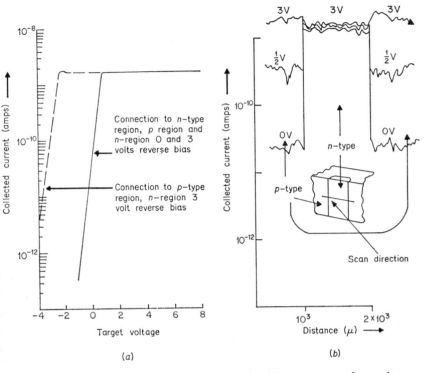

Figure 12.15. Quantitative data obtained with apparatus shown in figure 12.14. (*a*) 'Retardation' curves relating collected current to target voltage as function of diode bias and diode connection; (*b*) spatial variation of collected current as a function of diode bias; (*c*) charge collection current at very low beam voltages [39].

tion problem and the difficulties due to insulator charge-up. This is also the temperature range in which accelerated life-testing of devices is often carried out. Initial experiments [45] have shown that the use of elevated temperatures is very beneficial. For example planar transistors can be examined at 200°C with greatly reduced degradation in β. The situation with MOST structures is more complicated, but the changes induced, both as regard to changes in threshold voltage and in transconductance, are smaller at a higher temperature provided a suitable bias is applied. The use of low beam currents and, if possible, low beam voltages, helps. It has yet

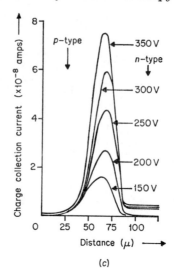

(c)

to be established whether SEM examination of specimens subjected to a flood beam of ultraviolet radiation can also be used. This method would, by photoemission, avoid charge build-up in the oxide and would appear to offer possibilities for reduced damage.

This is where the topic rests at present – with a need for relatively fundamental studies aimed at clarifying and using the semi-permanent effects introduced in the SEM as a diagnostic tool as a function of temperature and excitation. In particular there is a need to relate the observed changes to the initial properties of the device. These beam-induced changes are also relevant to the contents of the next chapter which deals with the fabrication of devices with electron beams.

REFERENCES

[1] See, for example, R. M. SCARLETT, W. SHOCKLEY and R. H. HAITZ, *Physics of failure in Electronics*, (ed. Goldberg and Vaccaro Spartan), Baltimore, (1963)

[2] For references, see H. A. SCHAFFT and J. C. FRENCH, *I.R.E. Trans. on Electron Devices*, **ED-9**, 129, (1962)

[3] C. J. VARKER and E. M. JULEFF, *I.E.E.E. 9th Annual Symposium on Electron, Ion and Laser Beam Technology*, Berkeley, Calif., (1967)

[4] D. GREEN and H. C. NATHANSON, *Proc. I.E.E.E.*, **53**, 183, (1965)

[5] T. E. EVERHART, O. C. WELLS and R. K. MATTA, *J. Electrochem. Soc.*, **111**, 929, (1964)

[6] J. W. THORNHILL and I. M. MACKINTOSH, *Microelectronics and Reliability*, **4**, 97, (1965)

[7] P. R. THORNTON, K. A. HUGHES, HTIN KYAW, C. MILLWARD and D. V. SULWAY, *Microelectronics and Reliability*, **6**, 9, (1967)

[8] A. G. CHYOWETH and K. G. MCKAY, *J. Appl. Phys.*, **30**, 1811, (1959). See references given in P. R. THORNTON, *The Physics of Electroluminescent Devices*, Spon, (1967)

[9] See, for example, M. POLESHUK and P. H. DOWLING, *J. Appl. Phys.*, **34**, 3069, (1963)

[10] R. A. LOGAN, A. G. CHYOWETH and B. G. COHEN, *Phys. Rev.*, **128**, 2518, (1962)

[11] M. GERSHENZON and R. M. MIKULAK, *J. Appl. Phys.*, **32**, 1338, (1961)

[12] A. G. FISCHER, *J. Electrochem. Soc.*, **110**, 733, (1963)

[13] O. W. LOSSEV, *Phil. Mag.*, **6**, 1024, (1928) and L. PATRICK, *J. Appl. Phys.*, **28**, 765, (1957)

[14] H. KRESSEL, *RCA Review*, **28**, 175, (1967)

[15] I. G. DAVIES, K. A. HUGHES, D. V. SULWAY and P. R. THORNTON, *Solid-State Electron*, **9**, 275, (1966)

[16] J. W. GAYLORD, *J. Electrochem. Soc.*, **113**, 753, (1966)

[17] D. V. SULWAY, Ph.D. Thesis, Bangor U.C.N.W., (1967)

[18] P. R. THORNTON, N. F. V. NEVE, D. V. SULWAY and R. C. WAYTE, *I.E.E.E. 9th Annual Symposium on Electron, Ion and Laser Technology*, Berkeley, Calif., (1967)

[19] N. F. B. NEVE, *Annual Report on CVD Contract No. 3622/66*, Bangor, U.C.N.W., (1967)

[20] N. F. B. NEVE, K. A. HUGHES and P. R. THORNTON, *J. Appl. Phys.*, **37**, 1704, (1966)

[21] N. F. B. NEVE, M.Sc. Thesis, Bangor, U.C.N.W., (1966)

[22] P. P. BUDENSTEIN and P. J. HAYES, *J. Appl. Phys.*, **38**, 2837, (1967)

[23] T. E. EVERHART, O. C. WELLS and C. W. OATLEY, *J. Electron. and Control*, **7**, 97, (1959)

[24] C. W. OATLEY and T. E. EVERHART, *J. Electron. and Control*, **2**, 568, (1957)

[25] C. V. SPIVAK, G. V. SAPARIN and N. A. PEREVERZEV, *Izv. Acad. Nauk, USSR.*, Ser. Fiz., **26**, 1339, (1962)

[26] P. R. THORNTON and D. C. NORTHROP, *Solid-State Electron*, **8**, 437, (1965)

[27] R. E. SIMON and W. E. SPICER, *J. Appl. Phys.*, **31**, 1505, (1960)

[28] H. R. POTTS, *Microelectronics and Reliability*, **6**, 173, (1967)

[29] J. J. LANDER, H. SCHREIBER, T. M. BUCK and J. R. MATTHEWS, *Appl. Phys. Letters*, **3**, 206, (1963)

[30] W. CZAJA and G. H. WHEATLEY, *J. Appl. Phys.*, **35**, 2782, (1964)

[31] W. CZAJA, *J. Appl. Phys.*, **37**, 918, (1966)

[32] N. C. MACDONALD and T. E. EVERHART, *Appl. Phys. Letters*, **7**, 267, (1965)

[33] P. R. THORNTON, N. F. B. NEVE and D. V. SULWAY, *Microelectronics and Reliability*, **5**, 299, (1966)

[34] D. V. SULWAY, HTIN KYAW and P. R. THORNTON, *Solid-State Electron.*, **10**, 545, (1967)

[35] T. P. CHANG and W. C. NIXON, *Solid-State Electron.*, **10**, 701, (1967)

[36] R. F. M. THORNLEY, Ph.D. Thesis, Cambridge, (1960)

[37] D. GREEN, *Proc. 8th Annual Sym. on Electron and Laser Beam Technology, Ann. Arbor*, (1966)

[38] D. V. SULWAY, N. F. B. NEVE and P. R. THORNTON, *Annual Report on CVD Contract No. CP 13436*, Bangor, U.C.N.W., (1966)

[39] E. D. WOLF, R. G. WILSON and J. W. MAYER, *2nd International Conf. on Ion- and Electron-beam Science and Technology, New York*, May, (1966)

[40] E. D. WOLF, *I.E.E.E. 9th Annual Symposium on Electron, Ion and Laser Beam Technology, Berkeley, Calif.*, (1967)

[41] R. F. W. PEASE, *I.E.E.E. 9th Annual Symposium on Electron, Ion and Laser Beam Technology, Berkeley, Calif.*, (1967)

[42] R. WILLIAMS, *J. Appl. Phys.*, **37**, 1491, (1966)

[43] A. M. GOODMAN, *Phys. Rev.*, **152**, 780, (1966)

[44] D. GREEN, J. E. SANDOR, T. W. O'KEEFFE and R. K. MATTA, *Appl. Phys. Letters*, **6**, 3, (1965)

[45] D. V. SULWAY and P. R. THORNTON, *Annual Report on CVD Contract No. CP 3632/66*, Bangor, U.C.N.W., (1967)

[46] J. P. MITCHELL and D. K. WILSON, *B.S.T. Journ.*, **46**, 1, (1967)

[47] P. R. THORNTON, M. J. CULPIN and I. W. DRUMMOND, *Solid-State Electron.*, **6**, 523, (1963)

CHAPTER 13

Application to Device Fabrication

13.1 Introduction

Here we are widening the field of application somewhat. So far we have been preoccupied with the use of electron beams to examine materials and devices and to diagnose microscopic faults and characteristics. The emphasis has been on the attainment of good resolution. As a result the beam currents have been usually very low (3×10^{-13} to 10^{-11} amp). This use of electron beams represents one extreme end of a complete spectrum of applications. The other end of the spectrum is represented by the very high voltage ($\geqslant 100$ kV), high current (≈ 1 mA) beams used for welding large structures. In this chapter, we will show how the low-current systems can be used to make devices, not, normally, by supplying the power necessary to fabricate the structure but by controlling the processes with high resolution and with a considerable degree of automation. In addition, reversible changes brought about in specimens by electron-beam irradiation are beginning to be employed to operate devices. Before discussing some instructive examples of the non-thermal use of electron beams for device fabrication we have to consider what kind of devices can be made by these methods and what are the advantages and limitations that electron-beam methods have over the existing methods. Wells [1] has reviewed the scope and potentialities of this technique.

There are two obvious fields of application, one is to thin-film technology and the second is to the manufacture of planar microcircuits. Thin-film assemblies are normally made by direct evaporation through suitable masks. The various patterns required in successive layers are obtained by the use of successive masks. By using suitable layers of conducting, insulator and ferromagnetic materials, resistors, capacitors and magnetic elements can be made. Additional contacts can be made later outside the vacuum. This use of successive masks is also inherent in current silicon planar technology. In this case the device elements are made by diffusion and by epitaxy [2]. These two technologies have one great virtue in common. Once the initial mask-making and processing has been evolved, the processes can be repeated many times thus producing large numbers of very complex and very small devices quickly and, with good process control, a moderate to good yield. The yield can be increased by suitable design, i.e. by including 'redundancies', by which are meant components to be used only if similar components fail to pass the necessary standards. Such redundancies can be

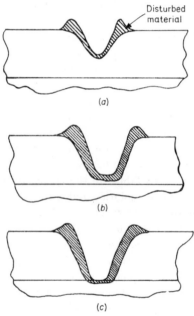

Figure 13.1. Shape of grove formed by electron-beam machining: (a) (b) and (c) represent the same grove subjected to increasing exposure.

included with a marginal increase in cost and time in mask preparation, because of the essentially 'parallel' nature of the process, i.e., many devices are made simultaneously. Therefore, if electron beams are to be used, they must either serve to make many device elements simultaneously or must have some significant advantages which overweigh the rather considerable loss of speed inherent in the use of scanning electron beams to give sequential fabrication. The possible advantages that come to mind are the increased resolution that may be obtained with electron beams and the possibility that such beams may be extensively programmed so that the complete process can be automated.

Electron beams can do three things of interest in this context. They can remove material to some pre-determined pattern, they can bring about chemical changes in the target or they can result in a reversible change in the localized charge distribution in the device. Consider the effect of material removal first.

13.2 Material removal by electron beams

The type of cross-section developed by an electron-beam-induced 'grove' is shown in figure 13.1. Not only does material get removed from the centre of the 'grove' but it gets redistributed to form 'hedges' on the grove sides. If the beam is scanned over the specimen too long the underlying substrate becomes damaged as well. Typically a beam of spot diameter 10μ will produce a grove of 15μ width with a total disturbance width of 25μ. The beam voltages used vary from 10 to 150 kV, the beam currents from 20 μA to 5 mA, the spot diameters usually from 2 to 20 μ and the power densities from 0·5 to 25 mW/cm². The writing speeds are of the order 1 to 25 cm/sec. The criteria used to judge the results and the system used are straightforward and are listed in table 13.1. The results obtained

Table 13.1. *Criteria used to judge electron-beam formed groves and systems* [3]

(a) Edge definition and contrast. Often such groves have to be electrically isolating.
(b) Hole depth to width obtainable.
(c) Restrictions, if any, on pattern geometry, or size (both maximum and minimum).
(d) Speed, repeatibility and flexibility.
(e) Compatability with the materials used, no damage to substrate etc.
(f) Economical factors.

---

depend strongly on the materials used. The resolution available on metal specimens is $\sim 10\ \mu$ in normal use although $2\ \mu$ can be obtained with difficulty. On the other hand $1·5\ \mu$ slots have been made in SiO_2 of thickness $150\ \mu$ [4].

Thermal effects associated with a focussed electron beam can also be used to form *p-n* junctions [5]. A layer of suitable dopant is deposited on the surfaces and an electron beam is used to alloy the dopant into the material where required. The unalloyed layer is then removed. Resolutions of the order of 5 μ can be obtained.

13.3 Non-thermal fabrication methods

The difficulties associated with thermal methods include the relatively poor resolution and the presence of strained or remelted material of uncertain geometry and of unknown impurity content. In an attempt to avoid these difficulties other methods have been pioneered. Shoulders and his co-workers [6, 7, 8] have developed a method in which a mask is used to interrupt an electron beam; subsequently the interrupted beam passes through a de-magnifying lens which throws a reduced image of the mask on the specimen. The specimen is coated with a chemical (such as triphenylsilanol) which gives a latent image under exposure to an electron beam. This latent image is made into a silica mask by heating to 200°C. The unexposed parts are etched away by a gaseous or molecular beam etch. Simple structures giving resolutions of better than 500Å have been obtained. Good resolutions can also be obtained by the use of other electron-beam activated resists; Wells [1] lists some ten chemicals used in this work. One that is often used [9, 10] is silicone oil introduced as a vapour into the specimen area. In this case we are concerned with the useful exploitation of the effects that give rise to what we have termed beam-induced contamination. The fast electrons strike absorbed molecules of the oil and free radicals are formed. These free radicals recombine to form polymer films which can be hardened by further exposure to the beam. These hardened films have the same order of resistance to chemical and ion etching as those exposed to sufficient doses of ultraviolet. There are really two interests centred on these films. One is the 'photo-resist' aspect outlined above and the other arises from the possibility that these films may have useful electrical properties [11].

A fair amount is known [11, 12] about the electrical properties of these films. These properties are best studied in films formed under low energy ($<$ 1kV) beams at rates $\approx$ 100 Å/minute. If higher energy beams are used the films become degraded electrically and, in particular, the d.c. resistivity drops from its best value $\sim 10^{15}\Omega$cm. The dielectric strength is $\sim 10^{6}$V/cm. The films interact with the oxygen and water vapour in the atmosphere if long-lived free radicals exist in the polymer. This tends to increase the film capacity as a function of time. On the other hand, if there is any unpolymerized monomer in the film this will be desorbed as a function of time and the capacity will decrease marginally. In general the room temperature VI characteristics of these films agree with characteristics predicted by Schottky thermal emission. At low temperatures ($4.2°K$) the same mechanism is applicable at low voltages but gives way to tunnel emission at higher voltages. Mechanically these films

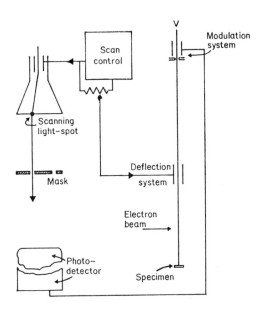

Figure 13.2. Use of a scanning light-spot and mask to control a high-resolution exposure pattern formed by an electron beam [13].

have two advantages over dielectric films formed by direct evaporation, the incidence of pinholes is greatly reduced and the stress built into the film is an order of magnitude less.

Of more immediate applicability is the use of beam-induced polymerization to make devices. One type of system in operation [13] for this work is illustrated in figure 13.2. A single-scan generator traces a raster on a CRT and on the specimen. The travelling light-spot is projected through a 'negative' of the required pattern and then focussed on a photomultiplier. The output from this photomultiplier is used to control the beam current either by controlling the grid voltage or by deflecting the beam over an aperture. When a photocurrent flows in the photomultiplier the beam current is switched on. In this way a relatively crude mask can be used to give a substantial demagnification in one step. The scan generator can be programmed so that the whole procedure is repeated on a predetermined matrix. Subsequent fabrication processes can be superimposed, provided the masks can be registered to a sufficient degree of accuracy. The magnitude of the problem becomes clear when it is realized that in order to make sufficiently fast transistors for this method to be of interest the tolerances have to be $\sim \pm 1000\,\text{Å}$ in order to make, for example, 1 μ strips on 2 μ centres [14]. The registration capability of optical methods is $\sim (2 \pm 0.5)\mu$ in normal use and $\sim 1\ \mu$ with extra care. Wells *et al.* [28] and Thornley and Hatzakin [14] have described how the registration can be made with electron beams.

Leaving aside the economic factors, we still have to ask what virtues this method can have over the existing, very effective, methods based on diffusion, photoresist and oxide masking. The answer is really contained in the above paragraph in terms of the increase in registration capability. This increase means that in general terms the active areas of devices can be dropped by a factor of ten or more. Emitter areas can be reduced to $\sim 1\mu \times 1\mu$ and we can aim at MOST channel widths $\sim 2,000\,\text{Å}$. As a result the inherent capacities drop and the devices can be operated at higher frequencies. Therefore, in situations where high speed (and packing density) are important, this technique has a potentiality, particularly if the process can be largely automated to overcome the time factor. It is also possible that the two methods can be combined when conventional planar technology makes the bulk of the components and certain critical components are superimposed by use of electron beams. This, at present, appears to be the main role of electron beams in micro-device fabrication: a useful addendum in specialized cases (such as computer devices) rather than a complete competitor. Nor should we forget that electron beams can be used for the writing of fast, random access data stores of high packing density [15] and for the fast recording [16] of data. It is under the stimulus of these possibilities that considerable effort is being devoted [17, 18] to the development of completely automated electron-beam systems which can run for weeks with minimal attention.

13.4 Use of ion beams for device fabrication

Shoulders [19] has stressed that the collimation inherent in the use
of ion beam-etching can be exploited to give a near-ideal etching
process in which a steep-sided cut is obtained with none of the
undercutting experienced with liquid etchants. We can see just
how steep an edge can be obtained by recording the results obtained
by Broers [20, 21, 22], using the system outlined in section 7.7.
The SEM was used to write a resist (silicone oil) pattern onto a
2,500 Å Au film on a silicon substrate. The writing speed was
$\sim 0.25\,\mu$/sec. The argon ion beam (5 kV, $\frac{1}{2}$ mA/cm^2) was then used
to remove the unexposed resist and the underlying Au. Provided
the exposed resist was thick enough, Au ridges 700 Å wide with
edge definitions of 200 Å and of height 3,000 Å were obtained. If an
insulating substrate (glass) was used, the Au ridges could be made
with heights of 4,000 Å, widths of 750 Å and edge definitions of
~ 300 Å. Once the beam reached the insulator the etching virtually
ceased. The best resolution was obtained with Au-Pt wires on Si.
This combination gives lines of width = 400 Å and edge definitions
≈ 150 Å. Broers indicated that the writing speed is low ~ 20 bits/sec
assuming an elementary recording unit of 500 Å linear size. The
speed depends on the sensitivity of the resist to beam exposure. In
situations where the ultimate in resolution is not required the beam
can be used to expose a KPR or KMER resist. In this case, line
widths of 2,500 Å with edge resolutions of 700 Å could be obtained
with writing speeds of ~ 7.5 cm/sec. The increased speed results
because the resolution obtainable is limited by scattering in the
resist film and so a higher beam current can be used. Recently
Chang and Nixon have shown [23] that scattering is probably the
limiting factor even when silicone oil vapour is used as the resist.
The exposed lines have a characteristic shape – an inner core and a
weaker, outer fringe – which can be explained in terms of scattering.
These workers were able to write 500 Å lines on $1.5\,\mu$ centres at a
writing speed of $5\,\mu$/sec.

13.5 Electron-beam 'writing'

The use of electron beams to write, store and erase information is
already actively exploited [24]. However, the recent development of
highly focussed scanning electron beams and of stable MOST structures has introduced a new possibility [25, 26] into the technique.
The ideas put forward here are those discussed in Chapter 12, in

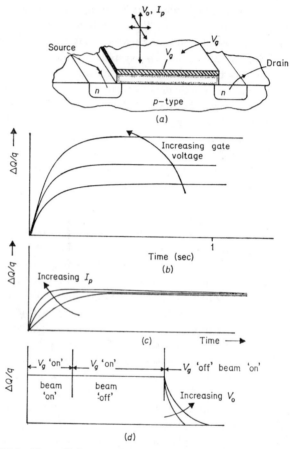

Figure 13.3. Use of electron beams to store information in MOST structures (schematic): (a) typical device structure used in relation to scan directions; (b) charge induced in semiconductor under gate as function of time and gate voltage (V_g); (c) effect of increasing primary current, I_p; (d) illustrating the retention of stored charge on beam 'turn-off' and the removal facility on irradiation in absence of bias.
[After MacDonald and Everhart [25]].

which we were concerned with the way in which imperfect devices could be diagnosed by electron-beam techniques. But now we must consider how similar interactions between well-made devices and electron beams can lead to reversible and predictable behaviour which can be used to make memory devices.

The kind of structure required for these studies is illustrated in figure 13.3. If the device has been suitably treated to reduce the surface-state density to a low value, and if it is irradiated with a positive voltage applied to the gate, a positive charge will be stored in the oxide near to the silicon – silicon oxide interface. The charge results because holes are trapped and electrons are swept out by the field, the trapped positive charge inducing an inversion layer under the oxide and the channel is then opened. The action observed is in accord with the ideas explained in Chapter 6. The stored charge density reaches a saturated value which depends on the gate voltage applied during the irradiation. The rate at which this saturated value is reached increases with increase in beam current. If the beam is switched off, the stored charge remains sensibly constant, if the gate voltage is reversed then the stored charge will die away. The stored charge increases the magnitude of the threshold voltage, typically from a few volts to a few tens of volts. These effects suggest that storage devices can be made this way. The electron beam can be programmed to write a two-dimensional distribution of stored charge. This distribution can be removed by reversing the gate voltage. A quickly restored readout can be obtained [26] in the manner outlined in figure 13.3. The channel is divided into two sections – the left and the right. Initally both sections are irradiated with V_g positive to increase the threshold voltage to $- (V_{to} + \Delta V_t)$. For the channel to represent the 'on' state, the left-hand side is irradiated with $V_g < 0$. This restores the threshold voltage to $- V_{to}$ in this region. Subsequently the right-hand side is irradiated with $V_g < 0$. If this opens the complete channel between A and B with the threshold voltage set between $- V_{to}$ and $- (V_{to} + \Delta V_t)$ then the left-hand side is in the 'on' state. If this irradiation does not open the channel then the left-hand side is in the 'off' state. To reset the read-out facility all the right-hand side elements are re-irradiated with $V_g > 0$ to reset the threshold voltage to $- (V_{to} + \Delta V_t)$. Obviously the approach is capable of considerable extension. Two groups [25, 26] have reported

AA

work on this method of information storage. The relevant data for a proposed system are listed in table 13.2.

Table 13.2. *Properties of an electron beam activated memory device* [25]

Beam properties required	10^{-3} amps/cm^2 at 10 to 30 kV
Charge dosage	10^{-6} to 10^{-5} C/cm^2
Time to store	$\sim 5 \times 10^{-6}$/specimen beam current density (secs.)
Random access time for storage time	$= 1\mu$S*
Random access time for reading (function of ancillary equipment)	0·1 to 10μS*
Storage capacity (using an array of devices to control a 'microspot' CRT)	$\sim 10^7$
Time to readout each element	$< 1\mu$S*

* = Estimated.

The attractive possibilities of this approach to data storage are random access, extension to analogue data and, possibly, stability.

13.6 Comment

The foregoing outline describes some ways in which electron beams are being exploited to fabricate devices. The examples chosen illustrate the ideas involved without too much complication. They are not, however, intended to be comprehensive nor do they, necessarily, represent the most up-to-date studies. Also any assessment of these techniques must be made against a wide background in which competing optical and laser techniques, existing planar technology, the new techniques of ion implantation and ion deposition are all taken into account. From the viewpoint of readers of this book the main interest will lie in the fact that most of these studies fall within the range of a scanning electron microscope. The modifications required are minimal and usually consist of omitting various components and adding further control systems. Higher beam currents than are usually required in the SEM can be obtained by increasing the aperture sizes and if needs be, by removing lenses from the column. If the ability to revert to high-resolution conditions quickly is incorporated, the processing can be completed and inspected [27] at once at high resolution.

REFERENCES

[1] o. c. WELLS, *Introduction to Electron Beam Technology*, (ed. R. Bakish), p. 354, Wiley, New York, (1962)

[2] See, for example, *Integrated Circuits*, (ed. R. M. Warner, Jnr., and J. N. Fordemwalt), McGraw-Hill, New York, (1965)

[3] P. L. HAWKES, G. BOWEN and S. MATHER-LEES, *Microelectronics and Reliability*, **4**, 65, (1965)

[4] J. KELLY and H. N. G. KING, *Microelectronics and Reliability*, **4**, 85, (1965)

[5] E. C. ORRIS, Ohio State Univ. Res. Foundation, Columbus Ohio, *Report on Contract AF 33/616/6416*, (1959)

[6] K. R. SHOULDERS, Office of Tech. Services Publication No. PB171027, (1960)

[7] K. R. SHOULDERS, Stanford Research Institute. *Final Report Contract No. AF 19/604/6114*, (1961)

[8] D. A. BUCK and K. R. SHOULDERS, *Proc. Eastern. Joint Computer Conf.*, *Philadelphia*, (1958)

[9] P. R. EMTAGE and W. TANTRAPORN, *Phys. Rev. Letters*, **8**, 267, (1962)

[10] L. MAYER, *J. Appl. Phys.*, **34**, 2088, (1963)

[11] R. W. CRISTY, *J. Appl. Phys.*, **31**, 1680, (1960)

[12] G. W. HILL, *Microelectronics and Reliability*, **4**, 109, (1965)

[13] See, for example, references [14] and [28] or I. M. MACKINTOSH, *Proc. I.E.E.E.*, **53**, 370, (1965)

[14] R. F. M. THORNLEY and M. HATZAKIN, *I.E.E.E. 9th Annual Symposium on Electron, Ion and Laser Beam Technology*, Berkeley, Calif., (1967)

[15] F. KURZWEIL, JNR., R. R. BARBER and M. H. DOST, *I.E.E.E. 9th Annual Symposium on Electron, Ion and Laser Beam Technology*, Berkeley, Calif., (1967)

[16] See, for example, Work at Ampex Corp., Redwood City. See *Electronics*, Nov. 29, 124, (1965)

[17] G. R. HOFFMAN, *Microelectronics and Reliability*, **4**, 59, (1965)

[18] K. H. LOEFFLER, *I.E.E.E. 9th Annual Symposium on Electron, Ion and Laser Beam Technology*, Berkeley, Calif., (1967)

[19] K. R. SHOULDERS, Publication PB 171027, Office of Technical Services, U.S. Dept. of Commerce, September, (1960)

[20] A. N. BROERS, *Proc. of 1st Inter. Conf. on Electron, Ion Beam Science and Technology*, *Toronto*, (ed. Bakish), (1964)

[21] A. N. BROERS, Ph.D. Thesis, Cambridge, (1965)

[22] A. N. BROERS, *Microelectronics and Reliability*, **4**, 103, (1965)

[23] T. H. P. CHANG and W. C. NIXON, *I.E.E.E. 9th Annual Symposium on Electron, Ion and Laser Beam Technology*, Berkeley, Calif., (1967)

[24] M. KNOLL and B. KAZAN, *Storage Tubes*, Wiley, New York, (1952)

[25] N. C. MACDONALD and T. E. EVERHART, *I.E.E.E. 9th Annual Symposium on Electron, Ion and Laser Beam Technology*, Berkeley, Calif., (1967)

[26] C. J. VARKER and E. M. JULEFF, *Proc. I.E.E.E.*, **54**, 728, (1966)

[27] J. W. THORNHILL and I. M. MACKINTOSH, *Microelectronics and Reliability*, **4**, 97, (1965)

[28] O. C. WELLS, T. E. EVERHART and R. K. MATTA, *I.E.E.E. Trans on Electron Devices*, **ED-12**, 556, (1965)

Author Index

Subject Index